THE NEW NATURALIST

A SURVEY OF BRITISH NATURAL HISTORY

SEA-BIRDS

The aim of this series is to interest the general reader in the wild life of Britain by recapturing the inquiring spirit of the old naturalists. The Editors believe that the natural pride of the British public in the native fauna and flora, to which must be added concern for their conservation, is best fostered by maintaining a high standard of accuracy combined with clarity of exposition in presenting the results of modern scientific research.

The text and line illustrations are here reproduced unaltered, but the process of manufacture used to achieve an economic price does not, unfortunately, do full justice to all the photographs; and those originally in colour appear in black and white.

Plate 1. Cahow. Painting by Roger Peterson, by kind permission of the artist and the American Ornithologists' Union

THE NEW NATURALIST

SEA-BIRDS

An Introduction to the
Natural History of the Sea-Birds of
the North Atlantic

by

JAMES FISHER

and

R. M. LOCKLEY

Bloomsbury Books
London

To
JULIAN HUXLEY
*in gratitude for his guidance
and encouragement, and in recollection of the
many happy days we have spent together,
watching sea-birds*

This edition published 1989 by
Bloomsbury Books an imprint of
Godfrey Cave Associates Limited
42 Bloomsbury Street, London WC1B 3QJ
under license from William Collins Son's & Co. Ltd.

ISBN 1 870630 88 2

CONTENTS

vi

It should be noted that throughout this book plate numbers in arabic figures refer to Colour Plates, while roman numerals are used for Black-and-White Plates

EDITORS' PREFACE

IT IS NATURAL that in a series dealing with the wild life of the British Isles sea-birds would be a subject planned for early publication; and in fact this book was announced as forthcoming five years ago. That it has not been completed earlier is not due to any want of industry on the part of its authors. On the contrary, in their researches for this book they have found their subject so absorbing that they have made the interval an opportunity to continue to publish numerous scientific papers, and two monographs, on sea-birds. James Fisher is the author of *The Fulmar* (1952); and R. M. Lockley, author of *Shearwaters* (1942), has just published *Puffins* (1953). There could, in fact, hardly be any other pair of authors better qualified to describe the sea-birds of the North Atlantic than these with their experience of many years of field work and visits along the coast and islands, from Spitsbergen and Iceland in the cool north, to Madeira and the Salvages in the warm south, of that great demi-ocean. They have made their visits often together, and lived much on the small remote islands where sea-birds breed.

The North Atlantic, busiest ocean in the world, is revealed in the opening chapters not as a monotonous watery plain, but as an intricately varied, densely inhabited foraging ground for sea-birds. This avian community, though remarkably homogeneous in different sections of the broad expanse of the North Atlantic, is fascinating in the variety of the species that compose it, and in the complexity of their movements and migrations. The annual migrations of some species extend the total range of the community from the arctic to the antarctic. These long transatlantic migrations, verified by ringing, take species from east to west between Europe and North America, and from north to south between Greenland and South Africa, Britain and South America.

The authors tell us of the primitive progenitors of the sea-birds, dating from over sixty million years ago, and the evolutionary adventures of their descendants, including the notorious extinction of the strange flightless great auk, the sad decline of many other fine species, also the rediscovery of the cahow after it had been presumed extinct.

ix

They have paid special attention to geographical distribution, and have provided a unique collection of maps, giving us, for the first time, the distribution of most species of North Atlantic sea-birds.

Chief among the authors' interests has been the study of sea-bird numbers. They were largely responsible for organising the surveys of that splendid and typical North Atlantic animal, the gannet, which provided biology with the first reasonably accurate figure for the world population of any single and fairly numerous bird species. They have, from their own notes and those of many amateur and professional bird-watchers, produced interesting statistics of the total population of the fulmar, the Manx shearwater, the puffin and many others. Incidentally, such careful counts, site by site, reveal the continuous change that is going on in sea-bird populations, often directly or indirectly due to man's influence.

The chapters on life-history are preceded by a general account of social and sexual behaviour, which throws light upon the significance of the prolonged and, to the observer, entertaining, mutual ceremonies of these strictly monogamous birds, their pair-formation, their fidelity to their mates, their nest-sites and their parental duties; at the same time problems of instinct and learning ability are discussed. The life-histories include much original field-work by the authors, who have been responsible for several discoveries concerning the incubation and fledging of a number of sea-birds.

We read of the birds' ecology, their sharing of the wild frontiers of the land where they nest, their niches in the economy of the ocean. We learn of the contrasts between cliff-dwelling and hole-nesting species, of how the guillemot and razorbill chicks, exposed to many dangers on the open rocks, hasten their feather-growth and depart to the sea in two weeks, while the young puffins, safe in the darkness of their burrows, delay their departue for seven weeks, and are finally deserted by their parents; we learn of the strange lives of the shear-waters and small petrels which wander after the breeding season between the North and South Atlantic Oceans, living in perpetual summer—the Tristan shearwater "wintering" in our northern summer, and the Manx shearwater enjoying its "winter" in the southern summer off the coasts of South America.

But we have said enough to indicate the richness of knowledge brought together in this volume, which we confidently recommend as indispensable to everyone interested in the birds of the sea.

THE EDITORS

AUTHORS' PREFACE

THE HEROES of our story are rather over a hundred species of birds whose life is a sea-life, whose habits enable them to earn at least part of their living in, or on, salt water, and which have been seen in the Atlantic Ocean north of the Equator.

The North Atlantic is the scene of our book, the great ocean that is now the most travelled by man. Its two sides are provided with an almost equal variety of sea-birds: sixty-eight species, or rather over half are common to both. Of all Atlantic countries Britain, considering its size, has the greatest number of sea-bird species; with no less than eighty, it can boast on its list all but six of those that have been seen on the Atlantic coast of Europe. The British Isles therefore make a good headquarters for a survey of the sea-birds of the North Atlantic. In Britain, and from Britain, the writers of this book have explored the eastern Atlantic sea-bird stations, and enjoyed many fine islands and memorable experiences. One or the other of us has sought the sea-birds south to the frigate-petrel burrows of the Salvages, near the Canary Islands; north to the ivory-gull colonies on the nunataks that rise from the ice-cap of Spitsbergen; or from 30°N. nearly to 80°N., a distance of more than three thousand miles; west we have ranged to Iceland, the Faeroes, Rockall, St. Kilda and the Blaskets of the Kerry coast; east we have travelled to Heligoland, and as far as Laesö in the Kattegat and Gotland in the Baltic, with their off-lying islands of sea-birds. There is no coastal county in England, Wales and Scotland that has not been visited by us both, and not one in Ireland that has not been visited by one of us.

No good British sea-bird cliff or island has been overlooked in our search for what the naturalist searches for; our experience and enjoyment has been long and continuous because both of us are, each in his somewhat different way, obsessed with sea-birds and with islands. We have spent a combined total of nearly seventy years sea-bird watching.

We have seen the little crags and green island swards of the Isles of Scilly and the drowned coast of Cornwall; the granite cliffs and

xi

puffins of Lundy; the chalk of south England east from Dorset; the flats and shingles and dunes of Essex and Suffolk and Norfolk, and the sanctuaries of Havergate and Minsmere and Walberswick and Cley and Blakeney and Salthouse, with terns and avocets and many kinds of marsh-birds. One of us has spent many years of his life in the county of Pembroke, living on Skokholm, and on other islands and peninsulas of the Welsh coast; of its sea-birds he has written in many books, and on Skokholm established the first permanent coastal bird observatory in Britain; the other has spent parts of twenty seasons in North Wales, and has worked its coast from St. Tudwal's Islands to the Little Orme. Both of us know the Yorkshire bird-cliffs most of the way from Flamborough Head to Saltburn; and we have explored the shore of Durham, where bird-cliffs and black industry mix. In Northumberland we know Cullernose Craster, and Dunstan-burgh and Bamburgh Castle, and the cliffs north of Berwick, and other places where sea-birds nest; and we have been to the Holy Island, and to Coquet Isle, and to various of the Farne Islands, where the guillemots and kittiwakes are tame. We have seen the steep cliff-hill of the south part of the Isle of Man, and the sanctuary of the Calf; and have visited the inland gull colonies of North Lancashire and the Lakes.

In Scotland we have, at one time or another, visited every important sea-bird station: in the east St. Abb's Head, Fast Castle, Tantallon Castle, the Bass Rock, the exciting Isle of May, and many others; in the west the Lowland coast from the Mull of Galloway in Wigtown-shire up-Clyde as far as Ailsa Craig, whose magnificent gannetry has been the scene of many weeks of enjoyment and experiment in efforts to improve the counting of nesting sea-birds. Our visits farther north have taken us to Fowlsheugh in Kincardineshire, and round the bird-cliffs of the Aberdeen-Banff border—Pennan Head, Troup Head and others. West along into the Moray Firth we have hunted out the bird-cliffs as far as they go, which is to Covesea in Morayshire.

In the West Highlands we have explored the mainland promon-tories of Kintyre and Ardnamurchan, and the islands of the Clyde and Inner Hebrides. We have searched the cliffs of west Islay closely from a slow aeroplane. The curious headland of Ceann a 'Mhara on the lovely sunny Island of Tiree has been investigated, as have the odd-shaped Treshnishs, home of seals, and the capes of Mull. The island of Eigg, where the shearwaters nest in a mountain; the magni-ficent but somewhat birdless island of Skye, and some of its attendant islets and stacks; both the lonely coast of Ross and its islands—Priest, Tanera, Glas Leac Beg and many others, where Frank Darling first worked out his theory of bird sociality by studying herring-gulls.

In the North Highlands we have watched the birds of the Black Isle Coast, and those of Easter Ross where the coast continues north of the Cromarty Firth to Tarbat Ness. In East Sutherland Dunrobin Castle itself becomes a bird-cliff, because fulmars are now prospecting it—and there we have seen them; in West Sutherland we have travelled nearly the whole wild coast, in instalments spread over several years; we know the crags of Stoer; the Torridonian sandstone precipices of Handa, the best bird island in Sutherland; the lonely cliffs on each side of remote Sandwood Bay—and Eilean Bulgach opposite which only half-a-dozen naturalists have visited; the high promontory of Cape Wrath, and the higher cliff of Clò Mor to the east of it—the highest mainland cliff in Britain—where the guillemots on two-hundred-foot stacks must be observed from six or seven hundred feet above; Fair-Aird Head and the home cliffs and caves of Durness; the huge white crags and stacks of Whiten Head; the complex of islands and cliffs that stretches thence to Caithness, whose headlands too, we know, and their birds—Holborn Head, Dunnet Head, John o' Groats and Duncansby Head, Noss Head, Berriedale Ness.

In many years, and many boats (as well as from aircraft), we have enjoyed the Outer Hebrides, from North Rona (which many call the loneliest place to have been inhabited in Britain) to Barra Head. We have seen the seals and birds of Rona, and counted the gannets of its lonely neighbour Sula Sgeir; and have hunted out the coast of the Lewis, and much of Harris. One of us has slept some nights on the Shiants, among the rats that may be affecting the population of that vast remote puffinry; and has several times threaded the maze of the Sound of Harris, and eight times has been to St. Kilda, whose unsurpassed cliffs and towering stacks have to be seen to be believed (and are sometimes then not believed). We have traversed the Long Isle—North Uist, Benbecula, South Uist and Barra—and many of its attendant isles, and carried on to sail close under the cliffs of Mingulay and Berneray, which for remoteness, grandeur and personality are rivals—much overlooked rivals—to those mighty precipices of St. Kilda, Conachair, Soay and Boreray.

One hundred and ninety-one miles west of St. Kilda, and about three hundred miles from the mainland of Scotland, lies a tiny rock which has been a magnet for us both—not only because of its bird-problems, but because it is a tiny remote rock! Fisher flew over Rockall in 1947. In 1948 Lockley spent twelve days in a trawler fishing within sight of, and on occasion very close to it. In 1949 Fisher sailed there in H. G. Hasler's sixteen-ton yawl *Petula*, and spent some time investigating it at close quarters.

One of us has visited Sule Stack, the lonely gannetry thirty miles west of Orkney; and we have enjoyed nearly every island, from North to South Ronaldsay, from Eynhallow to Hoy, and have seen sea-birds in a great range of surroundings. Neither of us is a stranger to the well-named Fair Isle, a great migration and sea-bird station. We know the Shetland gannetries of Noss and Hermaness, where thousands nest—though forty years ago there was none. We have stood at the top of Foula's Kame, and gazed twelve hundred and twenty feet to the auk-scattered sea below. We have sailed in and out, and round about, the stacks and rocks and skerries, and voes and geos of straggling Shetland, and seen many a fine cliff, from Sumburgh in the south to Saxa Vord in the north; from Noss on east to Papa Stour on west. We are no strangers to Fitful Head, or Hillswick, or Ronas Voe, or Burra Firth; or to Hascosay, the bonny isle of Whalsay, Fetlar, Bressay or Mousa; or to the Out Skerries, nearest British land to Norway.

Perhaps in Ireland we have not seen all we should; but one of us knows the windy corner of Kerry, the end of the world, where the pure Irish survives on the Blasket, and where the fulmars now glide and play round Inishtearaght, Inish-na-Bro, and Inishvickillaun; and where the gannets mass white on the serrated pinnacles of the Little Skellig, second gannetry of the world. He knows, too, the little gannetry of the Bull, and its neighbour the Cow, and other crags of Cork from Cape Clear Island and Dursey Island east to Great Newtown Head. In Clare the cliffs of Moher bring sea-birds to nest among many beautiful flowers. We have seen the bird-colony of the Great Saltee in Wexford, and that of Lambay not far from Dublin. One of us knows the many fine, high cliffs of Mayo and Sligo, and some headlands of the maze-coast of Donegal; the other has watched fulmars haunting the curious inland cliffs of Binevenagh in Derry, and hunted out the basalt coast of Antrim and the Giant's Causeway.

Between us, then, we have seen much of the coast of our glorious islands; but we have not seen nearly enough, and we hope to see what we have already seen, all over again. And we would see the west side of the ocean we have grown to love, and compare it with the Britain we know, and other sea-bird countries we have seen—the tuff and lava and basalt of Iceland, the basalt crags of Faeroe, the dissected plateaux of Spitsbergen, the misty cliffs of Bear Island, the drowned coast of Norway with snow-coated Lofotens and dark fjords like corridors, the friendly limestone of Sweden's Gotland, the skerry-guard of Stockholm and Uppland, the dunes of Denmark and the Dutch islands, the red sandstone cliffs of Heligoland (the only cliffs in western Germany), the chalk and granite of north France, and the islets of Brittany; the benign, sunny slopes and little scarp-precipices of the Channel Islands where one of us lived for a while; the warm, shearwater islands of the Portuguese Berlengas, the Madeiran Desertas, and the Salvages; and the gulleries and terneries of the Camargue, within the Mediterranean.

This book is not a comprehensive survey of a problem based upon a lifetime's experience nor yet a full bibliographical compilation. We have paused in field-work simply to offer this book as a stimulant, which we hope very much it will be. We intend it as no more. It is a statement of some of the facts concerning the wonderful sea-birds of the North Atlantic, and of some of the interesting problems connected with their lives and their evolution. It is intended to exhibit the ignorance of ornithology as much as its knowledge, and to draw attention to what needs doing as much as to what has been done. It is our wish, we must also add, not only to take the reader with us—if he will come—to the east side of the North Atlantic where the sea-birds are more in our personal experience, but also to the western seaboard, which is zealously worked by the ornithologists of the United States and Canada and described by them with such enthusiasm and thoroughness in numerous books and journals. One of us has corrected the galley proofs of this book in an aircraft bound for North America, on the beginning of a journey among the sea-birds of that continent; as he left Britain, Ailsa Craig flashed white with gannets in an April evening sun, and the first bird he saw in the New World, through Newfoundland clouds next morning, was a gannet.

For help, encouragement and information we have more friends to thank than we can mention. Our search of the literature has been chiefly pursued in books belonging to the Zoological Society of London, the Alexander Library at Oxford, the Royal Geographical Society and the London Library, and we thank G. B. Stratton and W. B. Alexander particularly. Among those who have given us valuable help or information (they have no responsibility for the use we have made of it) are B. M. Arnold, R. Atkinson, J. Buxton, T. Cade, F. Darling, E. A. G. Duffey, A. Ferguson, Finnur Guðmundsson, H. G. Hasler, P. A. D. Hollom, J. S. Huxley, the late P. Jespersen, G. T. Kay, Miss J. Keighley, T. C. Lethbridge, H. F. Lewis, C.-F. Lundevall, S. Marchant, R. C. Murphy, E. M. Nicholson, R. S. Palmer, R. Perry, R. T. Peterson, L. E. Richdale, M. Romer, F. Salomonsen, H. N. Southern, D. Surrey-Dane, N. Tinbergen, L. Tuck, L. S. V. Venables, H. G. Vevers, K. Williamson and V. C. Wynne-Edwards. Mrs. E. Marshall patiently typed several drafts of most of this book. J. F. Trotter prepared the final copies of most of the maps. One of these is on a mapnet invented by the late Professor C. B. Fawcett and is used with his permission and that of the Royal Geographical Society (e.g. Fig. 24, p. 145). Another mapnet, devised by one of us (J.F.) is used for the first time in this book; it is based on the South Pole with the oceans in three petals, and is useful for showing the range of the many sea-birds that have a primarily southern distribution (e.g. Fig. 22, p. 136). J. Fisher's fellow *New Naturalist* editors have been encouraging; and Eric Hosking in particular has found us many unique photographs. R. Trevelyan, of Messrs. Collins, has been most ingenious and helpful. The American Ornithologists' Union, who published our frontispiece first in the *Auk*, have very kindly allowed us the use of it; this fine painting by Roger Peterson of the interesting cahow, long thought to be extinct, embellished the paper by R. C. Murphy and L. S. Mowbray on their recent rediscovery of its breeding-grounds.

Ornithologists' wives do many (if not most) of the chores that husbands normally do. We thank ours for more things than they probably remember.

JAMES FISHER

R. M. LOCKLEY

CHAPTER I

THE NORTH ATLANTIC OCEAN
ITS STRUCTURE AND ITS SEA-BIRDS

THE ATLANTIC OCEAN is a big broad blind alley, kinked like a zig-zag, its jagged north end blocked with ice, its broader south butt cornered by the cold stormy narrow eastern entrance to the Pacific Ocean, and by the warm, windy and wide western gate to the Indian Ocean. It resembles two wedges, their apexes towards the North Pole, one of them truncated midway and at that point connected sideways to the base of the other.

The birds inhabiting the more northerly of these wedges, the North Atlantic, are the birds of this book. Two of these birds have become extinct in historical times: the great auk was never seen alive after 4 June, 1844, and the last Labrador duck was shot in 1875, though some say one was shot in 1878. The number of living species that remain is about one hundred and eighteen, of which eighty-six have been seen on the western seaboard of Europe (which includes Iceland), and ninety-three on the eastern seaboard of the New World (including Greenland).

However, for an understanding of the environment to which the North Atlantic birds are adapted, a description of the whole ocean is necessary, and to this we must proceed.

The extremely simple fundamental shape of the Atlantic invites diagrammatic caricature (fig. 1, p. 3). It is the second largest ocean in the world. It is, on an average, over two and a quarter miles deep, and in some places nearly six. It is, on an average, three thousand five hundred miles across (maximum about five thousand); and is nine thousand miles long. Its area has been estimated as thirty-three million square miles, and its volume as seventy-five million cubic miles. It is a vast place, with many miles of coast, upon which much of civilization depends: considering its size, it has few islands. In comparison, the Indian Ocean is not quite as large (about twenty-eight million square miles); but the Pacific (about sixty-four million square miles) has nearly twice the area, and is ten thousand miles across its widest part. The Arctic Ocean (about five and a half million square miles) is small and nearly full of ice at all times of year; in spite of this it is at times very full of life. Finally, it is usual to describe the cold waters round the Antarctic Continent (itself the same size as the Arctic Ocean) as the Antarctic Ocean.

South of the normal steamship route from Britain to New York the Atlantic is almost everywhere over two miles deep, and in large areas more than three. But down mid-ocean, following the tropical kink in the zig-zag, runs a very long submarine ridge, above which is less than two miles of sea; it is only broken by deeps for a short distance on the Equator, and it rises to the surface in places—in the northern hemisphere at the Azores and St. Paul Rocks, and in the south at the lonely isles of Ascension, Tristan da Cunha and Gough. Other oceanic Atlantic islands, such as Bermuda in the north, and South Trinidad and St. Helena in the south, rise abruptly from very deep parts of the ocean. A sketch-chart will be found on p. 30 (Fig. 2c).

It will be seen that there are prominent shallows along the east coast of southern South America, north of the mouths of the Amazon and along the Guianas, in parts of the Caribbean Sea and the Gulf of Mexico (there are also marked deeps in these tropical waters), off the New England States, Nova Scotia and (most particularly) Newfoundland, and round Britain, the Channel and the North Sea, and round Iceland. A submarine ridge, over which the sea is five hundred fathoms or less, cuts the North Atlantic entirely from the Norwegian Sea and the waters of the Polar Basin; Shetland, the Faeroes and Iceland lie on this ridge. Davis Strait is shallow, and the waters of Labrador and Hudson's Bay very shallow. Where the waters are less than a hundred fathoms deep, what they cover is usually described as the Continental shelf. This has its own particular community of birds.

For practical purposes, and because all charts and maps mark the Arctic Circle and the Tropics, we have classified the North Atlantic and its birds into arctic, temperate and tropical areas based simply on latitude. In our analysis of breeding-distribution, for instance (p. 22), we regard birds nesting north of the Arctic Circle as arctic, those nesting south of the Tropic of Cancer as tropical, and th

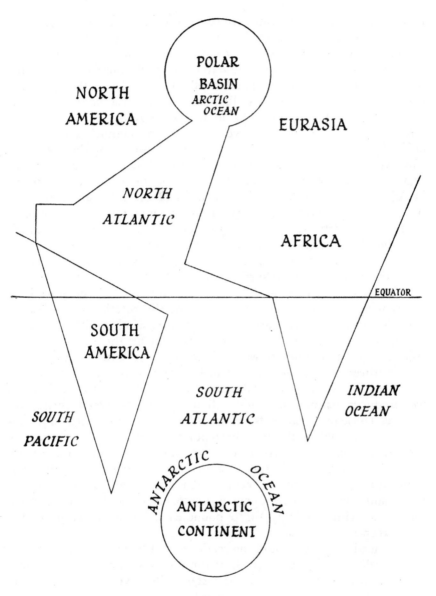

FIG. 1
Diagram of the Atlantic Ocean

nesting between as temperate. However, the temperature of neither air nor water arranges itself, in the Atlantic, according to latitude.* For instance, if we examine the July air isotherms over the world north of the Tropic of Cancer we see that that for 45° F. runs well south of the Arctic Circle in the areas Greenland-Baffin Island and Bering Strait, and well north of it off Scandinavia, avoiding Lapland altogether.

If we examine a map of the world (showing particularly the lands between the Tropics), we see that the summer isotherm for 80°F. (July in the northern hemisphere, January in the southern) runs well north of the Tropic of Cancer in Mexico and the southern States, and in Africa and Asia, and south of the Tropic of Capricorn in Africa and Australia; yet large parts of the tropical Pacific and Atlantic Oceans never reach an average summer air temperature of 80°F.

In the North Atlantic there is not only relatively little direct correspondence between isotherms and latitude, but there is a good deal of difference in position between the same isotherms under the surface, on the water surface and in the air.

The primary cause of the ocean currents, and of the prevailing winds which are associated with them, is the rotation of the earth. The plot of the Atlantic currents and Atlantic winds is almost, though not quite, coincident. To a very large extent the distribution of Atlantic water temperatures, and to a large extent that of air temperatures, is a consequence of these currents and prevailing winds. However, in parts of the Atlantic evaporation and the melting of ice produces temperature and salinity gradients which themselves produce consequent currents. Hence the web of sequence and con-sequence, of cause and effect, becomes complex. We must examine the great equatorial current first, for almost every one of the more important sea masses in the Atlantic owes its existence to it. It is quite justifiable to write in terms of sea masses, for, as we shall see, the Atlantic waters are by no means homogeneous and can be divided, sometimes with strikingly sharp boundaries, into volumes possessing very diverse properties.

We need scarcely remind the reader that if he faces a globe, poised in the ordinary way with North at the top, and spins it as the earth naturally rotates, the points on its surface will travel, as they face him,

*Maps of the northern part of the North Atlantic showing July surface-water isotherms, air-isotherms, vapour-pressure and relative humidity, and annual rainfall, are given by Fisher (1952, pp. 284-85); and a good map of August surface-water isotherms by Storer (1952, p. 186).

from left to right. The points travelling with the greatest velocity will be those on the equator, and the two points represented by the Poles will travel with no velocity relative to the earth's axis.

In general terms it is true that, as the earth rotates, its atmosphere rotates with it. However, there is a certain effect due to inertia or drag; and this effect, obviously, is greatest at the equator, where the surface velocity is greatest. The effect operates on all objects but can put only liquids and gases into a dynamic state. Upon these Corioli's force—the deflecting force of the earth's rotation—acts in a simple manner. It sets them in motion in a direction which, at the equator, is opposite that of the rotation of the earth. Thus if we examine a map of the prevailing winds and ocean currents of the world, we find pronounced positive east-to-west movements in all equatorial regions. The liquids and gases thus displaced circulate into the temperature regions and perform return movements in the higher latitudes where the Corioli's force is less. Consequently, in the northern hemisphere water and wind currents tend to turn right-handed, whereas in the southern hemisphere they turn left-handed. (Exceptions to this rule are mostly found in minor seas, where the impact of the currents upon coasts may cause contra-rotation.) The main clockwise movement of the northern hemisphere wind and currents is very obvious. (See the map on a back end-paper.)

The Atlantic equatorial current can be traced from the African coast south of the equator westwards as far as the sea reaches. Approaching the coast of Brazil it attains a remarkable speed. It sets past the isolated oceanic island of Ascension so that even in calm weather it leaves a wake of turbulence which must make that island unusually visible from far off by its numerous bird inhabitants.

Just north of the equator the lonely St. Paul rocks, which represent the pinnacles of a submerged, steep-sided mountain over thirteen thousand feet high, face the full strength of the great equatorial current, especially in August, when the associated south-east trades are blowing their hardest. During the cruise of the *Challenger* in 1860 H. N. Moseley saw the great ocean current "rushing past the rocks like a mill race." A ship's boat was quite unable to pull against the stream.

The equatorial current divides when it impinges on the corner of Brazil at Cape São Roque. The northern element—the Guiana coast current flows past the mouth of the Amazon with sufficient rapidity to displace the outgoing silt 100 miles or more in a northerly direction; and it continues steadily past the mouth of the Orinoco and Trinidad to flow with scarce-abated force into the Caribbean, mainly through the channel between Trinidad and Grenada in the Windward Islands.

Through the Caribbean the current flows from east to west, turning northerly and entering the Gulf of Mexico through the fairly narrow channel between Yucatan and Cuba. It is no doubt aided here by the climate, for this part of the world is very hot, and not excessively wet, and there is much evaporation of the waters of the Caribbean and the Gulf of Mexico, which has to be replaced. The current finally comes up against the coast of Louisiana and Texas and proceeds to mill right-handed, escaping finally through the narrow gap between Florida and Cuba, into the Bahama Seas.

Here the Gulf Stream is formed, not only by the waters escaping from the Gulf of Mexico but by more northerly elements of the equatorial current which impinge upon the outer shores of the West Indies and are deflected northwards. This north equatorial current flows across the ocean from the Cape Verde Islands and the joint product swings quickly east again, narrowing in width but probably gaining in velocity, to sweep past the tail of the Great Bank of Newfoundland and thence to carry on as what is now called the West Wind Drift (because of its associated air currents). The most direct continuation of this drift flows northwards and eastwards past the west coast of Ireland (giving off a branch towards Iceland), between Rockall and the Hebrides, through the channel between Shetland and Faeroe, north-eastward up the coast of Norway, whence elements strike east into the Barents Sea and north to reach Spitsbergen. It is because of this warm drift that, of all lands reaching latitude 80°, Spitsbergen has been the most accessible. If it was not for the Gulf Stream, many Oxford expeditions could never have explored there in the Long Vacation and got back in time for the Michaelmas Term.

So far we have described the simplest and best-known currents of the North Atlantic. The fate of the waters in their return circulation is more complex. Much of the return circulation is below the surface, for cool water is denser than warm water. In the lower latitudes of the North Atlantic, between the westward-flowing north equatorial current, and the eastward-flowing Gulf Stream and drift, there is an area of clock-wise milling. The centre of this area is the part of least water-movement, and bears some resemblance to an oceanic desert. This is the Sargasso Sea, usually windless, too, with masses of the floating Sargasso weed, which has berry-like air vessels, and is used by sea-birds as a resting-platform; but on the whole this stagnating area is as devoid of animal life as it is of movement.

There is a corresponding and not dissimilar area in the South Atlantic, which also has calms. It has never been named, though it could well be called the Southern Sargasso. These Sargasso areas contain fewer plants and animals than any other part of the ocean. In both there is a rather fluctuating and not very well marked line or lines of convergence between the warm equatorial waters and the comparatively cool temperate waters.

We must now return to the temperate waters, which, as we have seen, form a drift right across the Atlantic and into the Polar Basin. starting on the west below latitude 30°N. and reaching latitude 70°N, or more on the east side. The counter-movements and mills consequent on this great temperate drift are mostly in an anti-clockwise direction. Thus the waters of the North Sea tend to rotate anti-clockwise, running south down the British coast, east and north round the Heligoland Bight, and north-west from southern Norway. In the Norwegian Sea two major and several minor anti-clockwise mills can be detected, and the waters of the Barents Sea also tend to revolve anti-clockwise.

But the greatest counter-movement in the North Atlantic is composed of the Greenland and Labrador currents, carrying cold, heavy water south past Labrador, past Newfoundland and far down the United States' eastern seaboard. This great counter current sets south along the east coast of Greenland down the Denmark Strait between Greenland and Iceland, round Cape Farewell, the southern tip of Greenland carrying with it many bergs tumbled from the sliding glaciers of the inhospitable east Greenland coast, runs north some hundreds of miles up the west coast of Greenland, then west and once more south, collecting the ice of Davis Strait and Baffin Island, and pursues its final course down the·Labrador shore. As it turns the corner of Newfoundland and passes over the great shallow Banks, it deposits its last icebergs and suddenly impinges on the northern boundary of the Gulf Stream or West Wind Drift. Here a long, well-marked line of convergence extends for many hundreds of miles. The cold water sinks rapidly under the warm, and much turbulence is the result. Many organisms are brought to the surface. There is a steep temperature-gradient and frequent climatic upheavals, including fogs. It is largely because of the cold Labrador current that New York, though a full ten degrees farther south, enjoys a climate similar to that of London though with greater extremes of temperature.

The Atlantic thus is a mosaic, not a homogeneous area. Each patch in the mosaic is characterised by some peculiarity of climate. In practically all areas the water, the prime constituent, is in a state of continual movement. The fortunes and distribútion of our sea-birds depend on this environment, so continually in turmoil. We must beat the bounds, then, of the North Atlantic and discover how our birds and their lives are interlocked with this climate and scenery.

A suitable place from which to begin our tour of the North Atlantic is the St. Paul Rocks. Only three species of sea bird nest on them— the brown booby *Sula leucogaster,* and the noddy terns, *Anoüs stolidus* and *A. minutus.* The islands have been visited by many naturalists, including Charles Darwin, who spent some hours of the afternoon of 15 February 1832 obtaining bird specimens with his geological hammer!

From here we move to the coast of South America between the Equator and the Caribbean: this is a mud-coast and not, as are many tropical coasts, a coral coast. Indeed, there is no sign of the coastal coral barrier-reef off Brazil until some distance south of the Equator. If we start at the Equator, on the islands in the mouth of the Amazon, we find a typical river bird-community. The water is fresh for some considerable distance outside into the ocean and the birds consist of skimmers *(Rynchops nigra)* and various river-loving terns such as the gull-billed tern *Gelochelidon nilotica,* the yellow-billed river-tern *Sterna superciliaris,* and the large-billed river-tern *Phaëtusa simplex.* Off-shore the true sea-birds come in, and Murphy records species such as Leach's petrel, Wilson's petrel, the Tristan great shearwater, the great skua, boobies and tropic-birds. North of the Amazon mouth the Brazilian Guiana coast is forested down to the muddy shore. Many small rivers, often choked with the debris of tropical forests, flow into it.

In French Guiana, however, rocky promontories and islets appear, and they are inhabited by some sea-birds; regrettably little is known about the species involved, but they probably include boobies and tropic-birds. Along the coast of Dutch and British Guiana we are once more in a muddy coast with no headlands or islands. North-west of the mouth of British Guiana's main river, the Essiquibo, there are some shell-beaches, but most of the coast is of mangrove-swamp jungle, in which the only animal resembling a sea-bird is the Mexican or *bigua* cormorant *Phalacrocorax olivaceus.* Over the Venezuelan border we are at once in the delta of the great river Orinoco. It is a land of dense mangrove forest and a very large number of low wooded islands. Off-shore the immense tonnage of mud and silt is seized by the equatorial current and driven northwards towards Trinidad, which it thus provides with a very wide continental shelf. As Murphy (1936, p. 127) writes, "The delta of the Orinoco is not the home of birds that can be called marine. . . . Only our adaptable old friend the Bigua cormorant seems . . . at home."

Generally speaking, from the mouth of the Amazon to the mouth of the Orinoco the coast scarcely harbours a breeding sea-bird. However, the British islands of Trinidad and Tobago, off the north-east corner of Venezuela are provided with rocky promontories and many islets on which sea-birds nest. The brown pelican *Pelecanus occidentalis*, the red-footed booby *Sula sula*, the man-o'-war or frigate-bird *Fregata magnificens*, nest on low trees or on mangroves. On the bare Soldado rock the sooty tern *Sterna fuscata*, and the two species of noddy, nest. One tubenose, Audubon's shearwater *Puffinus l'herminieri*, nests on Tobago, which is its southernmost breeding place on this coast. The gull-billed tern nests in fresh water marshes.

West of Trinidad we are in the Caribbean Sea and following the coast, which for 250 miles more has a wide continental shelf, with small islands dotted in it. Opposite the western part of Venezuela, however, the water is much deeper close in-shore, and the off-coast islands of Curaçao and other Dutch possessions rise from a deep sea. Both the islands of the shallow shelf, such as Los Hermanos and the Testigos, and these Dutch islands, have many sea-birds, including three kinds of boobies, man-o'-war birds, tropic-birds, noddies and sooty terns. At least eight species of terns are found at Aruba, the western-most of the Dutch islands. But there are few species which can be described as oceanic, though the boobies are marine; many of the sea-birds probably nest on the islands rather than on the mainland because of the additional safety and the existence of outcrops of rock such as are not found along the interminable mangrove coast.

Of all coasts that we have so far considered, those of northern Venezuela are the driest, and the Caribbean is the hottest part of the North Atlantic region. The western Caribbean, however, has intense summer rain; in spite of this, evaporation is great and the equatorial current is boosted along, flowing into the Gulf of Mexico with some rapidity.

In the Antilles, which form the eastern and northern boundaries of the Caribbean Sea, we find islands clad still in fairly thick jungle vegetation, with coastal mangroves, but also many sandy islets and bars and real coral reefs. Though the Guiana coast was too muddy to support coral reefs, these are found fringing the islands north of Venezuela, such as Curaçao. There are also many reefs along the western shore of the Caribbean, particularly at the corner of Nicaragua and Honduras, at the end of the shallow Mosquito Bank. Throughout the West Indies the distribution of sea-birds is linked primarily with available food, but that of the breeding adults probably also with available nesting-sites. Islets where there are exposures of rock or sand are much favoured, but some species as we have seen, including the red-footed booby, the brown pelican, the bigua cormorant, the darter *Anhinga anhinga*, and some terns, nest in trees. One very rare petrel *Pterodroma hasitata* (p. 76) nests above the tree-line on some of the West Indian islands, among the rocks of steep mountains.

A typical sea-bird islet in the West Indies is Desecheo, described by Alexander Wetmore. This lies in the hot dry zone west of Porto Rico. It is a rocky islet with cliffs and a gravel beach, and a thin top-soil covered with a dense thicket of cacti and the curious West Indian birch. Here brown boobies nested on the ground among the thickets and floundered through the prickly pear and cactus. Sooty terns nested on ledges, on shelves on the limestone cliffs, and B. S. Bowdish found a few bridled terns *Sterna anaetheta*, nesting on flat ledges. This species also breeds on the little islets or cays of the Barrier Reef south of Jamaica, among the broken coral rock and the mangroves.

North of the Antilles the low-lying British islands of the Bahamas occupy a large area of the west Atlantic. The blue Atlantic beats directly against steep east-facing limestone cliffs, while to the west there are shelving beaches. Many of these islands are covered with cacti, and the sea-grape *Coccolobis*, which forms low, thick vegetation in which brown boobies nest, scraping slight hollows in the ground and lining them with grass. In some Bahamas the man-o'-war bird builds its nest quite on top of the prickly pears, though more normally on the mangroves in the swamps, together with brown pelicans and the double-crested cormorant of Florida *Phalacrocorax auritus floridanus*. Upon the more exposed sandspits in the Bahamas several kinds of tern breed, including the gull-billed tern, the little tern *Sterna albifrons*, the roseate tern *S. dougallii*, Cabot's tern *Thalasseus sandvicensis*, and the sooty tern.

The coast of the Gulf of Mexico is low-lying, with coral reefs and an extensive continental shelf, especially off Yucatan. Breeding sea-birds are scarce, except terns and the ubiquitous bigua cormorant, which is as much a fresh-water as a salt-water bird. The Sandwich tern, which is known as Cabot's tern in North America, breeds in several parts of the Gulf coast of Mexico, which is more suited for terns than for any other sea-birds. On the grassy islands among the lagoons and marshes of the Texas coast, the gull-billed tern and Forster's tern *Sterna forsteri*, are found. The beautiful Caspian tern *Hydroprogne caspia*, also nests in a few places on sandy islands, and there is an interesting outpost breeding-station of the white pelican *Pelecanus erythrorhynchos*, on the Laguna de la Madre, south of Corpus Christi, near the Border. The rest of the population of this fine bird is found in western North America.

Along the Louisiana coast, where there are many protected reservations, there are very big colonies of the laughing gull *Larus atricilla*, especially in the marshy islands of the Mississippi delta, which are overgrown with grass and low mangroves. One of the reservations is in the Breton Islands, 114 miles off the main Louisiana coast. Here are great colonies of terns on low flat sandy spits, including Caspian, Cabot's and royal *Thalasseus maximus* (Bent 1921). Forster's and common terns *Sterna hirundo*, also nest in the Breton Islands, as do numbers of the extraordinary black skimmer, an aberrant tern whose lower mandible is prolonged and with which it scoops food from the surface of the sea. The peninsula of Florida has to its west an immense continental shelf, along the lower end of which is a famous chain of Keys. Beyond Key West, at the terminus of the Key railway, many miles to sea, lie the dry Tortugas, flat islands of coral, their surface, largely of coral sand, clothed in parts with dense cactus as well as with bay cedar, with many bare and grassy spaces between. On the cedars and the cactus immense numbers of noddy terns nest: often over the nests of the sooty terns on the ground below.

The Florida coast has one of the best stations in the U.S.A. for the roseate tern. The darter, which most North Americans allude to as the water-turkey (it is a fresh water lover), and the double-crested cormorant of Florida, commonly nest in trees in many swampy places along the coast. Brown pelicans nest by lagoons and in mangrove-keys on both sides of the peninsula.

Naturalists accustomed to British coast conditions can have little notion of the interminability of the low-lying eastern coast of North America. Indeed, on the entire stretch of mainland coast from Southern

Mexico to Maine, about four thousand miles, there is not a single cliff, nor indeed a mountain coming down to the sea. All through Florida, Georgia, the Carolinas, Virginia and Maryland to the New England States, runs a complex of lowland and shallow shores, broken in places by inlets such as those of Chesapeake and Delaware Bays and Long Island Sound. This is a tern coast. In the northern parts the effect of the Labrador current is felt and there is a fairly steep decline in temperature, which is why such tropical forms as the brown pelican and Florida double-crested cormorant drop out of the community in South Carolina. One tropical species which is distributed all along this coast, however, is the laughing gull; and the gull-billed tern reaches north to Virginia. Rather oddly, two terns, the common tern and Forster's tern, appear to avoid the mainland coast from Florida to South Carolina, though they breed to the west and north of it.

The distribution of tern populations on this Atlantic coast has had a chequered history, and is dealt with in some detail in the chapter on Sea-Bird Populations (Chapter 3, p. 85).

In the New England States and Maine we encounter the first truly northern elements in the Atlantic sea-bird fauna, and a community of sea-birds which is intensively watched and studied, as is the very similar community on the eastern side of the Atlantic, ten degrees farther north. We now meet not only some of the terns but some of the gulls that breed in the British Isles. In Maine and New Brunswick, where little cliffs begin and the wooded coast closely resembles the skerry-guard of Stockholm, and other parts of the Baltic archipelago, we find the southernmost auks—black guillemots *Cepphus grylle*, puffins *Fratercula arctica*, and perhaps still a pair or two of razorbills *Alca torda*. We even find tubenoses breeding in Maine, birds which we had last encountered in the Caribbean Antilles. (Apart from Audubon's shearwater and the rare diablotin (p. 76), which nest in various of the Antilles, no breeding petrel is found in the western North Atlantic south of Maine, save on Bermuda.)

The rocks and coral reefs of Bermuda, which is 580 miles from Cape Hatteras, the nearest point on the United States mainland, support an interesting little community of sea-birds, which consists of the northernmost outposts of the breeding population of an otherwise completely tropical species, the white-tailed tropic bird *Phaëthon lepturus*, besides the common tern, the roseate tern, possibly the Manx shearwater *Puffinus puffinus*, Audubon's shearwater, and the cahow *Pterodroma cahow*, thought to be extinct for many years.

It is in the Bay of Fundy, then, on the borders of the U.S. and Canada (Maine and New Brunswick) that the northern birds really begin. Here in burrows in the island rocks nest the southern elements of the rather small Atlantic population of Leach's petrel *Oceanodroma leucorhoa*. Here, too, are the representatives of the northern race of double-crested cormorant, which are separated by a gap of some hundreds of miles from the geographical race of the same species belonging to Florida and the Carolinas.

Other birds which come on the scene between Cape Cod and the Bay of Fundy are the great black-backed and herring-gulls, *Larus marinus* and *L. argentatus*, which are now quickly spreading south down the coast, and the arctic tern *Sterna paradisaea*, which still nests as far south as Cape Cod. If we move north to the Gulf of St. Lawrence, we can also bring in an outpost population of the European cormorant *Phalacrocorax carbo*, the ring-billed gull *Larus delawarensis*, which is very closely related to our common gull, the common guillemot *Uria aalge*, and, rather surprisingly, an arctic species, Brünnich's guillemot *Uria lomvia*, whose breeding distribution extends from the Magdalen Islands *via* Newfoundland and Labrador to the High Arctic There is a curious relict population of the Caspian tern also here. In many ways the Gulf of St. Lawrence has arctic properties and there is, as we have seen, a very steep gradient in water temperature at its mouth, at the convergence of the west wind drift and the Labrador current. Here we find the southern outposts of the largest temperate North Atlantic sea-bird, the gannet *Sula bassana*—though the majority of its breeding-population is found on the other side of the ocean; and we meet our first kittiwakes *Rissa tridactyla*.

In structure the coasts of the Atlantic right round from Maine *via* Nova Scotia, the Gulf of St. Lawrence, Newfoundland, Labrador, Greenland and Iceland to Britain, have a good deal of similarity. They have a fairly even supply of estuaries, inlets, beaches, sands, cliffs, skerries, stacks and islands, and it is probable that the distribution of no sea-bird is seriously limited by lack of suitable nesting sites.

There are two inland species of North American dark-headed gull, Franklin's gull *Larus pipixcan*, and Bonaparte's gull *L. philadelphia*, neither of which breeds near the coast.

From the Gulf of St. Lawrence, *via* Newfoundland, Labrador, Greenland and the Canadian Arctic Archipelago, we find a gradual disappearance of the temperate, sub-arctic and some low arctic species as we progress towards the shores where the sea is still near-freezing in July—the true High Arctic. In Newfoundland we reach the limit for breeding gannets, ring-billed gulls and common terns, and perhaps also Caspian terns. The Leach's petrels breed as far as Newfoundland Labrador, but no farther, and it is doubtful whether the double-crested cormorant now breeds as far. South-west Greenland is less 'arctic' than opposite parts of the Canadian Arctic Archipelago at the same latitude; and it is not surprising that some species extend beyond Labrador to West Greenland, though not to Baffin Island and the other Canadian islands. Such species are the razorbill and common guillemot, the latter having only one small colony in West Greenland. The European cormorant extends to West Greenland and previously had a small outpost in Baffin Island, from which it has now disappeared, and it is also extinct in Newfoundland Labrador, after much human persecution. The puffin does not breed in the Canadian Arctic but goes far north in Greenland where it is of a distinctive, large arctic race.

Species which extend in breeding-range all the way from Newfoundland to Arctic Greenland and Canada are the herring-gull, great blackback, kittiwake, arctic tern and black guillemot. All these except the blackback reach the High Arctic, if we regard the Iceland gull *Larus argentatus glaucoides*, as a herring-gull, as we think we should.

The glaucous gull *Larus hyperboreus*, does not now breed in Newfoundland, but nests commonly from Newfoundland Labrador all the way to the High Arctic, as does the arctic skua *Stercorarius parasiticus*; two other skuas, the pomarine *S. pomarinus*, and the long-tailed skua *S. longicaudus*, do not breed in Labrador, but farther north in both Canadian and Greenland Arctic. On the west side of the Atlantic-Arctic the fulmar *Fulmarus glacialis*, breeds no farther south than Greenland and Baffin Island, although it nests south to about latitude 50° north on the east side of the Atlantic.

This leaves the three High Arctic sea-birds of the West Atlantic for consideration—the little auk *Plautus alle*, Sabine's gull *Xema sabini*, and the ivory-gull *Pagophila eburnea*. All three breed in the more northerly parts of the Canadian Arctic Archipelago and Greenland, though the first may not have more than one colony west of Baffin's Bay. Sabine's gull is a rare bird that often nests in arctic tern colonies. The ivory-gull is the most northerly bird in the world in the sense that it breeds nowhere south of the Arctic Circle, but as far north as the land goes. The extraordinary, rare, Ross's or rosy gull *Rhodostethia rosea*, which normally nests in the aldergroves of some north-flowing rivers of eastern Siberia, has once bred in Greenland.

	Canadian Arctic	Green-land	Jan Mayen	Bear Island	Spits-bergen	Franz Josef Land	Novaya Zemlya	Arctic European Russia	Arctic Norway
Fulmar	+	+	+	+	+	+	+	—	—
Shag ..	—	—	—	—	—	—	—	+	+
Cormorant	extinct	+	—	—	—	—	—	+	+
Pomarine skua ..	+	+	—	—	—	casual	+	casual	—
Arctic skua	+	+	+	+	+	+	+	+	+
Long-tailed skua	+	+	once	—	casual	—	+	+	+
Ivory-gull	+	+	—	—	+	+	—	—	—
Common gull ..	—	+	—	?	—	—	—	+	+
Herring-gull (incl. "Iceland" gull)	+	+	?	casual	—	—	—	+	+
Lesser blackback	—	—	—	—	—	—	+	+	+
Great blackback	+	+	—	recent	recent	—	—	+	+
Glaucous gull ..	+	+	+	+	+	+	+	+	—
Ross's gull	—	once	—	—	—	—	—	—	—
Kittiwake	+	+	+	+	+	+	+	+	+
Sabine's gull ..	+	+	—	—	+	—	—	once	—
Common tern ..	—	—	—	—	—	—	—	casual	casual
Arctic tern	+	+	recent	+	+	+	+	+	+
Little auk	?	+	+	+	+	+	+	—	—
Razorbill	—	+	—	?	—	—	—	+	+
Brünnich's guillemot	+	+	+	+	+	+	+	+	—
Common guillemot	—	+	—	+	—	—	+	+	+
Black guillemot	+	+	+	+	+	+	+	+	+
Puffin ..	—	+	+	+	+	—	+	+	+

The breeding sea-birds of the lands and islands north of the Arctic Circle belonging to the Atlantic or the Atlantic section of the Arctic Ocean.

With the exception of a few gulls, sea-birds entirely desert the arctic regions bordering Baffin's Bay and Davis Strait in October and do not return until April. From no other part of the northern hemisphere is there so great a withdrawal of sea-birds to avoid a period of inhospitable climate.

The eastern arctic islands—Jan Mayen, Bear Island and Spitsbergen, Franz Josef Land and Novaya Zemlya, which lie across the Polar Basin where it abuts on the North Atlantic, have a very similar breeding sea-bird community to that of Greenland, though none has so many members. We can best make this comparison in the form of a table, adding columns for the Canadian Arctic, Arctic Russia-in-Europe and Arctic Norway. (Page 15.)

We now come to the seabird community of Iceland, Faeroe, the British Isles, Scandinavia, the Baltic, and the North Sea and English Channel. This community is very homogeneous, considering the range of latitude over which it is spread, though there are some members which do not reach the south end of this range and a few which do not reach the north. Among the species which are found over almost the entire twenty degrees of latitude are the Manx shearwater, the storm-petrel *Hydrobates pelagicus*, the gannet, the shag *Phalacrocorax aristotelis*, the cormorant, the herring-gull, the lesser blackback *Larus fuscus*, the great blackback, the black-headed gull *L. ridibundus*, the kittiwake, the common and arctic terns, the razorbill, the guillemot, and the puffin. Species which occupy the more northerly parts of this temperate European stretch include the great skua *Catharacta skua*, and Leach's petrel (Iceland, the Faeroes and Britain only), the fulmar, the arctic skua, and the black guillemot. The glaucous gull, little auk and Brünnich's guillemot breed (in this part of the Atlantic) only in Iceland.

There is a central group of sea-birds which breeds neither as far north as Iceland nor as far south as Atlantic France; this is headed by the common gull *Larus canus*, and includes also the little gull *L. minutus*; its other members are terns, the whiskered tern *Chlidonias hybrida* (only casual, in Holland), the black tern *C. nigra*, the white-winged black tern *C. leucoptera* (casual only), the gull-billed tern and the Caspian tern. The populations of all these terns are low, and only two of them (black and gull-billed) have recently bred in Britain, and that casually; their headquarters lie between Holland and the South Baltic. The Baltic Sea, though it has as many breeding terns and gulls as any other part of this stretch of the east Atlantic, lacks

---

Plate 2. Storm petrel incubating in a rock-crevice on Skokholm, Pembrokeshire

Plate 2.

Robert Atkinson

tubenoses and has no gannets, shags, kittiwakes or puffins. The long-tailed skua has a somewhat specialised breeding distribution in Lapland, mostly inland. The remaining birds of this temperate stretch of the east Atlantic breed from Britain, the North Sea or the Baltic south beyond its limits; they are the roseate, little and Sandwich terns. Britain is the European headquarters of the roseate tern.

About half the members of this east and north Atlantic temperate sea-bird community are truly oceanic; that is, they may be found in mid-ocean, up to the greatest possible distance from land, wherever there are suitable feeding waters. Storm-petrels, Leach's petrels and fulmars are the oceanic tubenoses of this community, and we now find that the Manx shearwater also has a right to be considered oceanic. Among the auks the dovekie and Brünnich's guillemot from the north join the puffins, razorbills and guillemots in ocean wanderings. Here,too, are found all the four skuas of the northern hemisphere and one, but only one, gull—the highly specialised kittiwake. In the waters a hundred fathoms deep or less, that is, on the so-called continental shelf, we find all the birds previously mentioned, together with the gannet, the black guillemot, and gulls of the genus *Larus*—the great blackback, the lesser blackback and the herring-gull. Once we are within sight of shore quite a number of species are added to our list, and the tubenoses, except for the Manx shearwater and fulmar, drop out. Here are the terns, the black-headed and common gulls, and also the cormorant and shag, the one haunting mostly seas in sight of sandy shores, and other seas in sight of rocks.

By far the most impressive of the sea-bird haunts are the breeding cliffs, where the different species are zoned vertically as well as horizontally. Whether the rocks be volcanic or intrusive or extrusive or sedimentary, we are sure to find *Larus* gulls breeding on the more level ground a little way back from the tops of the cliffs—fulmars on the steeply sloping turf and among the broken rocks at the cliff edge, puffins with their burrows honeycombing the soil wherever this is exposed at the edge of a cliff or a cliff buttress, Manx shearwaters or Leach's petrels in long burrows, storm-petrels in short burrows and rock-crevices, razorbills in cracks and crannies and on sheltered ledges, guillemots on the more open ledges where they can stand; perhaps gannets on broad flat ledges or on the flattish tops of inaccessible stacks, cormorants with their nests in orderly rows along broad continuous ledges, shags in shadowy pockets and small caves and hollowed-out ledges dotted about the cliff, kittiwakes on tiny steps

c

or finger-holds improved and enlarged by the mud-construction of their nests, tysties or black guillemots in talus and boulders at the foot of the cliff. These wild, steep frontiers between sea and land are exciting and beautiful. They probably house larger numbers of vertebrate animals, apart from fish, in a small space, than any other comparable part of the temperate world.

Not many sea-birds of the east Atlantic do not breed on cliffs; but the skuas nest on moors, and the terns and black-headed gulls nest on sand and shingle. Many of the *Larus* gulls, and recently the fulmar, are catholic in their taste in nesting sites, and may be found on moors and even sand dunes. Quite a large number of sea-birds can be inland nesters, even including tubenoses. Fulmars now nest up to six miles inland in Britain, and many of the *Larus* gulls at much greater distances. The black-headed gull, in particular, is often a completely inland species, since some individuals nest in England as far as they can from the sea, e.g. in Northamptonshire, and may never visit it except in casual search for food.

As we go south along the Atlantic seaboard of the Old World we leave behind in the Channel Islands and Brittany the last elements of certain temperate cliff-breeding sea-bird species—the gannet, lesser blackback, great blackback, arctic tern (only a casual breeder so far south), razorbill and puffin. South of the Bay of Biscay we encounter a large sub-tropical and tropical community of about forty species (a few of which belong to sea-bird families but which have become river-birds or inland birds), which is distributed in four main geographical regions—the Lusitanian coast (the Atlantic coast of Spain and Portugal), the Mediterranean, the Atlantic coast of Africa north of the equator, and the Atlantic Islands. These last comprise the Azores, Madeira (to which pertain the Desertas and Salvages), the Canaries and—near the equator—the Cape Verde Islands. Many species breed, of course, in more than one of these regions, though only the herring-gull (rather doubtfully the little tern and cormorant) breeds in them all.

Of the species in the table, the crested pelican *Pelecanus roseus*, the pigmy cormorant *Haliëtor pygmeus*, the Mediterranean black-headed gull *Larus melanocephalus*, and the lesser crested tern *Thalasseus bengalensis* breed on no North Atlantic shore, and the rare slender-billed and Audouin's gulls, *Larus genëi* and *L. audouinii*, are primarily Mediterranean species. It will be noted that three tubenoses have established themselves in the Mediterranean, but that no less than eight species breed in the Atlantic Islands, which have a greater variety of species of this order than any other part of the North Atlantic. The distribution of breeding sea-birds on these coasts is best illustrated in tabular form :

	ATLANTIC SPAIN AND PORTUGAL	MEDIT-ERRAN-EAN	ATLANTIC ISLANDS				NORTH ATLANTIC AFRICA
			AZORES	MADEIRA DESERTAS & SAL-VAGES	CANAR-IES	CAPE VERDE ISLANDS	
North Atlantic shearwater ..	+	+	+	+	+	+	—
Manx shearwater	—	+	+	+	—	—	—
Little shearwater	—	—	+	+	+	+	—
Soft-plumaged petrel ..	—	—	—	+	—	+	—
Bulwer's petrel	—	—	+	+	+	+	—
Frigate-petrel	—	—	?	+	+	+	—
Storm-petrel ..	?	+	—	?	+	—	—
Madeiran fork-tailed petrel	—	—	+	+	—	+	—
Red-billed tropic-bird ..	—	—	—	—	—	+	—
White-tailed tropic-bird ..	—	—	—	—	—	—	+
Crested pelican*	—	?	—	—	—	—	+
White pelican*	—	?	—	—	—	—	+
Pink-backed pelican*	—	—	—	—	—	—	+
Brown booby ..	—	—	—	—	—	+	+**
Shag	+	+	—	—	—	—	+
Cormorant ..	?	+	—	—	—	+	+
Reed-cormorant*	—	—	—	—	—	—	+
Pigmy cormorant*	—	?	—	—	—	—	—
African darter	—	—	—	—	—	—	+
Man-o'-war-bird	—	—	—	—	—	+	?
Herring-gull ..	+	+	+	+	+	—	+**
Black-headed gull	—	+	—	—	—	—	—
Mediterranean black-headed gull	—	+	—	—	—	—	?**
Slender-billed gull	+	+	—	—	—	—	—
Audouin's gull	?	+	—	—	—	—	—
Grey-headed gull*	—	—	—	—	—	—	+
Whiskered tern	+	+	—	—	—	—	+**
Black tern ..	+	+	—	—	—	—	—
White-winged black tern ..	*casual*	*casual*	—	—	—	—	—
Gull-billed tern	+	+	—	—	—	—	?**

		ATLANTIC ISLANDS				
ATLANTIC SPAIN AND PORTUGAL	MEDITERRANEAN	AZORES	MADEIRA DESERTAS & SALVAGES	CANARIES	CAPE VERDE ISLANDS	NORTH ATLANTIC AFRICA
Caspian tern .. —	+	—	—	—	—	?
Common tern +	+	+	+	? extinct	—	—
Roseate tern .. —	+	extinct	extinct	—	—	—
Bridled tern .. —	—	—	—	—	—	?
Sooty tern .. —	—	—	—	—	—	?
Little tern .. +	+	—	?	?	—	+
Royal tern .. —	—	—	—	—	—	?
Lesser crested tern —	+	—	—	—	—	—
Sandwich tern ?	+	—	—	—	—	—
Noddy .. —	—	—	—	—	—	+
African skimmer* —	—	—	—	—	—	+
Guillemot .. +	—	—	—	—	—	—

The Sea-birds breeding in the Eastern North Atlantic south of the Bay of Biscay and in the Mediterranean.

*mainly fresh water and estuarine.   **Morocco only.

Of the four main groups of these Atlantic islands, Madeira and the Cape Verdes have probably the largest sea-bird communities, with ten or a dozen species each. One tubenose, the North Atlantic great shearwater, *Puffinus diomedea*, nests on all of them as well as on the Berlengas of Portugal. Bulwer's petrel, *Bulweria bulwerii*, and the little dusky shearwater, *Puffinus assimilis*, also nest on all four island groups. The Madeiran fork-tailed petrel, *Oceanodroma castro*, nests on all but the Canaries. The Manx shearwater nests on the Azores and Madeira, but not yet farther south. The little storm-petrel reaches south to the Canaries (although in small numbers and probably to these Atlantic islands only). The rather rare soft-plumaged petrel, *Pterodroma mollis*, is believed to nest on Madeira; it does so on the Cape Verdes. The beautiful frigate-petrel, *Pelagodroma marina*, breeds on the Salvages (which belong to Madeira but are nearer the Canaries), the Canaries and the Cape Verdes.

The red-billed tropic-bird, *Phaëthon aethereus*, the brown booby and the frigate-bird (man-o'-war bird) do not appear farther north than the Cape Verdes. Here the cormorant, which had dropped out in Morocco, reappears as a new race, primarily South African. The bird communities of these islands are only moderately well-known. Most of the sea-birds nest on rocks whose comparative inaccessibility has been both a temptation and a deterrent to the visiting ornithologist. As for the coast of West Africa and the islands lying close to it, no organised investigation of the sea-bird communities of this difficult region has yet been made. We know that one group of species breeds on the Atlantic African coast to Morocco, but no farther south— the shag, herring-gull, the whiskered tern, probably the gull-billed tern, possibly the slender-billed gull. Farther south both white and pink-backed pelicans, *Pelecanus onocrotalus* and *P. rufescens*, and the grey-headed gull, *Larus cirrhocephalus*, reach the tropical sea-coast in some places, and the brown booby nests on at least one island off the coast of French Guinea. The Caspian tern, whose world distribution is, to say the least, peculiar, may have breeding stations on this coast, and the little tern, which we had left behind in Morocco, reappears as a separate race on the coast and rivers of the Gulf of Guinea.

The African darter, *Anhinga rufa*, reed-cormorant, *Haliëtor africanus*, and the African skimmer, *Rynchops flavirostris*, haunt the rivers and in places reach the coast; but they are not sea-birds: and on islands in the Gulf of Guinea the noddy and the white-tailed tropic-bird, *Phaëthon lepturus*, breed. It is suspected that the frigate-bird may nest on this coast, but its breeding-place has not been found. Neither has that of the bridled tern, *Sterna anaetheta*, or the sooty tern, *S. fuscata*, although both species are seen in considerable numbers. There is at least one other riddle: a population of the royal tern, *Thalasseus maximus*, haunts almost the whole coast of West Africa from Morocco to some hundreds of miles south of the Equator. Systematists have separated it from the West Atlantic population as a subspecies (*albidorsalis*), on valid differences, and it does not appear to leave this coast, yet no ornithologist has yet seen its nest or even its eggs.

Only in the tropical parts of the Atlantic are there still these distributional queries. In the temperate and arctic zones the breeding places of the birds are well-known and described. And with this little mystery we conclude our tour of the Atlantic, for we are back on the equator and can strike west to the St. Paul Rocks, where we began.

The sea-birds of the North Atlantic can be listed in the form of a table (Appendix, p. 292), and plotted according to which parts of the ocean they breed in, in the form of a diagram (Fig. 2). For the purpose of completeness, the secondary sea-birds have been

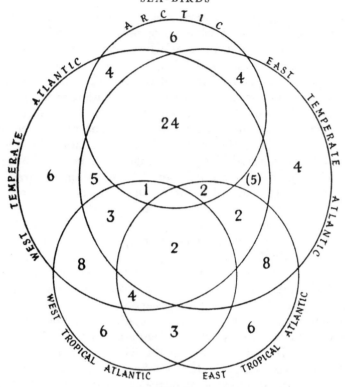

FIG. 2a

The breeding sea-birds of the North Atlantic, arranged by five geographical regions. No species breeds in more than four. Number of species; see opposite page for actual species

included, those belonging to families whose fundamental evolution has probably been non-marine (like anatids and waders) or which are only sea-birds in winter (divers and grebes). Only the more important of these are on the diagram, and they are not otherwise treated in this book. It is interesting that more than half of them are northern ducks which winter at sea, though usually within sight of shore.

It must also be pointed out that several species belonging to the families of primary sea-birds have secondarily taken to life inland, on rivers, or on estuaries, and may reach the sea only incidentally or not at all. Certain West African species, in particular, are river-birds (the pelicans *Pelecanus onocrotalus* and *P. rufescens*, the reed-cormorant *Haliëtor africanus*, the darter *Anhinga rufa*, the skimmer

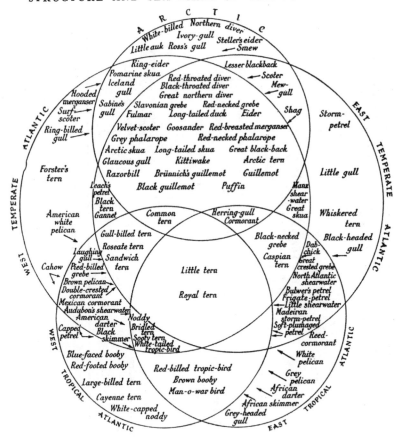

FIG. 2*b*

Actual species. Arrows point to replacement species or to nearest ecological counterparts

Rynchops flavirostris). The terns of the genus *Chlidonias* are primarily lake and marsh species throughout their range. In North America the gulls *Larus pipixcan* and *L. philadelphia* are purely inland species in the breeding season, and the tern *Sterna forsteri* and the pelican *Pelecanus erythrorhynchos* almost so. In South America the terns *Phaëtusa simplex* and *Sterna superciliaris* are purely river-species.

One hundred and eleven species of primary and thirty-two of secondary sea-birds have been identified by competent observers at sea or on some shore in the North Atlantic since 1800: a total of one

	WEST ATLANTIC			EAST ATLANTIC			COMMON TO BOTH WEST & EAST		
	Primary	*Secondary*	*Total*	*Primary*	*Secondary*	*Total*	*Primary*	*Secondary*	*Total*
Between Equator and Tropic of Cancer ('tropical')	27	1	28	27	3	30	10	—	10
Between Tropic of Cancer and Arctic Circle ('temperate') ..	45	22	67	43	22	65	26	16	42
Between Equator and Arctic Circle	55	22	77	56 (60*)	22 (22*)	78 (82*)	33	16	49
				(*including purely Mediterranean breeders)					
Mediterranean :				24	6	30			

Regions north of Arctic Circle ('arctic') communicating with

	WEST			EAST			COMMON TO BOTH WEST AND EAST		
	Primary	*Secondary*	*Total*	*Primary*	*Secondary*	*Total*	*Primary*	*Secondary*	*Total*
North Atlantic	10	—	10	23	24	47	3	—	3
All breeding sea-birds	12	—	12	85	31	116	5	—	5

	WEST			EAST		
	Primary	*Secondary*	*Total*	*Primary*	*Secondary*	*Total*
Purely 'tropical'	10	—	10	12	—	12
Purely 'temperate'	12	—	12	13	—	13

	Primary	*Secondary*	*Total*
Purely 'arctic'	3	3	6
Purely western } south of circle ..	20	4	24
Purely eastern } ..	24	2	26
Western and arctic	2	2	4
Eastern and arctic	3	4	7

hundred and forty-one. Of these one primary sea-bird, *Alca impennis* the great auk, and one secondary sea-bird, *Camptorhynchus labradorius* the Labrador duck, are now extinct. Of the survivors, eighty-two primary and thirty secondary sea-birds actually nest, or have nested, on or near a North Atlantic or Mediterranean shore or a shore of that part of the Arctic (north of the Circle) that communicates directly with the North Atlantic (this brings in six arctic species: ivory-gull, Ross's gull, little auk, white-billed northern diver, brent-goose and Steller's eider). Two further species (*Larus pipixcan* and *L. philadelphia*, see above) are purely inland breeders.

Most remarkably, the number breeding on the Old World and New World sides is almost exactly the same. We can derive the following summary of breeding-species from Appendix A ; the totals include the two North American purely inland species, and the two extinct species. Doubtful ("?" in the Appendix) and casual cases are deliberately included—most of them are from tropical West Africa north of the equator where the breeding of the species in question seems likely but, owing to the scanty exploration of the coast, is not formally proved.

We can see that if we add the six purely arctic breeders to those species which are common to both east and west sides of the North Atlantic, we have fifty-five, out of a total of 116, or about half. Of the remaining sixty-one species, 24 breed only on the west side of the North Atlantic, four on the west side and in the Arctic; and six purely on the east side, and seven on the east side and in the Arctic. Those on the east side include four 'sea-birds' which breed in the Mediterranean area but not in the North Atlantic (the crested pelican, pigmy cormorant, Mediterranean black-headed gull and the lesser crested tern).

The general conclusion is of considerable ecological interest, showing how exactly the sea-bird communities of both sides reflect one another. Although only about two-thirds of the members of the community on one side of the Atlantic are found in that of the other, the species comprising the remaining third 'balance each other' and occupy very much the same 'niches' or places in nature. Opposite species which pair off by occupying similar niches are grouped together in the list in the Appendix, p. 292.

A Note on Non-breeders and Casual Wanderers

Apart from these 116 breeders, the limbo of twenty-six primary sea-birds and one secondary sea-bird (the spectacled eider *Somateria fischeri*, which has been recorded twice in Norway, though it breeds on the other side of the Polar Basin) consists of casual wanderers, with three remarkable exceptions. These are all tubenoses (two shearwaters and a storm-petrel) which breed in the southern hemisphere but which cross the equator in large numbers to 'winter.' The most familiar of these in Britain is the Tristan great shearwater *Puffinus gravis*, which is rather similar, and certainly closely related to the heavier North Atlantic or Cory's shearwater, P. *diomedea*. Incidentally we suggest confusion between the two would be reduced if P. *diomedea* were consistently called 'North Atlantic shearwater' and P. *gravis* 'Tristan great shearwater'—not just 'great shearwater.'

The Tristan great shearwater nests only on Nightingale and Inaccessible Islands, in the Tristan da Cunha group; possibly a few may survive on Tristan itself. The population remains vast, though 'farmed' by the Tristan islanders, and an annual penetration of the North Atlantic by off-season birds has put the species on the list of regular and expected visitors to both West Atlantic and East Atlantic waters, as well as some arctic waters of Greenland. The northward movement reaches the North Atlantic in May, mostly on the west side at first, but odd birds appear in Irish and west British waters in June and have even been seen then in the Skagerak; one of us saw a few already at Rockall in mid-May (1949), and they were abundant there and in moult by late June (1948).

The Tristan great shearwater seldom comes close to land, and it is never common in British waters within sight of shore; but some distance to sea off west England, Ireland and the Hebrides it is always present in July and August; and some elements usually penetrate nòrthabout into the North Sea, descending to the latitude of Yorkshire. The Tristan great shearwater is much more common than the Northern Atlantic shearwater in our seas; indeed, the Mediterranean race of the latter P. *d. diomedea*, and Cory's race P. *d. borealis*, have each only once been taken ashore in Britain, although birds which may have been of Cory's subspecies have several times been seen at the entrance of the Channel. The only Scottish record is of one, seen at sea close to Aberdeen on 10 September 1947, by R. N. Winnall. Normally as Wynne-Edwards and Rankin and Duffey have shown, *Puffinus diomedea* does not get much farther north in the Atlantic than 50°N., and that at about 30°W. It is much more common on the North American coast than on that of Britain, although this coast is much farther from its base; 'they seem to arrive on our coasts early in August,' writes Bent, 'and spend the next three months with us, mainly between Cape Cod and Long Island Sound.' The Tristan great shearwater also probably reaches its greatest abundance on the North American coast, particularly in the area of the Newfoundland Banks, where it is known as the 'hagdon'; from here it extends every season along the coast of Labrador to Greenland;—it has been recorded near Iceland.

The other southern hemisphere shearwater that regularly visits North Atlantic waters is *Puffinus griseus*, the sooty shearwater. It is much rarer than the Tristan great shearwater, though it has been seen in British waters regularly enough to be classed as an autumn visitor. It breeds in New Zealand and its islands, in southern South America and its islands, and the Falkland Islands (in places many miles inland), and ranges the Pacific as well as the Atlantic; its Atlantic population is low compared with that of the other southern shearwater. Unlike the Tristan great shearwater, it probably makes its way into the North Sea by the Channel; and it is regular in small numbers in the Western approaches. At Rockall on 17 May 1949 J.F. saw none, but from 18 to 27 June 1948 R.M.L. found them always present there, singly and up to eight together, that is in the proportion of about one to a hundred hagdons. On the Newfoundland Banks, where it is in the same proportion, the fishermen called it the *haglet*. It reaches Greenland and Icelandic waters, and has been seen once as far north as Bear Island.

The storm-petrel from the south is Wilson's petrel *Oceanites oceanicus*, which nests in vast numbers in the antarctic continent and on the southern islands of South Shetland, South Orkney, South Georgia, Falkland, Tierra del Fuego and Kerguelen. It disperses into, and across, the Equator in the Atlantic, Indian and Pacific Oceans. Wilson's petrel has been the subject of an exhaustive monograph by Brian Roberts (1940), who mapped the dispersal in the Atlantic month by month (Fig. 29, p. 168). Records north of the Equator are only irregular and sporadic between November and March, but in April the species is spread widely over the western half of the North Atlantic as far as Cape Cod. In May the petrels spread eastwards reaching from Cape Cod across the Atlantic towards Portugal and the Bay of Biscay, off which there is quite a concentration in June. By July there is a band of Wilson's petrels across the whole North Atlantic with its northern border at about 40°N., but not reaching Britain. In August the eastern Atlantic petrels disappear, though on the west a concentration remains with its nucleus near Long Island Sound; and this persists in reduced population in September, by which time most Wilson's petrels are making their way home. In September they reappear again off Portugal, and the homeward stream in October runs south along the north-west coast of Africa, continues its line across the Atlantic to the corner of Brazil, and carries on mainly down the east coast of South America; in November and December the concentration is at its greatest in the triangle Rio de Janeiro-South Georgia-Cape Horn.

There are only about ten records for this abundant and successful species, in Britain. It does not normally reach our islands, though elements cannot be within much more than a few hundred miles of Cornwall in June and July. Most of the British records are between October and December—suggesting young non-breeding birds, inexperienced in the ways of wind and wave.

Among the two dozen casual sea-bird visitors to the North Atlantic undoubtedly the most exciting are the kings of the tubenoses—the albatrosses, whose occurences in the North-Atlantic-Arctic are really monuments not so much to the fact that from time to time the best-adapted birds make mistakes and get right out of their range, as to the extraordinary powers of endurance and flight of the world's greatest oceanic birds. Five albatrosses have strayed into the North Atlantic, four of the genus *Diomedea*, which includes the largest kinds, and one *Phoebetria*. All breed in the southern regions of the southern hemisphere.

The most frequent in occurrence has been the black-browed albatross *D. melanophris*, of which we can trace nine records. The first of these is astonishing; on 15 June 1878, north-west of Spitsbergen and north of latitude 80°N., the whaler-skipper David Gray shot one that is now in the Peterhead Museum; it was farther north than the species ever gets south, even though it nests to latitude 55°S. Another northerly record is from West Greenland, and others have been shot south-west of the Faeroes and in the Oslo Fjord, Norway; one is even alleged to have reached Oesel in the Baltic. In 1860 (Andersen 1894) a female black-browed albatross turned up among the gannets of Mýkinesholmur in Faeroe, and came to the cliff every season with them until 11 May 1894, when it was shot by P. F. Petersen. For many years the only British record was of one which was caught exhausted in a field near Linton, Cambridgeshire, on 9 July 1897; but on 14 May 1949 an immature albatross which was probably of this species was seen at the Fair Isle, between Orkney and Shetland. It was first noticed soaring off the south face of the Sheep Craig, the famous landmark on the east side of the island, and obligingly glided over George Waterston, G. Hughes-Onslow and W. P. Vicary, who got a fine view of it (Williamson 1950, 1950b). Further, in September 1952 one was picked up alive in Derbyshire (Edmunds, 1952; Serventy, Clancey and Elliott, 1953).

No other albatross has been certainly seen in Britain: a record of the yellow-nosed albatross from the Lincolnshire-Nottinghamshire boundary on 25 November 1836 is not admitted to the British list. This species, *D. chlororhynchos*, has been certainly obtained, however, in south Iceland, at the mouth of the St. Lawrence river, in the Bay of Fundy (New Brunswick), and in Oxford County, Maine. A record of *D. chrysostoma* from Bayonne in France* may possibly refer to this species, for *D. chlororhynchos* and *D. chrysostoma* are extremely similar, and almost impossible to distinguish in the field. *D. chrysostoma*, the grey-headed albatross, has, however, certainly been recorded once in the North Atlantic—from South Norway in 1837 (or 1834). The light-mantled sooty albatross *Phoebetria palpebrata*, a relatively small species which breeds on sub-antarctic islands, has been recorded from Dunkirk, France*. The greatest of all the albatrosses, the wandering albatross *Diomedea exulans*, has been taken, in France (Dieppe), Belgium (Antwerp) and on the Atlantic coast of Morocco; this magnificent animal has a wingspread up to 11½ feet and may weigh seventeen pounds or more; we can imagine the excitement of those humans who encountered these South Atlantic wanderers on their North Atlantic wanderings! Sometimes these wanderings may end in queer places; for instance, F. J. Stubbs (1913) found an albatross that he judged to be *D. exulans* hanging among the turkeys of Christmas 1909 in a game-dealer's shop in Leadenhall Market. When he saw it 'the bird appeared quite fresh, and bright red blood was dripping from its beak.' There was no indication whence it had been obtained.

Unidentified albatrosses have been seen at sea west of Spitsbergen on 2 May 1885, by the Captain David Gray who shot the 1878 black-browed albatross; off the mouth of Loch Linnhe, West Highlands of Scotland, in the autumn of 1884 by W. Rothschild; and twenty miles north-west of Orkney on 18 July 1894, by J. A. Harvie-Brown (1895).

Apart from the three regular non-breeding summer visitors and the albatrosses, at least six other tubenoses have wandered into the North Atlantic from the South, or from the Pacific. The Cape pigeon *Daption capensis*, has been recorded from France*, Holland and Maine, but the three British records have been rejected from the official list on the grounds that sailors have been known to liberate captured specimens in the Channel. Quite probably they are valid. Peale's or the scaled petrel *Pterodroma inexpectata*, has once been taken in New York State. *Pterodroma neglecta*, the Kermadec petrel, has been once found dead in Britain (on 1 April 1908 near Tarporley in Cheshire). One Trinidad petrel *Pterodroma arminjoniana*, was driven to New York

* Not included by N. Mayaud (1953) in his *List of the Birds of France*

by the hurricane of August 1933, and possibly this close Atlantic relative of the Kermadec petrel may cross the equator fairly often, as it breeds on South Trinidad Island (only), which is fourteen hundred miles south of the equator, surely no very great distance for a petrel. One collared petrel *Pterodroma leucoptera*, a Pacific species, was shot between Borth and Aberystwyth in Cardiganshire, Wales, at the end of November or the beginning of December 1889. The last wandering tubenose is the black-bellied storm-petrel *Fregetta tropica*, a sub-antarctic species which was first collected off the coast of Sierra Leone and has also been taken in Florida. It seems likely that this last species may cross the equator fairly regularly, at least as far as the Tropic of Cancer.

One Pelecaniform wanderer has crossed the equator into the North Atlantic from South Africa—the Cape gannet *Sula capensis*, which may reach north to the Canaries.

From the western United States the California gull *Larus californicus* (which may be a race of the herring-gull, see p. 38) winters fairly regularly to Texas, and thus (in our definition) to the North Atlantic region. Another gull which enters the North Atlantic, from more distant breeding-grounds, is the great black-headed gull, *Larus ichthyaëtus* of the Black Sea and farther east, which has reached Madeira and Belgium and has been seen in Britain about eight times.

Four exotic terns have wandered into the North Atlantic. The South American Trudeau's tern *Sterna trudeaui*, has once reached New Jersey. On the east side *Sterna balaenarum*, the Damara tern of South Africa, has migrated across the equator as far as Lagos in Nigeria. *Thalasseus bergii*, the swift tern, breeds on the west coast of South Africa north to Walvis Bay, whence occasional individuals may sometimes pass north across the equator. The elegant tern *Thalasseus elegans*, of the Gulf of California, has accidentally reached Texas. And finally *Gygis alba*, the tropical, white, almost 'transparent' fairy tern breeds north in the Atlantic to Fernando Noronha, and therefore probably occasionally operates across the two hundred miles that would bring it to the North Atlantic, though there is so far no formal record of this. It has a wide distribution in all tropical seas, but is very much attached to, and does not often fly far from, its breeding-grounds; nevertheless R. C. Murphy (1936) ponders: 'Since there are seasons when powerful southeast trade winds blow from Fernando Noronha across the equator almost as far as the mouth of the River Orinoco, speculation offers me no clue as to why *Gygis* has not succeeded in jumping the next gap and establishing itself in the West Indies.'

The remaining wanderers are from the North Pacific—auks from that cradle of the sub-order of auks. *Aethia pusilla*, the least auklet, has not actually reached the Atlantic, but one was found 'halfway' from the Pacific to the Atlantic, in the Mackenzie delta in May 1927. The ancient murrelet *Synthliboramphus antiquus* has been found three times in the Great Lakes area, but no farther east. *Aethia psittacula*, the paroquet auklet,* has actually reached the Atlantic by turning up in, of all places, Sweden: in December 1860 one was captured in Lake Vattern! If the least auklet has not reached the Atlantic, its congener *Aethia cristatella*, the crested auklet, has, for even if we reject (as most do) the alleged Massachusetts record, we must accept that of 15 August 1912 when one was shot north-east of Iceland. Finally *Lunda cirrhata*, the tufted puffin, was obtained by the great naturalist Audubon in Maine: other records from the Bay of Fundy and Greenland are erroneous.

*Ludwig Kumlien (1879) may possibly have seen this species off North Labrador, see Finn Salomonsen (1944).

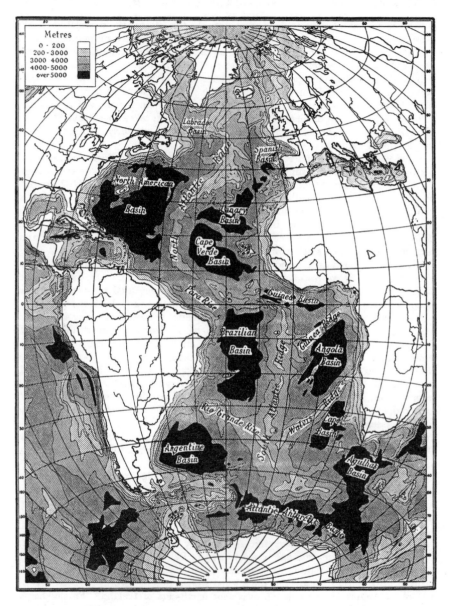

FIG. 2c
Bathymetrical sketch-chart of the Atlantic Ocean

CHAPTER 2

EVOLUTION AND THE NORTH ATLANTIC SEA-BIRDS

GEOLOGISTS DIFFER in their opinions of the origin of the Atlantic Ocean. The followers of the geomorphologist Alfred Wegener believe that it is a real crack in the earth's crust whose lips have drifted away from each other, and this opinion is lent verisimilitude by the neat way in which the east coast of the Americas can be applied to, and will fit with extraordinary exactitude, the west coast of Europe and Africa. It must be stated that, while the present opinion of most geographers is that the resemblance of the Atlantic to a drifted crack is purely coincidental, this is not shared by all students of animal distribution and evolution, some of whom, find the Wegener theory the most economical hypothesis to account for the present situation.

Whatever the truth is, there is no doubt that the boundaries of the Atlantic, and their interconnections, have varied considerably; thus half-way through the Cretaceous Period, about ninety million years ago (during this long period nearly all the principal orders of birds evolved), there were bridges between Europe, Greenland and Eastern North America cutting the Arctic Ocean from the North Atlantic completely; and from then until the late Pliocene—perhaps only two million years ago—there was no continuous Central American land bridge, but a series of islands.

Our present knowledge of the tree of bird evolution owes much to Alexander Wetmore and his school, who have so notably added to our knowledge of fossil birds during the last twenty years, especially in North America. Birds do not appear very frequently in the sedimentary rocks—their fossil population does not generally reflect their true population in the same way as that of mammals is reflected. However, if land-birds are rare in the beds, water-birds are relatively common, and the periods and epochs in which all our sea-bird orders, and many of our sea-bird families and genera, originated are quite well known. A recent paper by Hildegarde Howard (1950), of the school of Wetmore, enables us to show a diagrammatic family tree of birds (Fig. 3), with special reference to sea-birds, and to collate its branching with the approximate time scale of the epochs, so cleverly established by geomorphologists in recent years from studies of sedimentation-rate and the radioactivity of rocks. It will be seen that the primary radiation of birds and the great advances into very different habitats consequent upon the first success of the new animal invention—feathered flight—took place in the Cretaceous period, the first bird-like feathered animals having been found as fossils in Jurassic deposits of the previous period, over a hundred and twenty million years old. In the Cretaceous period—the period of reptiles—ostriches were already foreshadowed, as were grebes and divers, and the pelican-like birds, and the ducks.

In the Cenozoic period—the period of mammals—the radiation of birds into all nature's possible niches continued rapidly, especially in the first two of its epochs—Eocene and Oligocene—from sixty to thirty million years ago. In these epochs grebes can be distinguished from divers, and a bird of the same apparent genus (*Podiceps*, or, as the North Americans have it, *Colymbus*) as modern grebes has been found. Gannet-boobies of the modern genus *Sula* have been found in the Oligocene, as have cormorants of the modern genus *Phalacrocorax*. The only penguin fossils known are later—of Miocene age—but it seems probable that they share a common stem with the tube-noses, which would mean that their ancestors branched off in the Eocene. The tubenoses diversified in the Oligocene—from this epoch we have a shearwater of the modern genus *Puffinus*; and from the Miocene *Fulmarus* and albatrosses. The ducks started their main evolution in the Cretaceous, and by the Oligocene we find modern genera such as *Anas* (mallard-like) and *Aythya* (pochard-like); in the Pliocene we have *Bucephala* (*Charitonetta*)—one of the tribe of sea-ducks.

For the Lari-Limicolae, the order which includes waders, gulls and auks, the fossil record is rather indefinite, mainly owing to the difficulty of distinguishing the present families by bones alone. How-ever, we know that the auk family was early—an Eocene offshoot; that the waders and gulls diverged in the Oligocene; and that the gulls, terns and skuas probably diverged in the Miocene—which means

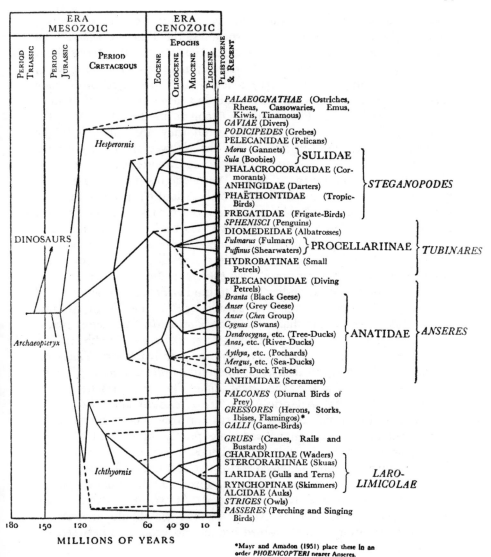

FIG. 3
Diagrammatic family tree of sea-birds, mainly after Hildegarde Howard (1950)

that an important part of the adaptive radiation of this order was comparatively late. One of the early auks, the Pliocene *Mancalla* of California, out-penguined the great auk, *Alca (Pinguinus) impennis,* for it had progressed far beyond it in the development of a swimming wing.

According to Howard (1950) a few living species of birds have been recorded from the Upper Pliocene, but large numbers of modern forms occurred in the Pleistocene. Of course in the Pleistocene the oceans approximated very closely to what they are today, with the Central American land-bridge closed, the Norwegian Sea wide open between Arctic and Atlantic Oceans, the Mediterranean a blind diverticulum of the North Atlantic. We need this picture as a background to a consideration of the North Atlantic's present sea-bird fauna, for we shall find that it has few sea-bird species of its own, and only two genera; for the primary sea-bird species which now breed in the Atlantic (and Mediterranean) and in the neighbouring parts of the Arctic, and nowhere else in the world, are no more than twelve : the Manx shearwater *Puffinus puffinus*;* the very rare diablotin and cahow of the West Indies and Bermuda (*Pterodroma hasitata* and *P. cahow*); the storm-petrel *Hydrobates pelagicus;* the North Atlantic gannet *Sula bassana;* the shag *Phalacrocorax aristotelis;* the lesser blackback *Larus fuscus;* the great blackback *L. marinus;* the Mediterranean gulls *L. melanocephalus* and *L. audouinii;* the Sandwich tern *Thalasseus sandvicensis;* the razorbill *Alca torda,* the puffin *Fratercula arctica;* besides the extinct *Alca impennis,* the great auk. The two present genera peculiar to the North-Atlantic-Arctic are *Hydrobates* and *Alca.*

The sea-birds which qualify by birth and residence to be members of the North Atlantic fauna (excluding purely Arctic and Mediterranean species) include thirteen tubenoses, seventeen cormorant-pelicans, fourteen gulls, nineteen terns, two skimmers, four skuas and five auks (besides various secondary sea-birds, notably about eighteen ducks, three divers and two phalaropes). If we are to understand how these have got into the North Atlantic we should analyse the present distribution of the sea-bird orders and groups as between the different oceans.

The most primitive group of sea-birds, yet the most specialized, is that of the penguins. The Sphenisci have fifteen species in all,

*Murphy (1952) has recently united as races of this species several Australasian and Pacific forms hitherto considered full species, and has suggested that the species may date from the Oligocene period when the Mediterranean communicated directly with the Indian Ocean.

of which eight breed in the South Pacific, seven in the Antarctic Ocean, five in the South Atlantic and two in the Indian Ocean. One (and one only) reaches the Equator, and thus the North Pacific, at the Galapagos Islands. No live wild penguin has ever been seen in the North Atlantic.* It seems certain that the evolution of this order of birds has taken place in Antarctica and in the neighbouring sectors of the South Pacific.

The great order of Tubinares the albatrosses, petrels and shear-waters, probably originated in what is now the South Pacific. Nobody knows exactly how many species belong to this order, as there is a good deal of disorder in the published systematics of this very difficult group; but the number is certainly eighty-six, and may be over ninety Of these fifty-four breed in the South Pacific, twenty-seven in the Antarctic, twenty-five in the North Pacific, twenty-four in the South Atlantic, seventeen in the Indian Ocean, thirteen in the North Atlantic, three in the Mediterranean, and only one, the fulmar, in the Arctic Ocean.

The Steganopodes are an order which is particularly well repre-sented in the South Pacific and Indian Oceans. The pelicans, gannets, cormorants, darter, tropic- and frigate-birds number fifty-four species in all. Thirty-one breed in the South Pacific. Twenty-eight breed in the Indian Ocean. The North Pacific has twenty-three, the South Atlantic twenty, the North Atlantic sixteen, the Mediterranean six, the Antarctic three, and the Arctic two. The present distribu-tion suggests that the order radiated from what is now the East Indian region—from south-east Asia or Australasia.

In the order Laro-Limicolae the family Chionididae, two curious pigeon-like sheathbills, *Chionis*, are found in Antarctica; and one also breeds in the South Atlantic and South Pacific.

In the family Laridae the gulls (subfamily Larinae) number forty-two. In the North Pacific sixteen of these breed, in the North Atlantic fourteen, in the Arctic eleven, in the South Pacific nine, in the Indian Ocean six, in the South Atlantic five, in the Mediterranean five, in the Antarctic two. Besides these two breed inland only in North America, one inland only in South America, and three inland

*Apart from nine king-penguins, *Aptenodytes patagonica*, introduced into the Lofotens and West Finmark, Norway, in 1936; most soon disappeared or died, but at least two survived on the coast until 1943 and one to 1944 (C. Schøyen in K. Curry-Lindahl, 1947, and W. E. Glegg, 1949). Some macaroni and jackass penguins (*Eudyptes chrysolophus* and *Spheniscus demersus*) were also released in the Lofotens in 1938 but these were never seen again.

only in the Palearctic Region. This appears to be the only group of sea-birds whose evolutionary radiation may have taken place from the north; the Arctic and neighbouring parts of the North Pacific and Atlantic appears to be the origin of the gulls. The terns (sub-family Sterninae) number thirty-nine, of which twenty-three breed in the North and twenty-two in the South Pacific, nineteen in the Indian Ocean, nineteen in the North Atlantic, fifteen in the South Atlantic, ten in the Mediterranean, two in the Antarctic, two in the Arctic and one inland only in South America. The radiation of terns appears to be pretty general over the world's seas, and they may have originated in the tropics, perhaps in the Indian Region. The skuas (subfamily Stercorariinae) have only four species, one of which (*Catharacta skua*, the great skua) has its breeding-headquarters in the Antarctic; it also breeds in the South Pacific, South and North Atlantic. The other skuas have an arctic breeding-distribution which extends into the North Pacific and North Atlantic. The three skimmers *Rynchops* belong to a separate family, Rynchopidae; North Atlantic, South Atlantic and South Pacific each have two; the Indian Ocean has one. Some workers regard them as all of one species.

The family Alcidae (the auks) take the place in the north of the penguins of the south. Undoubtedly their origin has been in or not far from the Bering Sea. Of the twenty-two species, sixteen belong to the northern part of the North Pacific, twelve to the Arctic Ocean north of the Circle, and six to the northern part of the North Atlantic.

This concludes the list of sea-birds belonging to groups of super-family or higher status whose evolution has been marine. There are several further (secondarily marine) groups which contain sea-birds, or part-time sea-birds; thus all four members of the order Gaviae the divers, breed in the Arctic, and North Atlantic and Pacific regions, and winter at sea on the coasts of the oceans. Many of the twenty species of grebes, order Podicipedes, are marine outside the breeding-season, and six of them visit the coasts of the North Atlantic at that time. Among the geese and ducks many (see Appendix, p. 295) are partly marine, and some (*e.g.* eiders and scoters) are largely marine in the breeding—as well as in the off-season: two eiders and three scoters breed in the North Atlantic-Arctic. Among the waders (Charadriidae) the subfamily Phalaropinae contains only three members, all of which breed in the Arctic, North Atlantic and North Pacific, and two of which winter in the open sea.

If we ignore these secondary sea-birds, and consider the 267 species of the primary marine groups, we find that the hierarchy is this: South Pacific 128 (51 per cent.); North Pacific 107 (40 per cent.); North Atlantic 74 (28 per cent.); South Atlantic 73 (27 per cent.); Indian Ocean 73 (27 per cent.); Antarctic 44 (16½ per cent.); Arctic 31 (11½ per cent.); Mediterranean 24 (9 per cent.); and purely inland only 7 (2½ per cent.).

It can be seen that the North Atlantic, with its seventy-four species, is much lower than either half of the Pacific than would appear warranted by its area. There is not the faintest hint, from the radiation of any of the sea-bird groups, that either North or South Atlantic has been the arena of any great evolutionary changes. The Atlantic has been colonised from without; by penguins from the Antarctic; by petrels from the South Pacific; by pelecaniform birds and terns probably from the Indian Ocean; by gulls and auks from the Arctic. The North Atlantic and the immediately neighbouring parts of the Arctic have but two present sea-bird genera and only thirteen species of their own. We need not be surprised at this indication that the Atlantic's bird fauna is derived from that of other oceans if we accept Wegener's theory of the origin of the Atlantic; but whether the Wegener theory is true or not it is quite clear that the North Atlantic has not been the home in which any important group of sea-birds has evolved. This is not to say that there has been no sea-bird evolution in the North Atlantic; but it has not usually gone beyond the differentiation of species. Of this it has, indeed, much to show. Some of the classic examples which E. Mayr (1942) has discussed are North Atlantic species. Mayr's thesis is that one species can only become two after it has been differentiated geographically. He opposes the notion which has found favour in some quarters that speciation may occur by ecological differentiation or by the differentiation of behaviour.

So far the available evidence appears to uphold Mayr's view—at all events, for birds. During the present century much systematic work in the description and measurement of birds has been conducted in American and European museums, and much practical and theoretical work on evolution has also been done. But it needed the persuasions of Mayr and Julian Huxley (1942), amongst a few others, to collate the work of the systematists and the evolutionary zoologists. Sea-birds lend themselves to evolutionary study because they are so largely confined to coasts for breeding purposes. This makes their distribution often linear rather than of the ordinarily spatial two-dimensional type; and this linear distribution makes it easy to apply Huxley's concept that the characteristics of animals tend to grade from one part of their range to another in an orderly way. Some of these gradations had been recognised long before Huxley thought of the word "cline" because they are adaptations to the environment. For instance Bergmann's Rule states that from the warmer parts of an animal's distribution-area to the colder parts there tends to be an increase in its size. Thus the puffins, black guillemots and eider-ducks of the Arctic are considerably bigger than those of Britain. The main adaptive reason for this is that larger animals have less surface in proportion to their weight, and consequently heat is not lost from them (if warm-blooded) so rapidly as it is from small animals. Another rule, Allen's Rule, states that warm-blooded animals of cold climates tend to have their heat-radiating surfaces decreased by a reduction in size of their extremities and limbs such as ears, tails, necks, legs and noses. There is also a general tendency (Gloger's Rule) for animals to become darker as humidity increases.

If we examine those sea-birds which are widely distributed, we find clines in various characteristics, notably in size, i.e. total size, and also size of limbs and extremities, beak-length, wing-length, etc., and in colour. There are also clines in shape; for instance the fulmars of the north-east Atlantic have very thick bills, those of Baffin Island rather more slender bills, those of the North Pacific more slender bills still, and those of the Antarctic very slender bills indeed. No sea-bird is arranged quite evenly in its geographical distribution. Just as the distribution in space is never even, so are the gradations in character never even. From one part of the geographical distribution of a species to the other, change often occurs more as a series of steps rather than as continuous ramp.

Most working ornithologists today will agree that there are more subspecific names about than a true understanding of bird evolution requires. It is the species which has reality and significance. In this book we have tried to be sparing in the use of subspecies, and have rejected some that appear in many current text-books. Nevertheless, a study of the geographical races of the species of the North Atlantic sea-birds will lead us to examine here some of the more fascinating examples of geographic differentiation. The classic example among the sea birds is the chain of the *Larus argentatus* and *fuscus* group, the herring-gulls and lesser blackbacks, which may include some birds which are regarded as separate species, e.g. the California gull *L.*

californicus, and the so-called 'Iceland' gull, or better the Greenland herring-gull, *L. glaucoides* or *leucopterus*. The relationships of this superspecies (Fig. 4a) were first worked out by B. Stegmann (1934): we have included the results of subsequent systematic work in this map (Fig. 4b) and in the discussion which follows.

It will be seen that the subspecies is composed of three chains of subspecies which unite in Central Siberia, where the resident breeding subspecies is Birula's herring-gull *Larus argentatus birulai*. The two northerly chains link round the Polar Basin, the two end links of one overlapping with the two end links of the other. Where they overlap, the two races of one chain-end are 'herring-gulls,' of the other 'lesser blackbacks.' These behave as different species. It can be found convenient to make the 'species' separation in the chain, between the two races *birulai* and *heuglini*, thus calling the latter *Larus fuscus heuglini* (it is the first really dark-mantled gull in the chain). This is more practical than splitting the chain into *argentatus* and *fuscus* in the Bering Strait area, though this is probably the place of origin of the ancestral gull that gave rise to the whole chain; for if all the palearctic group were *fuscus* some confusion would surround the light-mantled Mediterranean forms.

Special comments can be made on various members of the chain. In the zone of overlap in Western Europe the herring-gulls are distinguished from the lesser blackbacks not only by form but by many habits. The lesser blackbacks breed often inland on moors, and when coastal tend to colonise flattish ground set back from the cliff-tops beloved of the herring-gulls. While the herring-gulls are dispersive in winter, the lesser blackbacks are almost entirely migratory, wintering south of all but their most southerly breeding-places, though some of the dark *L. f. fuscus* of Scandinavia winter in Britain, and recently a minority of the British race *L. f. graellsii* has 'revived' an old habit of wintering in England, especially in Cheshire and Lancashire. Both species are also extending their breeding-range north; *L. a. argentatus* has colonised east and north-east Iceland since 1909, and a herring-gull of this or the Scandinavian race *omissus* was breeding on Bear Island in 1932, though not 1948. The *graellsii* lesser blackback has established itself in south Iceland since about 1925, and a group intermediate between *graellsii* and *fuscus* in Denmark since 1922.

The North American situation is of great interest. As the herring-gulls range north-east they become generally paler in colour. The much-discussed Kumlien's herring-gull *L. a. kumlieni* was for a long

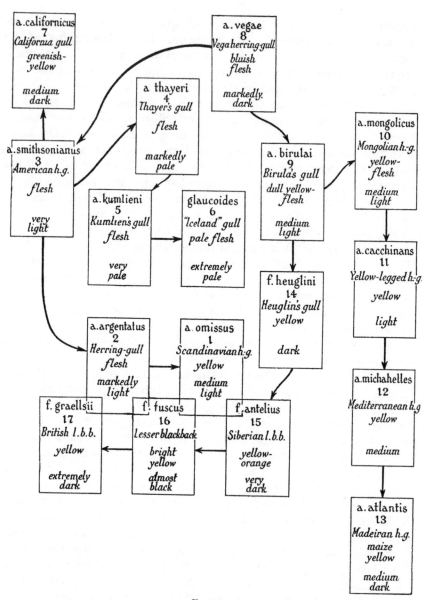

FIG. 4

Breeding distribution and relationships of all subspecies of *Larus fuscus*, *L. argentatus* and related forms.

a Diagram of forms, with leg and mantle-colour

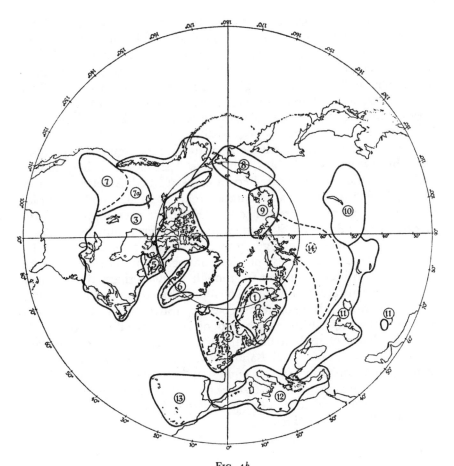

FIG. 4*b*

Broken line: in Eurasia, *L. fuscus;* in North America southern limit of
possible area of overlap between *L. californicus* and *L. argentatus smithsonianus.*
FIG. 4*a*, opposite, gives the key to the numbered forms.

time held to be a hybrid between the 'Iceland' gull of Greenland and *L. a. thayeri*, Thayer's gull of the Canadian Arctic and Thule corner of north-west Greenland. But there seems no doubt that it is a valid race (Taverner, 1933) with its own discrete breeding-distribution in southern Baffin Island, though on the western marches of its distribution there are apparently some forms intermediate between it and *thayeri* (Hørring, 1937) and colonies off south-west Baffin Island have been described as mixed (Soper, 1928).

The palest of all the herring-gulls is the 'Iceland' gull. Unquestionably this extremely pale bird, with pale flesh legs, is a herring-gull, and conspecific with the other herring-gulls of North America. Reports of its breeding in the Canadian arctic archipelago are due to confusion with *thayeri*; there is no evidence whatever of its overlapping with this or any other subspecies of *L. argentatus* anywhere; and its similarity in size, structure and plumage is obvious. It is just a very pale kind of herring-gull; and at the same time happens, through convergence, to be extraordinarily similar to, though smaller than, the glaucous gull.* It is entirely confined to Greenland, breeding north to Melville Bay on the west (this inhospitable coast separates it from *thayeri*) and to Kangerdlugssuaq (at the south end of the Blosseville coast) on the east. Evidence of its breeding farther north in east Greenland, and elsewhere (e.g. Franz Josef Land, Novaya Zemlya) is quite unsatisfactory, and probably due to confusion with the glaucous gull; on Jan Mayen it was stated by F. Fischer to be as abundant as the glaucous gull in 1882-83, and to be nesting on low ledges, but it has not been proved to breed there since.

In a complex situation, such as this, a confusion of scientific names is to be expected. In other cases it is often found that the vernacular name is less equivocal, and certainly more stable, than the scientific name! Such is not the present case, however; for the name 'Iceland gull' makes confusion worse confounded. It has never bred

---

*It is an interesting and additionally confusing fact that the "Iceland" gull resembles the larger glaucous gull, *L. hyperboreus* (with which it overlaps throughout its breeding-range), more than it resembles the neighbouring subspecies of its own species; and that the western forms of the *fuscus* group resemble in plumage the larger great blackback *L. marinus* (with which they overlap geographically) more than do the eastern *argentatus* herring-gulls (with which they also overlap). The glaucous gull and great blackback are closely related to each other, but are distinct species whose breeding range considerably overlaps; within the overlap hybridization is not unknown, though extremely rare. Hybridization between herring-gulls and lesser blackbacks in the zone of their overlap is also not unknown, though rare. Hybridization between glaucous gulls and herring-gulls has also been recorded.

in Iceland. Hørring and Salomonsen (1941) have already used the English name *Greenland Gull* to describe it, and regard it as a race of *Larus argentatus*. We commend to our readers, and to the compilers of the Lists of the American and British Ornithologists' Union : the Greenland Herring-Gull,

Larus argentatus glaucoides (= *L. a. leucopterus*)

Among the North Atlantic sea-birds are others whose species have differentiated geographically and whose range-end populations have become different enough to occupy the same geographical area— but separate ecological niches, and thus preserve their identity. For instance, it is probable that the ring-billed gull *Larus delawarensis*, of North America, and the common gull of the Old World, *L. canus*, have not long since shared a common ancestor, though a subspecies of the common gull, which has probably spread across the Bering Straits from the Old World, now occupies Alaska and parts of the Canadian North-West, where it overlaps with the western element of the ring-billed gull (Fig. 5). Here the two act as different species. The glaucous gull and the great blackback, which overlap in eastern North America, Iceland and parts of the European Arctic (Fig. 6) may be not long ago descended from a common ancestor. They very rarely hybridise. How the three species of terns—the arctic, common and Forster's—which are very closely related, arrived at their present distribution (Fig. 7, p. 46) is difficult to imagine at this stage of their evolution, but they all may be descended from a common tern of north-east Asia or an arctic tern of the North Pacific—from which part of the world the species has probably spread, differentiated and overlapped.

Various suggestions could be made as to the origins of the two guillemots, the common and Brünnich's guillemot (Fig. 8). Possibly the original guillemot was a common guillemot (*Uria aalge*) type which got divided into two subspecies in the Atlantic and Pacific by the Ice Age, but not before it had had time to give rise to an arctic race adapted to the harder life. After the Ice Age, with the ameliorating conditions, perhaps both the Atlantic and the Pacific guillemots began pushing north again, this time to meet and overlap with their arctic descendant, which, meantime, had differentiated sufficiently to offer no direct competition. It is interesting to note that the most arctic of the common guillemot races, *Uria aalge hyperborea* of Iceland, Novaya Zemlya, and Lapland, has a very thick bill and a considerable resemblance to Brünnich's guillemot, with which it, however, does not

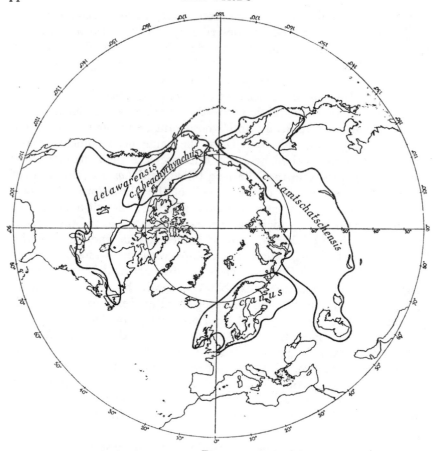

FIG. 5

Breeding distribution of *Larus canus*, the common gull, and the closely
related *L. delawarensis*, the ring-billed gull

interbreed, nor apparently compete. Perhaps it is recapitulating some
of the early stages in the origin of Brünnich's guillemot. To some
extent Brünnich's guillemot, with its razorbill-like beak, appears to
replace the razorbill in the arctic, where it may occupy the same
ecological (feeding and breeding) niche in relation to the common
guillemot as the razorbill does in relation to that bird in the south
part of the common guillemot's range.

The student of variation will find much material for his researches
among the North Atlantic sea-birds. Several species of North Atlantic

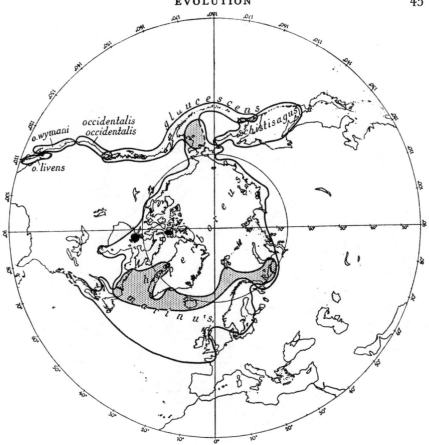

FIG. 6

Breeding distribution of a group of closely-related gulls: *Larus occidentalis*,
the western gull: *L. glaucescens*, the glaucous-winged gull; *L. schistisagus*, the
slaty-backed gull; *L. hyperboreus*, the glaucous gull; and *L. marinus*, the great
black-back. Areas of overlap shaded. Black areas in Canadian Arctic
represent outpost breeding-places of *L. marinus*

birds, notably the common guillemot, the three smaller skuas and the
fulmar, are polymorphic or dimorphic. They exist in several so-called
phases. Some common guillemots have a white ring embracing their
eye from which a white line runs back towards the back of their heads.
These are called 'bridled' guillemots, and were for long actually
thought to be of a different species. The phases of the skuas range

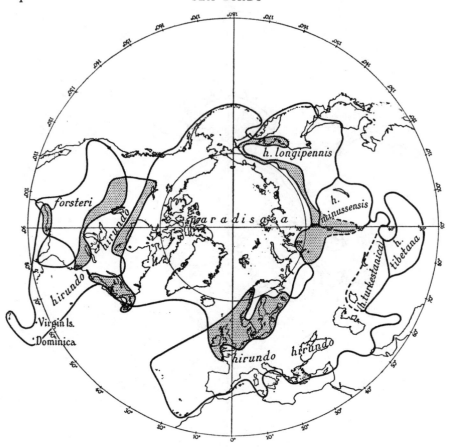

FIG. 7

Breeding distribution of three closely-related terns: *Sterna hirundo*, the common tern; *S. paradisaea*, the arctic tern; *S. forsteri*, Forster's tern. Areas of overlap shaded. *S. h. turkestanica* is a doubtful subspecies

from very light phases with yellow over their ears and the back of their necks, white throats and bellies, to those which are almost uniformly brown. The breeding fulmar population of Britain, the Faeroes, Iceland, Jan Mayen and West Greenland are all light-coloured with white bellies, necks and breasts, but in Baffin Island, Spitsbergen and Franz Josef Land the fulmars are nearly all very dark coloured. Between the light forms of Britain, etc., and the dark forms of Spitsbergen, there are a number of puzzling intermediates, most in evidence

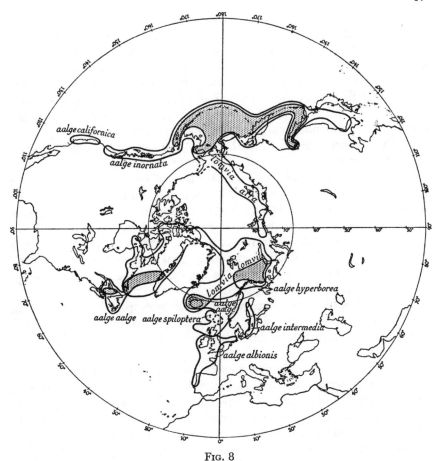

FIG. 8

Breeding distribution of two closely-related guillemots or murres: *Uria aalge,* the common guillemot; and *U. lomvia,* the arctic guillemot (Brünnich's guillemot* in the Atlantic, Pallas's murre in the Pacific). Areas of overlap shaded.

on Bear Island (and often to be seen at sea in the Rockall area), and the situation among the fulmars is therefore one not of dimorphism but of polymorphism, as it is among the skuas.

*The Brünnich's guillemot, *U. lomvia, does* nest in Newfoundland on Funk Island on a little island on the east side of the Avalon Peninsula just south of St. John's (Green Island in Witless Bay) and on Cape St. Mary, S. W. Avalon. These colonies were discoved by Leslie Tuck; the last in company with J.F. in April 1953, too late to alter the map.

Southern, who has carefully studied the problem of the differential distribution of the bridled guillemot, thinks that its 'bridle' is probably controlled by a single Mendelian factor, which appears to control also a slight difference in the skull structure and the shape of the tail-feathers. He organised counts of the percentage of bridled guillemots throughout Britain in the years round 1939 and again in those round 1949; and he has also collected as much evidence as he could from the rest of the guillemot's range. Two main conclusions are apparent: first, the percentage of bridled birds increases from SSE to NNW (with a reversal in Iceland); and secondly the percentage is not always constant at any one place—there are signs of trends towards increase or decrease, and of shifts, or drifts, of the balance. Possibly the possession of a bridle gives a guillemot an advantage over other guillemots in some environments, and a disadvantage in others, though we do not know why: the alternative is that possession of the bridle is the result of an advantageous mutation that is spreading through the population; which is unlikely to be the case on the evidence, though Southern has been careful to show that the possibility still exists. There is no indication that bridled guillemots prefer to mate with each other rather than with unbridled guillemots; mating in a mixed colony appears to be completely, or almost completely, at random.

Southern shows that the percentage of bridled birds marches fairly closely with humidity and cloudiness; but, as he points out, many other factors may be involved. The changes between c.1939 and c.1949 may be linked with the climatic amelioration, but "might very well be due to random fluctuation." The actual percentages as recorded in the paper of Southern and Reeve (1941) and Southern (1951), and in a few notes published by other observers, are shown on the maps (Figs. 9a, 9b). The results of Southern's enquiry of 1949 have shown that out of the very many colonies studied in Britain at only five has a *significant** change been recorded in ten years, four of which show decreases of the percentage of bridled birds and one an increase. One of the decreases is at St. Kilda, where the expedition of 1939 found 16.5 per cent. of the guillemots bridled and that of 1948 only 10.3 per cent. (one of us took part in both counts). Other decreases in Britain have been significant, as at the Isle of May, 5.3 to

*This means, here, not only mathematically significant by the ordinary χ^2 test (not likely to occur by chance more than once in twenty times), but also based on counts by observers whose reliability has been checked against other observers.

3.2 in ten years; and at Unst in Shetland—23.8 to 16.9 per cent. in the same period. There has also been a significant decrease—of about one-third—in Iceland; thus at Grímsey in the north, from 8.7 in 1939 to 6.9 per cent. in 1949; at Hafnaberg, in south-west Iceland, from 29 per cent. in 1939 to 18.1 per cent. in 1949; in the Westmann Islands a parallel decline from 75 per cent. in 1935 (Lockley, 1936) to 50 per cent. in 1949.

Increases noted in the 1939-1949 enquiries were several, but only one, at Foula in Shetland, was significant and by checked observers (from 24 per cent. in 1938 to 29.4 per cent. in 1948-49). Increases on the margin of significance were recorded from St. Bee's Head in Cumberland, Marwick Head in Orkney, and the Fair Isle. Apart from these small increases in the last decade, there was a significant increase of the percentage on Noss in Shetland from 15.5 in 1890 to 26.5 in 1938, which seems great enough to embrace a possible slight observer-error.

Unfortunately, too few of the early bridled guillemot counts are reliable, though some from Berneray and Mingulay ('Barra Head') in the Outer Hebrides may be so. This had 20.2 per cent. in 1871; 12 in 1939; 9.8 in 1949; 12.6 in 1950. The decrease between 1871 and 1939 is significant, though the other apparent changes are not so. Elsewhere we have followed Southern in discarding such vague records as 'about one in every nine or ten.'

Nothing is yet known about the percentage of bridled guillemots along the coast of Norway, except that it has remained slightly over 50 per cent., at Bear Island from 1932 to 1948. At the Karlov Islands off the Murmansk coast the percentage was 42 in 1938. It seems likely, from the rather scanty figures from Novaya Zemlya, which Southern slightly misdates and misplaces, that the percentage may be about the same on islets in Pukhovy and Bezymiannaya Bays off that island (36.4 and 50).

These changes are curious and it is clear that much remains to be solved about this interesting problem in distribution and evolution. Nor is much known about the distribution of the bridled form in the New World, save the following: H. F. Lewis found 128 bridled out of a sample of 724 (17.7 per cent.) in the colonies along Quebec Labrador in 1929. One of us found 51 bridled out of a sample of 295 (17.3 per cent.) at Cape St. Mary, on the south-west corner of the Avalon Peninsula of Newfoundland, in 1953. In June, 1940 at Funk Island and other parts of the east coast of Newfoundland within forty miles

E

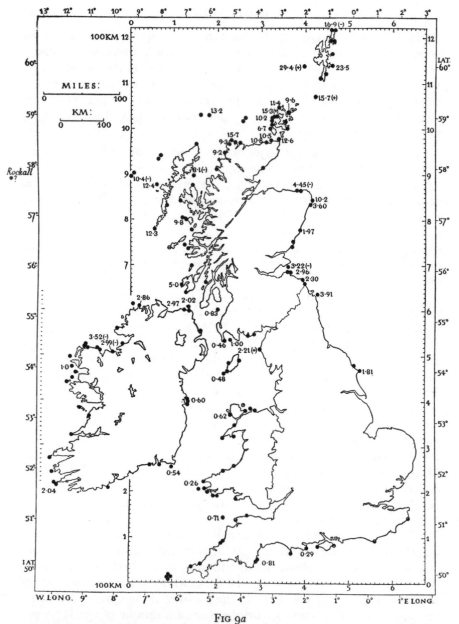

Fig 9a

The principal breeding-colonies of the common guillemot in Britain. The percentages
of bridled forms in the breeding-populations, as determined chiefly by H. N. Southern
and his colleagues, are shown. Minus and plus signs in brackets indicate changes in
the decade *c.* 1939–*c.* 1949 which are significant, or on the borderline of significance.
Crossed circles mark sites of former colonies.

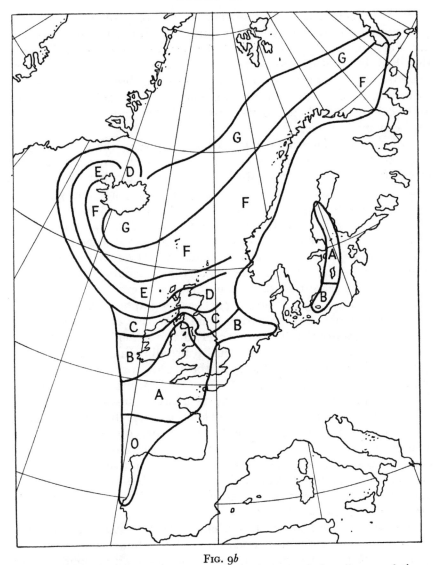

FIG. 9*b*

The distribution of bridled guillemots in the East Atlantic breeding-populations:
O: *no bridled birds observed.* A: *under 1 per cent bridled.* B: *under 2 per cent bridled.* C: *under 5 per cent bridled.* D: *under 10 per cent bridled.* E: *under 20 per cent bridled.* F: *under 50 per cent bridled.* G: *over 50 per cent bridled.*

of it W. Templeman (1945) collected twelve common guillemots (? at random) of which six (50 per cent.) were bridled. When Hørring and Salomonsen (1941) compiled a list of all the common guillemots that had been then collected on the west coast of Greenland they recorded six out of thirty-two (18.7 per cent.) as bridled, but knew of no breeding-colony. Soon afterwards Salomonsen (1944) became aware of the colony in the Sukkertoppen district; but no count has apparently yet been made there.

All the four skuas appear to vary in plumage; the bonxie (great skua) particularly in the amount of rufous colour, especially among some of its southern forms; the three smaller skuas have a 'normal' pale phase of plumage with light breast and underparts, and yellowish or buff on the sides of their necks; and a 'dark' phase which is almost uniformly, or uniformly, dusky; and intermediates. The dark phase of the long-tailed skua is so rare that it has hardly ever been seen. Among the population of pomarine skuas, wherever they may breed, from five to twenty per cent. are dark; the distribution of dark birds is even, in the sense that there is no detectable gradient. Southern's detailed analysis (1944) shows that no geographical area contains significantly more dark pomarine skuas than any other. Among the arctic skuas (Southern, 1943), however, the situation is quite different. In the southern parts of this bird's breeding-range about three-quarters of the birds are dark; in the middle parts about half, in the Low Arctic less than half, and in the High Arctic a quarter or less. In north-east Greenland, indeed, the dark form is unknown. There are a few, rare, birds intermediate in colour between the pale and dark forms. This looks like a quivering balance between two 'stable' types. The proportion of the colour-forms in the British colonies is (Southern points out) subject to rather special considerations, since the colonies are generally small and scattered, and thus liable to random fluctuations—in fact between the limits of 50 and 86 per cent. dark. The mean probably lies at about 75 per cent.

Southern has attempted to correlate the distribution of the dark arctic skuas (Fig. 10) with temperature, relative humidity and various ecological factors. His material carries darkness with humidity over a considerable part of the bird's total range; but the correlation breaks down in Norwegian Lapland—also, good meteorological figures are not available for all the arctic regions.

We found the same difficulty in correlating the distribution of the colour phases of the fulmar, *Fulmarus glacialis*, with climate and other

Plate 1. ROCKALL lies over 200 miles west of the Outer Hebrides: a granitic rock 70 feet high, it is an Atlantic resting-post for sea-birds rather than a breeding-place. Heavy seas wash over the top in bad weather. The shallow seas around are a rich feeding-ground for tube-noses, auks and Gannets

Plate IIa. ELDEY, ICELAND: one of the last refuges of the Great Auk. The flat top is occupied by *c.* 9,000 pairs of nesting Gannets (*James Fisher*)

b. ELEGUG STACK, PEMBROKESHIRE.   Occupied by Common Guillemots on top, and Razorbills in crevices at sides, with Kittiwakes on the sheer walls (*R. M. Lockley*)

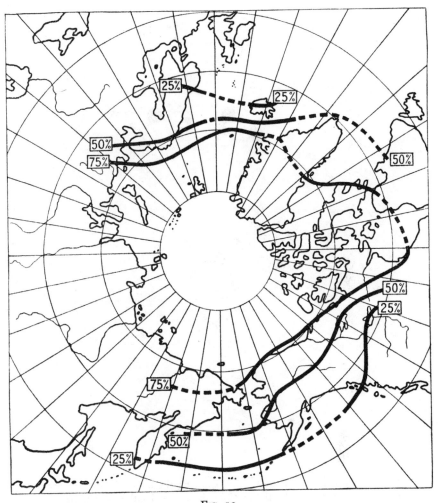

Fig. 10

Distribution of colour-phases of the arctic skua, *Stercorarius parasiticus,* from H. N. Southern (1943), showing isolines for percentage of the pale phase in the breeding population.

environmental factors. In the Atlantic (though not the Pacific) part of the fulmar's range the situation is in many ways the opposite of that among the arctic skuas; where the surface of the sea is above freezing (i.e. in the Low Arctic and rest of the range) the fulmars are nearly all light. The gradient runs from 0 per cent. dark in Britain to a hundred

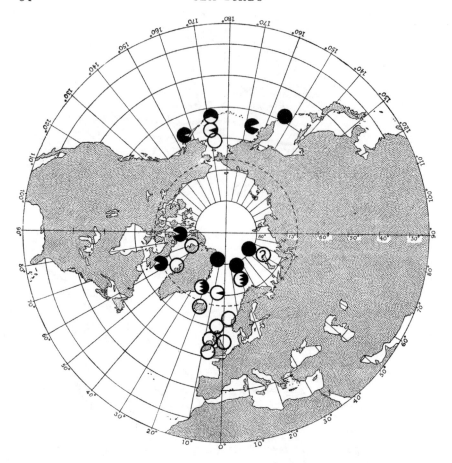

FIG. 11

Breeding distribution of the fulmar, showing the approximate preponderance of dark birds in the populations, indicated by the dark parts of the circles (*from Fisher, 1952*)

per cent. (probably) in the High Arctic of Spitsbergen and Franz Josef Land; in West Greenland (Low Arctic) the fulmars are very nearly all light. Finn Salomonsen suggested to Fisher (1952) a correlation between this distribution (Fig. 11, above) and surface water-temperature. Dark fulmars are only found in the areas where the water is nearly freezing, or freezing, in July, in which month the adults collect food for the chick fulmar. It is interesting to note that approximately the fifty-fifty situation in the distribution of colour-phases of the fulmar (as also of the bridling in the guillemot) is found at Bear Island, whose position is between Low and High Arctic. However, the Pacific fulmar appears to reverse the situation found in the Atlantic; the dark fulmars are found in the warmer parts of the Pacific fulmar's range, and the light fulmars progressively towards the colder parts, though nowhere does this race of the fulmar breed in truly High Arctic waters.

The existence of these polymorphic forms of some birds constitutes a problem of the greatest interest, which travellers and amateur naturalists might well help to solve by collecting simple counts of the relative proportions of easily recognisable forms.

CHAPTER 3

SEA-BIRD NUMBERS AND MAN

E VERY BIRD has a history, which is a tale of adventure and fluctuating
fortunes, of success, or of failure; for every bird, like every other
animal, suffers change. In any study of the life of birds, and the place
of birds in nature, an understanding of their numbers is fundamental.

Since most sea-birds are social animals, and nest in colonies in
wild and beautiful places, their numbers can often be studied very
closely, and with a great deal of enjoyment. So enthusiastic is the
average amateur bird-watcher about visiting sea-bird stations, and
'collecting' islands, that it is safe to say that every *important* sea-
bird colony on both coasts of the United States (not Alaska), and on
those of the Faeroes, Britain, France, Belgium, Holland, Denmark,
Germany, Finland, and Sweden is known to somebody who can distinguish its birds from each other; and *most* of those in Norway, Spain,
Portugal, Iceland and St. Lawrence-Canada are known. The sea-bird
stations of Greenland, thanks to a tradition of accurate observers
from Giesecke to Bertelsen and Salomonsen, are better known than
those of the Canadian Arctic, Newfoundland, the U.S.S.R., China,
and perhaps even Japan. Those of the Antarctic and Subantarctic,
and South America, are perhaps better known than those of the tropical
Pacific. Probably a very adequate list of the sea-bird stations of the
United States (excluding Alaska) or of north-west Europe could be
compiled by some bibliophilic ornithologist with access to all the local
as well as national bird and natural history journals of those countries.
Such lists would be useful documents; they would have to be carefully
dated, because of what history tells us of the fortunes of animals, and
of change. Fisher has recently compiled a dated list of all the fulmar
colonies of the world, and we have both, at different times, compiled
lists of the world's gannetries. It is surprising how certain it is possible
to be of being complete, within reasonable limits. Thus after the publication of his *Report on the 1938 survey of black-headed gull colonies*

P.A.D. Hollom (1940) had no colony known (or not known) to be occupied in 1938 to add or subtract from his list of 342 such colonies. When Fisher and Vevers (1943-44) organised a census of the North Atlantic gannet in 1939, only two small colonies of the twenty-three which then existed were overlooked in that year. When Fisher and Waterston (1941) reported on the fulmar colonies known to them in Britain in 1939 they believed that there were 208 separate stations at which the fulmars were breeding. Ten years later, after carrying on research and correspondence with the same intensity to discover the situation in 1944 and 1949 (during which 'back information' was also collected), Fisher discovered that he had overlooked only nineteen, all small (and some in very remote parts), and unimportant as far as the fulmar's population, or the actual *extent* of its range, were concerned.

A census of the sea-birds of the North Atlantic is no longer a wild dream. A start has been made with certain obvious species, with limited distribution or small populations. The organisational problems are not insuperable; we have an ever-increasing body of highly competent bird-watchers available for, and keen on, the counting of nests: for a sea-bird census depends on the assessment of the number of occupied nests. Such a census has already been performed for several species on the coasts of Germany (Schulz, 1947), and, judging from the descriptions of the distribution of sea-birds in Sweden (Lundevall, unpublished), Denmark (Jespersen, 1946, and Løppenthin, 1946), the Netherlands (van Ijzendoorn, 1950) and Belgium (Verheyen, 1951), it need not be long before a census of the southern North Sea and Baltic could be complete. In Britain good surveys, if not censuses, exist for the sea-bird colonies of most counties in England, and there are records published in the present century concerning almost every bird-cliff in mainland Britain (though not every species on the cliff) and many in the Hebrides, Northern Isles and Ireland. Complete censuses, or careful estimates, have been made of many species of sea-birds in various countries with a North Atlantic-Arctic seaboard; of which a selection is:

Some Censuses

of apparently occupied nests (i.e. an approximation to the apparent total breeding *pairs*) of North Atlantic sea-birds in some parts of their range (in a few cases, world census). Censuses of single colonies are not included unless these are of great importance.

Fulmar, c.100,000 in Britain, including St. Kilda, in 1949 (and five-yearly estimates since eighteen-seventies; Fisher, 1952): c.350 in Norway in 1947 (P. Valeur, 1947): c. 200,000 in West Greenland (F. Salomonsen, 1950): c.200,000 on Bear I. in 1932 (Bertram and Lack, 1933): c.100,000 + at Cape Searle, Baffin I. in 1950 (V. C Wynne-Edwards, 1952).

North Atlantic (Cory's) shearwater, c.20,000 on the Salvages, pertaining to Madeira, in 1939 (R. M. Lockley, 1952).

Great (Tristan great) shearwater, world population between 2 and 2½ million, all on Tristan da Cunha in 1949-50 (M. K. Rowan, 1952).

Cahow, world population all on Bermuda where 13 or 14 nests found and 1951 population "perhaps of the order of 100 adult birds, there may be fewer, but there are not likely to be more." (Murphy and Mowbray, 1951).

Leach's petrel, c.2,000 in Britain; this estimate contains a guess of 1,000 nests on St. Kilda in 1931 which is unreliable since not all the St. Kildan islands on which the species nests were visited (Atkinson and Ainslie, 1940): c.13,000 in Newfoundland in 1942-45 (Peters and Burleigh, 1951).

American white pelican, world population c 15,000 in 1932 (B. H. Thompson, 1932).

North Atlantic gannet, world population c.83,000 in 1939, of which c.70,000 in Iceland-Faeroes-Britain; in 1949 c.82,000 in Iceland-Faeroes-Britain (Fisher and Vevers, 1943-44, 1951). See p. 83.

Double-crested cormorant, Population entire n.e. subspecies *P. a. auritus*, c.20,000 in 'twenties (H. F. Lewis, 1929); re-established on eastern seaboard U.S. c.1925 (E. H. Forbush, 1925, H. L. Mendall, 1936); c.900 in 1931 (Norton and Allen, 1931), over 10,000 in 1944 (A. O. Gross, 1944).

European cormorant, in Holland c.1,200 in 1926, c.2,600 in 1934, c.4,000 in 1937, 4,622 (peak) in 1940, 4,359 in 1941 (van Ijzendoorn, 1950); in Belgium 30 in 1950 (R. Verheyen, 1951); in North America 1,086 in 1940 (H. F. Lewis, 1941).

Great skua, just over 100 in the Faeroes in 1942, c.200 in 1946 (K. Williamson, 1945b, 1948, L. Ferdinand, 1947); c.1,000 in Great Britain (all Shetland and Orkney) around 1946 (R. Perry, 1948, Royal Society for the Protection of Birds watchers and other sources).

Ring-billed gull, c.1,750 in Gulf of St. Lawrence in 1940 (H. F. Lewis, 1941b.).

Common gull, c.500,000 in Denmark in 1939 (P. Géroudet, 1946); 20,221 in Germany in 1939 (Schulz, 1947); *c*.250 in Holland in 1949 (van Ijzendoorn, 1950); a few occasionally on the Belgian border (Verheyen, 1951); *c*.30 in England in 1941.

Herring-gull, c.27,500 in Holland in 1938 (van Ijzendoorn, 1950); 28,569 on North Sea coast of Germany in 1939 (Schulz, 1947); under 9,000 in Maine in *c*.1900, *c*.16,500 in 1921, *c*.25,000 in 1931 (Norton in Palmer, 1949).

Lesser blackback, 1 in Germany 1927-28, *c*.6 in 1938-47 (Schulz, 1947); colonised Holland since 1926, not more than 50 (van Ijzendoorn).

Great blackback, c.1,100 in England and Wales in 1930 (Harrisson and Hurrell, 1933); *c*.20 in Denmark in 1941 (F. Salomonsen, 1943); 16 on Bear Island in 1948 (Duffey and Sergeant, 1950); 3 in United States in 1928, at least 1,250 in 1944 (A. O. Gross, 1945).

Laughing gull, c.25 in Maine in 1860-70, 1, 2, 3 or 4 from *c*.1884 to *c*.1918, *c*.150 in 1931, 1936, *c*.250 in 1937-38, *c*.300 in 1940, *c*.50 in 1941, none since. (Palmer, 1949); in Western U.S. 2 in 1928 (Miller and van Rossem, 1929).

Black-headed gull, 35,000 in England and Wales in 1938 (P. A. D. Hollom, 1940, S. Marchant, 1952).

Little gull, 15 in Holland in 1942, 18 in 1943, 13 in 1944, 1 or 2 in 1945, *c*.8 in 1949 (van Ijzendoorn).

Kittiwake, 6,000 to 8,000 in England in late 1940's (J. Fisher, from literature and notes); 11 in Denmark in 1941, 15 in 1942, 124 in 1946 (Salomonsen, 1941, Løppenthin, 1948); 1-3 in Germany in 1938-39 (R. Drost, 1939); 24,400 in Newfoundland in 1941-45 (Peters and Burleigh); probably *c*.10,000 in Gulf of St. Lawrence in 1940 (H. F. Lewis, 1941b and others).

Black tern, 8 in Britain in 1941, 5 in 1942 (R. Cooke, 1946); none in other recent years.

Whiskered tern, 8 in Holland in 1938, 9 in 1945 (invasions; van Ijzendoorn).

White-winged black tern, 1 in Belgium in 1937 (R. Verheyen, 1951).

Gull-billed tern, 1 in Holland in 1931, 1 in 1944, 2 in 1945, 3 in 1949 (van Ijzendoorn).

Caspian tern, 300 in Germany in 1819, 25 in 1874, none since 1918; 7 in California in 1922, 296 in 1930, 378 in 1943 (A. H. Miller, 1943); *c*.200 in Gulf of St. Lawrence in 1884 (M. A. Frazar, 1887), 30-55 between 1925 and 1940 (H. F. Lewis, 1941b.), 45 in 1945 (O. H. Hewitt, 1950).

Common tern, c. 4,450 in Maine in 1931-36 (Palmer, 1949); *c*.15,000 in Cape Cod region of Massachusetts in 1930-44 (O. L. Austin, 1946) ; 15,000–16,000 in Germany in 1939 (Schulz); *c*.19,000 in 'de Beer' sanctuary, Hook of Holland, in 1939 (van Ijzendoorn); doubtful whether in any year in the present century more than 7000 in England and Wales, and likely that over half of these have been in Norfolk (J. Fisher from literature and notes).

Arctic tern, c.5,970 in Maine in 1931-36 (Palmer); c.4,700 in Germany in 1939 (Schulz); probably under 200 in Holland (van Ijzendoorn); doubtful whether in any year more than 3,000 in England and Wales, and likely that over half of these have been in the Farne Islands (J.F.).

Roseate tern, c.276 in Maine in 1931-36 (Palmer); 1 or 2 in Germany in most years since 1904 (Schulz); 2 in the south of France in 1951 (R. M. Lockley); over 1,000 in the British Isles in recent years, about a third of which are in Anglesey and about half of which are in Ireland (J.F.)

Sooty tern, in Pacific c.166,950 on Laysan Island (Dill & Bryan, 1912); in Indian Ocean over 25,000 in 1937 on Goelette, c.65,000 on Bird Island (Seychelles), c.5 million in 1931 and at least ¼ million in 1937 on Desnoeufs (D. Vesey-Fitzgerald, 1941); in U.S.A. (breeds Dry Tortugas only) c.7000 in 1903, 9,000 in 1907, 10,000 in 1908, 9,000 in 1917, 15,000 in 1935, 20,000 in 1936, 50,000 in 1937, 32,029 in 1938, 35,000 in 1939, c.50,000 in 1940, over 50,000 in 1941, 32,500 in 1942, 54,500 in 1945, 48,600 in 1946, 32,135 in 1947 (P. Bartsch, 1919; A. Sprunt, 1948).

Sandwich tern, c.40,000 in Holland in 1940 (van Ijzendoorn, 1950); this perhaps four-fifths of whole population of north-west Europe; other occupied countries, all with very fluctuating numbers, Sweden (200-300 nests in early 'forties), Germany (3,957 in 1940), Denmark (unknown number), the British Isles (fluctuating between two and five thousand nests, and about 3,500 in early 'forties, J. F. from literature and notes), and Danzig, Brittany and Portugal (a few each).

Noddy, in U.S.A. 200 in 1903, 2,000 in 1907, 700 in 1908, 2,000 in 1917; 1,500 in 1935, 2,000 in 1936, 1,000 in 1937, 206 in 1938, 125 in 1939, 90 in 1940, 500 in 1941, 225 in 1942, 375 in 1945, 275 in 1946, 125 in 1947 (as sooty tern).

Little auk, in Iceland, now breeds Grímsey only, where c.50 in 1820, 150-200 in 1903, c.20 *birds* in 1934, at least 19 *birds* in 1949 (see p. 123.)

Razorbill, 12 in Germany in 1939 (Schulz), all on Heligoland; 318 in Denmark in 1939 (Salomonsen, 1943), all on Græsholm, where 60 pairs in 1944 (K. Paludan, 1947). Peters and Burleigh (1951) suggest that there may not be more than 450 in Newfoundland.

Common guillemot, c.25,000 pairs in Sweden in early nineteen-forties (F. Salomonsen, 1944), nearly all on Störa Karlsö, where only 10 in 1880, c.1,250 in 1918; in Denmark established Græsholm in 1928, c.60 in 1936, 100 in 1938, 122 in 1939, 127 in 1940, 208 in 1941, 158 in 1942 (Salomonsen, 1943, 1943b); c.200 in c.1946 (P. Jespersen, 1946); in Germany c.2,000 all on Heligoland (Schulz and ourselves). Peters and Burleigh (1951) suggest that there may not have been many more than 25,650 in 1941-45 in the whole of Newfoundland, but it seems clear that

Plate III. A sandy shore habitat: Sooty Terns at Bush Key, Dry Tortugas, Florida, U.S.A.

Plate IV. The Double-crested Cormorant often nests in trees with egrets. Redfoot Lake, Tennessee, U.S.A. (about 1,000 birds in colony)

the total west Atlantic common guillemot population is at least 40,000, of which there are about 7,700 in Quebec Labrador (R. A. Johnson, 1940), *c.* 10,000 on Anticosti Island (H. F. Lewis, 1941c.), and perhaps 500 on Bonaventure Island in Quebec and 700 on the Bird Rocks in the Magdalen Islands (A. C. Bent, 1919).

Brünnich's guillemot, c. 2 million in Greenland (Salomonsen, 1951).

*Black guillemot, c.*250 in Maine in 1948 (Palmer); 3 in England in 1940 (Cumberland; Blezard and others, 1943).

Atlantic puffin, world population 1952, not less than 7,612,500, of which 2,500,000 each Iceland, Faeroes; 2,000,000 Brit. Is. (J.F. thinks this an under-estimate); 62,500 France, Channel Is. (R.M.L., 1953).

Though this list includes some very small numbers of sea-birds breeding in some countries and lands desultorily, or at the very edge of their range, there have been some big censuses; and of five North Atlantic sea-birds, Tristan great shearwater, cahow, American white pelican, gannet and puffin, we have estimates of the world population.

We must again remind readers that the figures do not refer to *birds* (unless this is particularly pointed out); but to occupied nests or breeding 'pairs.'

Not many of the censuses made so far are of the species with very large populations. Indeed, if we were to judge solely from completed censuses, we might come to the conclusion that the populations of sea-birds were not high. In fact, they are often extremely high. "The Fulmar Petrel lays but one egg," wrote Darwin in *The Origin of Species,* "yet it is believed to be the most numerous bird in the world." We now know (Fisher, 1952) that, while there may be over two million, there are under ten million fulmars in the world, and that, far from being the most numerous bird, the fulmar is less numerous than many sea-birds, and even some land-birds. One of us has already suggested (Fisher, 1940) that "the most abundant bird in the world is certainly a sea-bird, and probably Wilson's petrel," and nothing discovered in the last ten years has encouraged him to change that view. Nevertheless, many species of sea-birds are astonishingly abundant, and quite a number of North Atlantic species, if not vastly numerous in the Atlantic proper, certainly darken the sky round their arctic breeding-haunts just as Wilson's petrels darken some antarctic skies. The miles of cliffs round Bear Island (especially at its south end) harbour millions (an unknown number of millions) of Brünnich's and common guillemots. Some of the buttresses rise fourteen hundred

feet sheer from the sea, and, as Bertram and Lack say, "have been
described with justice as the finest bird-cliffs in the Northern Hemi-
sphere." However, those of St. Kilda are (in one place) also fourteen
hundred feet high, and are more varied, with a better-known history.
Those who have seen both may think St. Kilda finer, though Bear
Island has more birds and is more magnificently sinister. It certainly
has a higher sea-bird population than any comparable place in the
North Atlantic-Arctic; though it seems to have competitors in the
Pribilov, Aleutian and Kurile Islands and other parts of the North
Pacific. But there are many great bird-stations besides Bear Island
and St. Kilda, where the observer may behold a community of a
million birds or more. On the basalt cliffs of the Faeroes, particularly
north-west Streymoy, he may find this number. Perhaps nowhere
in Iceland is there a cliff-site with a million birds, but there are many
rocks with many thousands, from the Westmann Isles in the south
to Grímsey in the north; from Latrabjarg in the west to Skruður
and Papey in the east. Jan Mayen has at least a million sea-birds;
and there may well be millions at more than several places in Spitsbergen; perhaps on the hills of Horn Sound, Cloven Cliff off the
north-west, Magdalena Bay and Brandy Bay in North-east Land;
almost certainly on the Vogel Hoek of Prince Charles Foreland, the
great auk hill of Advent Bay, and the dolerite Alkrange of Hinlopen
Strait. A pioneer ecologist and student of animal numbers (Elton in
Longstaff, 1924) wrote of the Alkrange:—

"It is impossible to describe the multitudes of the Guillemots on
the bird cliffs. The place was teeming with them: literally hundreds
of thousands. The cliffs are made of columnar dolerite which weathers
into pinnacles and which rise several hundred feet sheer out of the
sea. On the numerous narrow ledges the birds were so crowded that
there was room for no more. The rows of black and white birds rising
in tiers up to near the top, and the ghostly noise of the combined
twitter made by them, made it seem as if one was in a vast opera house,
packed with crowds of people in white shirt-fronts and black tails,
all whispering comments on each other and rustling their pro-
grammes."

It seems clear that either the little auk or Brünnich's guillemot is
the most abundant bird of the north. It is hard to decide which;
the little auk colonies are perhaps fewer, and certainly less obvious
as dense loomeries, because the birds nest in crevices and not on flat
open ledges. But the dark cloud of circling, twittering dovekies

betrays their density, and we believe with Salomonsen that their actual numbers are greater. Nevertheless, some Brünnich's guillemot loomeries are vast, and those at Bear Island, Jan Mayen and Spitsbergen are not the only ones that are stupendous. The largest loomery in the U.S.S.R. is probably that at Bezymiannaya Bay in Novaya Zemlya, where S. K. Krasovskii (1937) has estimated that about 1,600,000 Brünnich's guillemots (birds, not pairs) nest. But Salomonsen (1944) has estimated that in 1936 over *two* million Brünnich's guillemots (birds) bred at the rock Agparssuit (Cape Shackleton), north of Upernavik in West Greenland. This was about half the population of this species in Greenland. There are many other huge bird rocks in Davis Strait and Baffin's Bay; in West Greenland several on Disko Island, in Umanaq Fjord (notably Sagdleq, which may have a million Brünnich's) and in the Upernavik district (notably Qaerssorsuaq, or Sanderson's Hope, where the guillemot cliff is at least three miles long and over three thousand feet high and has two hundred thousand Brünnich's), and several in the Thule district in the far north-west, notably Saunders and Hakluyt Islands, and Cape York, which contains what is probably the largest little aukery in the world;* nobody has been able to guess how many millions nest there.

Other huge bird-colonies in the western Arctic are to be found in Ellesmere Island, North Devon Island, Bylot Island and Baffin Island. Indeed, throughout the Arctic, where the naked rock escapes from the clutch of ice, and precipices rear to the sky from shores, the kittiwakes and dovekies, the puffins and guillemots, the fulmars, the glaucous gulls and pale herring-gulls, make their nests, and operate from them to the feeding grounds, to the leads in the ice, the convergences of tide and current, the upwelling zones at glacier faces and by the side of big icebergs. And below the cliff-ledges is the tell-tale of the bird city, rich plants, sudden patches of green in the arctic drab, green swards indeed, bright yellow-green grass; the round leaves of scurvy-grass, lush, six times as high as in the barren places, which means six inches high. On the slopes of scree and talus and broken rocks below is a special mat of little flowering plants, benefiting from the bird-dung leached and washed down from above; perhaps not the purple opposite-leaved saxifrage, which shuns this community (it is too rich for it), but alpine foxtail, the arctic poppy, the arctic buttercups, and

---

*Rivalled by those of Scoresby Sound and the Liverpool Coast in East Greenland, whose little auk population (A. Pedersen, 1930) has been estimated at about five million birds.

the polar creeping willow; and tufted, drooping, alpine brook saxi-
frages; and the alternate-leaved golden saxifrage; and alpine mouse-
ear chickweed, various arctic whitlow-grasses, poas and a woodrush,
and *Wahlbergella;* and sometimes carpets of Jacob's ladder. There
are many mosses, too, with bright colours; and all over these arctic
cliffs—not only below the bird ledges—grow lichens. One of them
is the beautiful orange *Caloplaca elegans;* it grows all over the bird
rocks of Spitsbergen, shines yellow orange among the dark rock and
green grass-ledges of the fulmar-haunted bastions of Disko in West
Greenland, and colours from top to bottom the mighty buttresses of
Cape Searle in eastern Baffin Island, the site of what may be the world's
largest fulmar colony. Grey fulmars sit on green ledges above orange
rocks.

In Britain, St. Kilda is the greatest sea-bird station. Upon its
thousand-foot precipices nests one of the densest communities of
vertebrate animals in the North Atlantic—probably the densest
south of the Arctic Circle. The gannets of Boreray and its stacks have
about seventeen thousand nests—one-sixth of the world population
of this species. A quarter of Britain's fulmars (up to forty thousand
pairs) nest on St. Kilda. Undoubtedly more than a million puffins'
eggs are laid on St. Kilda in a normal year; the question is, how many
million? There are seven separate puffin-slopes on St. Kilda each of
which is larger than the largest puffin colony anywhere else in the
British Isles, even the largest puffinry in the mossy talus-slopes of the
Shiant Isles, where blocks of columnar basalt lie below the cliffs
like the forgotten bricks of a child. The puffin is certainly one of the
most numerous birds in the North Atlantic. In his monograph on the
puffin (1953) Lockley estimates a minimum world population of
15,000,000 adults.

*   *   *

From the study of the ecology of animals we are learning that their
numbers are controlled primarily by the amount of food they can
get, and only secondarily by their parasites and predators; and
parasites are probably more important than predators. But there
are exceptions to this; and the chief one is when the predator is man
(another is when new predators are introduced through his agency).
Except in a few places such as most of Greenland, Jan Mayen, Spitsbergen, Franz Josef Land and a few other arctic islands, man is,
or has been, the most important predator of sea-birds. He has been

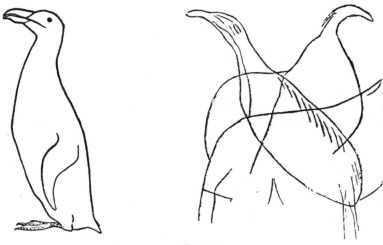

FIG. 12
Upper Palaeolithic (probably Magdalenian) rock-engraving at El Pendo,
near Santander, North Spain, showing what are probably great auks
of which modern sketch on left.
(After H. Breuil, 1911; G. Clark, 1948)

one, of a kind, ever since he has been Man—even before; for there
is ample evidence that during the second of the two advances of
the ice in the second of the two glaciations of the Great Ice Age, some
of the latest members of the species *Homo neanderthalensis* ate great
auks. This was about twenty thousand years ago; the Neanderthals
left their auk bones in the cave of St. Brélade in Jersey and in the
Devil's Tower at Gibraltar. Their successors, the first of *Homo sapiens*,
Men of the Aurignacian age (the early part of the Upper Old Stone
Age, *c.*16,000 to *c.*11,000 B.C.), were of two main races, the tall short-
faced Crô-Magnons, and the shorter Grimaldians, perhaps closely
related to African bushmen (W. J. Sollas, 1924). Great auk bones
have been found in Grimaldian deposits in the Grotta Romanelli
in the heel of Italy* and in another cave whose habitation goes back
to the end of the Old Stone Age, El Pendo in north Spain, a wall-
etching (Fig. 12, above) of Magdalenian age (*c.*8,000 B.C.) may
represent a great auk (H. Breuil and others, 1911; G. Clark, 1948).

*It is of interest to point out that the modern razorbill, the great auk's nearest
relation, which had a similar breeding-distribution, penetrates into the Mediterranean
as far as this in winter.

D

It is probable that between the end of the last glaciation of the Ice Age (about 15,000 B.C. in southern Europe, about 10,000 B.C. in northern) and the present day, i.e. during the Upper Old Stone, Middle Stone, New Stone, and Iron Ages the great auk had quite a wide distribution; judging by the number of bones, and the presence of the bones of young, in some prehistoric kitchen-middens in Britain and western Scandinavia, its breeding-range was possibly wider than it was found to be in historical times (Gulf of St. Lawrence, Newfoundland, Iceland, Faeroes and Britain). We cannot, however, quite agree with Clark (1948), who has collected the information about these deposits, that it was *certainly* wider, for it seems to us likely (see p. 268) that the young great auk left its breeding skerry very early, perhaps, like the razorbill, without either primary or secondary wing-feathers, not much more than a fortnight after hatching; and probably swam with its parents many hundreds of miles before 'fledging.' Clark's list shows great auk bones in middens of the Middle Stone Age in France, Denmark, West Sweden and Norway, of the New Stone Age in France, Denmark and Norway, of the Iron Age in west Sweden and Norway. Several brochs (small forts) in Orkney and Caithness inhabited by the Picts also contained great auk bones; this practically brings the great auk to historical times.

We suspect that the prehistoric exploitation of the great auk was largely confined to interception of the birds on passage and in their winter quarters;* the final collapse and extinction of the species took place only when Man in modern ships reached and attacked its main breeding-haunts.

These, as far as can be discovered, were the *certain* breeding-colonies of the great auk:

In Britain, St. Kilda and Papa Westray
In Iceland, Geirfuglasker and Eldey, S.W. of Cape Reykjanes and
    Geirfuglasker in the Westmann Islands
In the Magdalen Islands (Gulf of St. Lawrence), Bird Rocks
In Newfoundland, Funk Island (east)

---

*One of the reasons for thinking that the prehistoric exploitation was at least partly of at-sea birds is that the taking of auks at sea is a technical possibility; Williamson (1948, p. 157) describes a method of snaring them on a floating board covered with plaited hair loops, to which the auks are attracted by a dummy or decoy bird. This has been, and still is, in use in Iceland and the Faeroes; there is no doubt that primitive hunters were capable of devising such engines.

Other stations at which it possibly nested, but about which the evidence is not entirely satisfactory, are:

In Britain, the Calf of Man
In the Faeroes, Fugloy and Streymoy
In Iceland, Hvalbakur and Tvísker
In Maine, the Georges Islands in Knox County
In Nova Scotia, an island near Yarmouth (? in Tusket Is.)
In the Gulf of St. Lawrence, Cape Breton
In Newfoundland, 'Penguin Island' off Cape La Hune (south) and 'Penguin Island' near Cape Freels (east)
In Greenland, Leif's and Erik den Røde's Islands, near Angmagssalik.

There is no doubt that the main population, when history overtook the great auk, was around the island of Newfoundland, and particularly upon Funk Island, where, according to Peters and Burleigh (1951), it was probably first seen in 1170 by some early Norse explorers of the New World from Greenland.

When Jacques Cartier visited Funk Island on his first voyage to Newfoundland in May 1534 his crews filled two boats with the birds in less than half an hour, and every ship salted down five or six barrelfuls. Two years later the voyager Robert Hore came to one of the Penguin Islands or Funk Island, and found it full of auks and their eggs. They spread their sails from ship to shore and drove a great number of the birds on board upon the sails; and they took many eggs. By 1578 it was the normal thing for French and British crews in the Gulf of St. Lawrence or on the Newfoundland Banks to stock their ships with auk-meat, stopping at the Bird Rocks, or Penguin Islands or Funk Island, and driving the great auks aboard on planks. Today there is nothing but old ships' logs and travellers' diaries to record where the western auks once lived in thousands, save on Funk Island, where a great many bones have been found.

It seems clear, from the account of Peters and Burleigh, that the great auk became extinct in Newfoundland in about 1800. George Cartwright (1792), who lived in Newfoundland Labrador for most of the period 1770-1786, and who often sailed across the Straits of Belle Isle to northern Newfoundland, only logged personal meetings with great auks in his diary twice, on 4 August 1771 and 10 June 1774. On a visit to Fogo Island harbour on 5 July 1785 he wrote:

"A boat came in from Funk Island laden with birds, chiefly penguins. Funk Island is a small flat island-rock, about twenty leagues

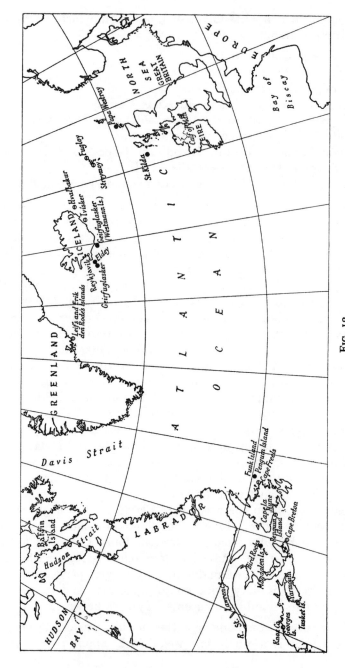

FIG. 13

Known (●) and putative (⊖) breeding-places of the great auk.

east of the island of Fogo, in the latitude of 50° north. Innumerable flocks of sea-fowl breed upon it every summer, which are of great service to the poor inhabitants of Fogo; who make voyages there to load with birds and eggs. When the water is smooth, they make their shallop fast to the shore, lay their gang-boards from the gunwale of the boat to the rocks, and then drive as many penguins on board as she will hold; for, the wings of those birds being remarkably short, they cannot fly. But it has been customary of late years, for several crews of men to live all the summer on that island, for the sole purpose of killing birds for the sake of their feathers, the destruction which they have made is incredible. If a stop is not soon put to that practice, the whole breed will be diminished to almost nothing, particularly the penguins: for this is now the only island they have left to breed upon; all others lying so near to the shores of Newfoundland, they are continually robbed. The birds which the people bring from thence, they salt and eat, in lieu of salted pork. It is a very extraordinary thing (yet a certain fact) that the Red, or Wild Indians, of Newfoundland should every year visit that island; for, it is not to be seen from the Fogo hills, they have no knowledge of the compass, nor ever had any intercourse with any other nation, to be informed of its situation. How they came by their information, will most likely remain a secret among themselves."

Nobody knows when the Norse-Gaels of St. Kilda came first to Hirta, their main island, and established Britain's most interesting colony of wildfowlers. Certainly by 1549 there was a stable human community on St. Kilda, whose life was based to a large extent on "wyld foullis" (D. Monro, 1774). In about 1682 the Lord Register, Sir George M'Kenzie of Tarbat, gave an account (1818) of St. Kilda to Sir Robert Sibbald. He probably did not visit St. Kilda himself, but he says: "There be many sorts of . . . fowls; some of them of strange shapes, among which there is one they call the Gare fowl, which is bigger than any goose, and hath eggs as big almost as those of the Ostrich. Among the other commodities they export out of the island, this is none of the meanest. They take the fat of these fowls that frequent the island, and stuff the stomach of this fowl with it, which they preserve by hanging it near the chimney, where it is dryed with the smoke, and they sell it to their neighbours on the continent, as a remedy they use for aches and pains."

When Martin Martin (1698), tutor to the son of the islands' laird, the MacLeod of MacLeod, arrived at St. Kilda in June 1697 he wrote a classic and accurate account of its natural history, which included this:

"The Sea-Fowl are, first, *Gairfowl*, being the stateliest, as well as the largest Sort, and above the Size of a *Solan* Goose, of a black Colour, red about the Eyes, a large white Spot under each, a long broad Bill; it stands stately, its whole Body erected, its Wings short, flies not at all; lays its Egg upon the bare Rock, which, if taken away, she lays no more for that year; she is whole footed, and has the hatching *Spot* upon her Breast, *i.e.* a bare spot from which the Feathers have fallen off with the Heat in hatching; its Egg is twice as big as that of a *Solan* Goose, and is variously spotted, Black, Green, and Dark; it comes without Regard to any wind, appears the first of *May*, and goes away about the middle of *June*."

We quote this in full, as it is really a most remarkable and convincing description. As we explain elsewhere (p. 268) the interval between the first of May and the middle of June is about seven weeks, the combined incubation and fledging period of the great auk's closest surviving relative, the razorbill. The description also otherwise fits the bird perfectly. Martin arrived at St. Kilda on 1 June 1697 by the calendar of his day, which would be 12 June by our present calendar. If great auks had actually been breeding on one of the islands (Soay would have been the most likely) in that year it is almost certain that he would have been shown them by the inhabitants, and made some comment thereon in his careful notes: as it is his passage that we have quoted reads very much as if the information in it had been taken from natives who themselves had seen the bird nesting and remembered it clearly, but not from Martin's own observations. From this we conclude that the great auk nested at St. Kilda not in 1697, but within the memory of some alive in that year, *i.e.* most probably in the second half of the seventeenth century; we can also conclude from the account that its eggs were sometimes taken. The M'Kenzie information for *c.*1 682 also suggests breeding in this period.

The great auk appears to have been seen at St. Kilda occasionally after Martin's visit. The notes of A. Buchan, who was minister on St. Kilda from 1705 to 1730, respecting the bird derive from Martin; but Kenneth MacAulay (1764) who was on the island for a year in 1758-59, alludes to irregular July visits (not every year) by the great auk; he did not see one himself. "It keeps at a distance from [the

St. Kildans]," he writes, "they know not where, for a
From what land or ocean it makes its uncertain voya;
is perhaps a mystery in nature." After MacAulay's
certain records of great auks at St. Kilda are two: on
Hirta in the early summer of 1821 and kept alive un
this month it was being taken to Glasgow by ship; nea
to the Firth of Clyde it was put overboard, with a line tied to its
leg for its daily swim, and escaped. Another was found on Stac an
Armin, the highest rock-stack in the British Isles (though no doubt
the auk got ashore at the shelving corner), in about 1840, and was
beaten to death by the St. Kildans L. M'Kinnon and D. MacQueen
as they thought it was a witch. Obviously it had been a generation
or more since any St. Kildan had seen a garefowl.

The existence of the great auk in the Isle of Man is indicated by
a picture of an adult in breeding plumage standing on a ledge on the
Calf of Man, drawn by Daniel King, probably in 1652. Williamson
(1939), who draws attention to this earliest British depiction of the
bird, comments that there is no parallel indication in contemporary
Manx literature that the great auk inhabited the Calf. It is quite
possible that it may have bred, though this of course is not proved;
there are suitable low rock-shelves on the Manx coast on which it could
have hauled ashore.

In Orkney one pair certainly bred in 1812. It is not at all certain
that the great auk had previously been a regular breeder at Papa
Westray (the place of the 1812 nest), or anywhere else in Orkney.
The site in 1812 was in a recess low down on the Fowls Craig on this
island. The female was killed with a stone while sitting on her egg.
In 1813 the male was also killed; it was shot by the native Willy
Foulis for William Bullock, the collector, having lived on the ledge
after the death of its mate. The natives called them the King and
Queen of the Auks (Buckley and Harvie-Brown, 1891).

So much for the great auk in Britain; the last of all, except for
St. Kilda's 1840 'witch,' was an odd bird which was found at the entrance to Waterford Harbour in Ireland in 1834, was kept alive for
four months on potatoes, milk, and trout, and which is now in the
museum of Trinity College, Dublin.

The early historians of the Faeroe Islands, Ole Worm (1655),
who died in 1654, and Lucas Debes (1673), both knew the great auk
and handled live specimens caught in the islands. J. K. Svabo (1783)
who was in the islands in 1781 and 1782, records the capture of a

...le on the island of Fugloy which was found on dissection to contain a well-formed egg; and Jørgen Landt (1800, 1810), who wrote his MS. not earlier than 1797, mentions great auks as "climbing up the low rocks." C. J. Graba (1830), who was in the Faeroes in 1828, met old natives who had formerly seen the great auk at Vestmanna on Streymoy, and one who told him that he had killed one on an egg at this place. J. Wolley (1850) in 1849, interviewed an old man who "had seen one fifty years ago, sitting among the Hedlafuglur,* that is young Guillemots and other birds upon the low rocks, and old men told him it was very rare. This was about the time when Landt wrote." Wolley was told that formerly, when many were seen, it was considered a sign of a good bird year; which suggests that the auks may have been desultory visitors for a long time. Finally H. W. Feilden (1872) interviewed an old fowler in 1872, who claimed to have killed a great auk on the island of Stóra Dímun on 1 July 1808; the last record for the Faeroes. K. Williamson (1948) points out that none of these records constitutes proof of breeding, though we agree with him that, though scarce, it probably *did* breed in the Faeroes until the eighteenth century.

The great auks of southern Iceland are well documented, and their history has often been related. They certainly bred on two, and perhaps bred on four *Geirfuglaskers*, or gare-fowl skerries off the coast; from east to west these can be identified as *Hvalbakur*, the most easterly point of Iceland, about 26 statute miles east of the island of Papey, near Djúpivogur; *Tvísker* off Breiðamerkursandur under the great southern ice-cap of Vatnajökull; *Geirfuglasker*, the southernmost islet of the Westmann Islands, and the most southerly point of Iceland; and (until it sank beneath the waves in a volcanic disturbance in 1830) *Geirfuglasker*, nineteen or twenty miles south-west of Cape Reykjanes, the most south-westerly point of Iceland save a rock Geirfugladrangur less than a mile further to sea, which still stands but was probably never inhabited by great auks. After the volcanic disturbance the garefowls went for as long as they were spared to the island of *Eldey*, almost exactly between Geirfuglasker and Cape Reykjanes.

It would seem from the accounts of Ólafsson (1772) and Olavius (1780) that Hvalbakur, the distant whale-back skerry of east Iceland, may have been inhabited by great auks when those historians were in

*Williamson (1948) gives "*Hellefuglar:* sea-birds 'fleyged' [see p. 99] when flying at the foot of the cliffs."

Iceland (between 1752 and 1777); but when N. Mohr (1786) visited nearby Djúpivogur in 1781 he evidently found no news of occupation in that year. If it was true, as Ólafsson thought, that Tvísker (a skerry which at present slopes up to a height of about 46 ft.), was a breeding-place, its occupation must be put before 1764, the last year he was in Iceland; there is no subsequent history here. In the eighteenth century the Westmann islet of Geirfuglasker (which rises to 190 ft., but, as we have seen, has a low platform on one side and low skerries around), had a big colony but, as Friedrich Faber (1822), records, the last known breeding-pair and egg were seen there in about 1800.

The end of the great auk in Iceland, and in the world, took place south-west of Cape Reykjanes. It seems probable that the great auks nested only on Geirfuglasker and afterwards Eldey, and never on the satellite stacks belonging to these rocks—Geirfugladrangur and Eldey-ardrangur. It was known that great auks occupied Geirfuglasker, and were at least occasionally raided by Man, in the first half of the seventeenth century. Though the accounts of the eighteenth century (e.g. J. Anderson, 1746; N. Horrebow, 1752) sometimes slightly conflict it seems clear that Geirfuglasker was occupied in 1729 and that in some years of the first half of that century (if not, perhaps, in that particular year) its great auk population was a "great multitude." Nevertheless, it could have been exaggerated. Horrebow stated that at his time the Geirfuglasker fowlers "filled their boats with the eggs of the Garefowl." (All through the early, uncritical literature of fowling we find boatloads of eggs—they have even been allegedly taken from Rockall, where seldom have more than a couple of dozen guillemots been seen in attitudes of incubation.) But a manuscript of c.1760 (S. Grieve, 1885, p. 19) states that the "garefowl is there not nearly so much as men suppose . . . the space he occupies cannot be reckoned at more than a sixteenth part of the skerry . . . and this only at the two landing-places; further upwards he does not betake himself, on account of his flightlessness." Mohr, who visited Iceland in 1780-81, also thought Horrebow's account exaggerated, though he did not go out to the skerry himself.

In the nineteenth century the doom of the auks was sealed by the raid of the *Salamine*, a private pirate-ship which had plundered Tór-shavn in the Faeroes on its way north. The crew of this ship was ashore on Geirfuglasker on (it is said) 8 August (? a late date) 1808, and killed many birds and their young. There may have been another raid from the Faeroes in 1809 (H. C. Müller, 1862); there was certainly a big one in 1813, when, during the war between Britain and Denmark, the armed schooner *Faeroe* landed a party which killed all garefowls that came within their reach, and arrived later in Reykjavík with twenty-four on board, besides numbers that had been salted down; fifty or sixty were taken back to the Faeroes. On 1 July 1821 Friedrich Faber and H. C. Raben visited Geirfuglasker, and Raben actually climbed Geirfugladrangur. They saw no garefowls at all: it is possible that the auks might have already gone to sea (especially if their eggs had already been taken that season). In 1828 at least one adult was taken, for a skin for the Copenhagen Museum. This is the last visit to Geirfuglasker that we hear of; in early March 1830 a series of earthquakes took place in which the skerry sank beneath the sea. The great auks moved at once to Eldey, ten miles nearer the coast, and attempted to breed there in the same season.

Eldey is a remarkable block of volcanic tuff with sheer sides and a flattish top that is distinguished by being the site of the second largest gannetry in the world (p. 83). It is about 250 feet high, at its highest point. On the east side of its north end, below the cliff, is a broadish ledge which slopes and slants into the sea (Pl. IIa, p. 53), and, as one of us (Fisher) who visited it in 1949 saw for himself, was a suitable landing place and, under the sheer cliff, also a suitable nesting-place for the garefowls. Eldey is made of a particularly resistant type of volcanic tuff; normally such a formation weathers and erodes easily, but Eldey has not significantly changed in a century,* and the Icelanders, who are sensitive to tradition and history, and whose fowlers work with their fathers and sons, are positive that the garefowl ledge is still as it was. It was certainly easy, in 1949, to imagine the great razorbills bobbing buoyantly in the fuss of spray and breakers round the landing-places, clawing a foothold and waddling and struggling clumsily ashore. But they only did this at Eldey for fifteen years. In the first year, the year of the earthquake 1830, two boats took twenty or twenty-one skins for dealers; in 1831 twenty-four were taken; in 1834 at least nine skins and several eggs; in 1840 at least one egg; in 1841 three skins and one egg (the egg was probably laid by a female which laid an egg taken in 1840, judging by their remarkable similarity). On a day between the second and fifth (most probably the fourth) day of June 1844 a boat of fourteen men, under the leadership of Vilhjálmur Hákonarsson, sailed the fourteen

---

*Just after this was written, in April 1951, a large piece of Eldey's top *did* slide off; the garefowl ledge was unaffected.

miles from Kirkjuvogur to Eldey; the sea was rough, and only three men could get ashore, Sigurður Íslefsson, Jón Brandsson and Ketil Ketilsson. They found two garefowls and an egg. Ketilsson smashed the egg, because it was already cracked, and the others each caught and killed an auk. On their way home the men sold the skins to a certain Christian Hansen, who sold them to the bird-stuffer at Reykjavík, Möller. Since that day no great auk has been certainly seen alive by anybody, anywhere.

There is only one other place at which the great auk has been suspected to have bred; it is certainly the most remote and romantic of the lot—romantic because it is the first place in the New World to have been seen by an European. In 877 a Norwegian, Gunnbjörn Ulfsson, on his way to Iceland to settle, was driven west past Iceland by storms, to some skerries, beyond which was land. The land was the the east coast of Greenland, and the skerries, once thought to be what are known as Graah's Islands, at about the same latitude as the Snæfell Peninsula of Iceland, and now thought (G. Holm, 1918) to be Leif's and Erik den Røde's Islands north-east of Angmagssalik. It was from Snæfellsnes that Erik the Red set sail in 982 to found the first European colony in the New World—and he navigated west to Gunnbjörn's skerries on his way. In the old sailing directions they are regarded as "midway between 'Greenland' (the Norse colonies in S.W. Greenland) and Iceland"; which is correct. Many fishermen and voyagers to Greenland after Gunnbjörn and Erik sailed to, or by, Gunnbjörn's skerries, and in the twelfth or thirteenth century at least one such voyager, according to the M.S. sagas of Iceland (Anon., 1838, W. Preyer, 1862), discovered a great multitude of great auks on them. Between 1586 and 1596 the fisherman Látra Clemens from Adalsvík in Iceland is said to have taken a 'boatload' of garefowls here. There is no later record of great auks at this place,* and it may have become too ice-bound with the deterioration of climate at about that time.

Such is the grim history of the great auk. As Salomonsen (1945) points out, the downfall of the great garefowl probably began when the Indians of the east coast of North America exterminated it on the mainland and neighbouring islands; by the time the hungry sixteenth-century transatlantic sailors found it in the Gulf of St. Lawrence and

*Grieve quotes a date 1652, but this refers to a voyage of David Danells on this coast, on which he did not visit Gunnbjörn's skerries, and could not have done so because of the ice.

Newfoundland it was probably already driven to skerries out of reach of the Indians' canoes. Maybe in prehistoric times the great auk also had a wider breeding-distribution in north-west Europe, or at least a very much denser distribution in Iceland-Faeroe-Britain. At the last, in its final miserable nineteenth-century years of slaughter, it was demanded for collectors (though while it was alive they did not pay much for it, contemporary accounts show). For years its passing was not known, and it was still sought high and low, by Steenstrup, Wolley, Newton, Grieve, Lucas; the devoted interest of these ornithologists only served to show that ornithology came not quite in time to save the auk, and that ignorance and greed are sometimes more powerful than knowledge and truth.

*　　*　　*

The end of the great auk was the only extinction in historical times of a primary North Atlantic seabird; but a secondary sea-bird, the Labrador duck, followed it in 1875 or 1878. Man the ignorant killer was again the agent of its death, armed this time with a shotgun. The evidence against him, in this particular case, is circumstantial; for nobody knows much about the population of *Camptorhynchus labradorius*, except that within colonial times it never appears to have been great. Nobody knows where it nested, though it was probably on the Labrador coast of the Gulf of St. Lawrence; no doubt it suffered from nesting-time persecution by Indians as well as winter-shooting by the colonists in the Nova Scotia and eastern U.S. coast; it wintered south to New Jersey.

Two North Atlantic sea-birds which were nearly exterminated by heedless exploitation are the diablotin of the West Indies, and the cahow of Bermuda, two closely-allied gadfly-petrels. The diablotin (or black-capped petrel), *Pterodroma hasitata*, still survives, probably in very small numbers, on Haiti and Dominica, while its close relation, *P. cahow* of Bermuda, now numbers probably fewer than a hundred individuals. But once these birds did not merely survive; they swarmed. The diablotin was first discovered by J. B. du Tertre (1654) on Guadeloupe; he thought it a rare bird of the mountains. In 1696 J. B. Labat (1722) describes a remarkable hunt for diablotins on the Soufrière of Guadeloupe, using eight-foot poles, hooked at the end, in the burrows; six men caught 213 in a morning. Already, Labat commented, the settlers were wiping the birds out. By the nineteenth century it was rare, and most of the surviving burrows on the Soufrière were destroyed by the great earthquake of 1847. But one was caught by a dog on Guadeloupe "a few years" before 1891 (G. N. Lawrence, 1891). On Dominica, Labat recorded it in 1696, and it was known in 1791, and recorded as "abundant" as late as *c*.1858 (G. N. Lawrence, 1878). But it seems quickly to have given way in the nineteenth century, for the Morne Diablotin, the petrel mountain of Dominica, was searched in vain for the birds by Ober (1880), Feilden (1890) and in 1917 by Beck (Murphy, 1936). However, the diablotin reappeared on Haiti (Hispaniola) in 1928 and on Dominica in 1932; and in 1938 a bird was found alive in Haiti which had not long left the nest. Moreover, the diablotin has been seen at sea in the present century in the triangle West-Indies-Bermuda-Azores, and the survival of a small breeding-population upon some Caribbean hillside is scarcely a matter of doubt; it would be exciting to be the discoverer, or re-discoverer, of its present breeding ground. Probably a very small population has survived all through, hidden in the mountains on Dominica and on Haiti. But in Jamaica, where a dark form of the petrel existed on Blue Mountain, no specimen has been found on the old breeding-places since some years before 1891 (W. E. D. Scott, 1891). It is probable that man's introduced animals, including opossums and mongooses, may bear some responsibility for the diablotin's undoubted extinction in Jamaica and Guadeloupe, and extreme rarity in Haiti and Dominica. But it seems clear that Man himself bears most.

Pterodroma hasitata has wandered to the North American seaboard or inland about a dozen times, as specimens from five of the United States and the province of Ontario in Canada show. It has actually been recorded in Britain; one was caught alive on a heath at Southacre, near Swaffham in Norfolk in March or April 1850. In the British list it is called 'capped petrel.' The story of the other rare petrel of the West Atlantic, the cahow of Bermuda (of which two skins only exist) is much the same.

In 1603 the galleon of Diego Ramirez, a famous Spanish captain, sheltered in a Bermudan anchorage in a storm, and the crew found themselves among nocturnal petrels. The cahows were yelling fearfully and eating squids, and it was only after some preliminary skirmishes with what some members took to be devils that the crew settled down to eating, drying and storing some thousands of the fat birds. Within a few years from this first known encounter Man had eaten all, or nearly all, the cahows, for by 1616 the governor of the island tried to stop the killing to save the stock; but it was too late. There was no indication, after 1629, that any cahows had survived.

But on 20 February 1906, two hundred and seventy-seven years after the existence of the peculiar bird had been last mentioned, a black-capped petrel with white under-parts was discovered in a rock-crevice on Castle Island, Bermuda, by Louis L. Mowbray. It was like no other petrel that had ever been seen, though it bore some resemblance to *Pterodroma hasitata*. With J. T. Nichols, Mowbray described the new bird in 1916 as *Pterodroma cahow*. In the same year, though a few months later, R. W. Shufeldt described a new petrel from a large collection of bones gathered from the floors of the old bird-caves in Bermuda by Mowbray and others; he also believed that this was the old, real cahow. The issue had by then become somewhat confused, for Bermuda then harboured breeding colonies of shearwaters. There is no doubt that some of the nineteenth-century accounts of 'cahows' on Bermuda—such as those of J. M. Jones (1859) and S. G. Reid (1884)—refer to Audubon's shearwater, *Puffinus l'herminieri*. Both Jones and Reid alluded to their birds, not inappropriately, as *Puffinus obscurus*, an old synonym of both *P. l'herminieri* and *P. assimilis*.

On 8 June 1935 a boy on a bicycle brought a bird to William Beebe (1935) in his research laboratory at New Nonsuch, Bermuda, from the lighthouse-keeper at St. David's. Beebe sent it to R. C. Murphy, who confirmed that it was the second known specimen of *Pterodroma cahow*. It was a young bird, probably only a few days out of the burrow, and had died by flying against the light. The bones of this bird were, rather luckily, preserved; and were identical with the sub-fossil and recent cave-floor material described by Shufeldt. So there is no doubt that *Pterodroma cahow* (frontispiece) is the old cahow; and that it survived and bred in 1935.

In June 1941 a cahow was killed by striking a telephone-wire on Bermuda. In March 1945 F. T. Hall, stationed on Bermuda, found old bones, fragments of birds apparently killed by rats, and a partly disintegrated adult that had floated ashore.

Murphy and Mowbray (1951) who recount this, were responsible for the uncovering of the cahow's present breeding-grounds in 1951. Study of this group of petrels had suggested that the cahow might have an early breeding-season, and their exploration of the islands off Castle Roads occupied the period from 25 January to 10 February. On 28 January they found a cahow on an egg at the end of a six-foot horizontal burrow at the rear of a rocky niche on a much-eroded islet. Eventually they found three occupied islets, one with perhaps nine, another with three or four, and the last with one occupied burrow. Gurnet Rock, the type-locality of the species, could not be visited. They conclude that there may be fewer than a hundred adult cahows surviving, and that there are not likely to be more. Much of the old nesting-grounds have been destroyed, and rats have established themselves on some of the islets, where no burrowing tubenoses consequently now nest. Louis S. Mowbray (son of L. L. Mowbray) is now experimenting with artificial burrows on some of the remoter, rat-free rocks to encourage breeding. Human exploitation seems to have made the first inroads on the cahow population, but its subsequent recovery has certainly been inhibited by other factors. Murphy and Mowbray conclude that "if a suitable alteration of present circumstances may eventually enable the cahows to spread to neighbouring islands well covered with soil, the future of a beautiful and historic sea-bird will be assured."

*   *   *

The history of the gannet in the North Atlantic shows well the transition from Man the predator to Man the husbandman and Man the protector. In the eighteen-thirties there were probably a third of a million individual adult gannets breeding yearly in the North Atlantic. By the end of the century the number was down to not much more than a hundred thousand. A diagram of the change in population is shown as Fig. 14, p. 80; it is based on the work of Fisher and Vevers (1943-44). The history can usefully start with the visit of J. J. L. Audubon to the Bird Rocks in the Gulf of St. Lawrence in 1833. He made no actual estimate of the number of occupied nests on this island (it was then much bigger than it is today, after erosion), but it has been possible to calculate from the size of the area occupied, and from the known density (one nest to just over a square metre) of this and other 'flat-top' gannet-colonies like Eldey and Grassholm, that Audubon saw a colony which probably then harboured between a hundred and a hundred and twenty-five thousand nests, or about two-thirds of all the gannets then living.

Audubon learned from his pilot, Godwin, that the Labrador fishermen annually visited the Bird Rocks to get flesh to bait their cod-fish hooks. Godwin himself had visited the rocks, with the fishermen, for ten years in succession, for this purpose; and on one occasion "six men had destroyed five hundred and forty gannets in about an hour, after which the party rested a while, and until most of the living birds had left their immediate neighbourhood, for all around them,

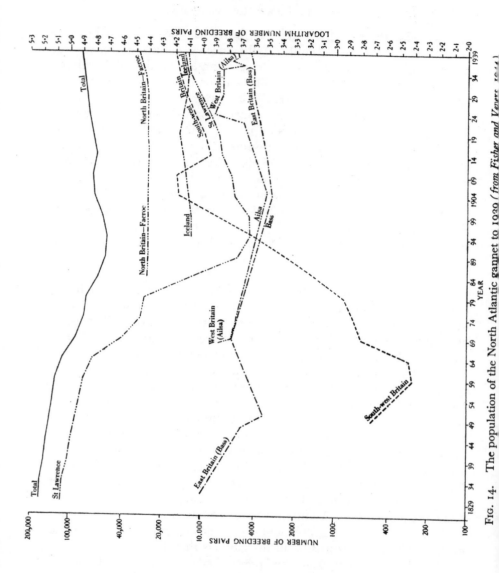

FIG. 14.   The population of the North Atlantic gannet to 1939 (from Fisher and Vevers, 1944)

beyond the distance of about a hundred yards, thousands of gannets were yet sitting on their nests, and the air was filled with multitudes of others." Enough were taken to supply bait for forty boats. The taking of gannets for bait at the Bird Rocks went on until the end of the century (in 1898 the nests reached their lowest number, probably not more than 750), and in 1900 some gannets were shot on the nest and a couple of pails of eggs were taken. From 1904 the birds were protected by Government order, and in 1919 the rocks were made a Federal Bird Sanctuary. Owing to the persecution, erosion of the gannets kept ahead of the erosion of the Bird Rocks, but during the present century the breeding-places have gradually become full up. Much reduced in area by erosion, they now hold fifteen hundred nests or more.

In the sixty years of steady decrease of the world population (1834-94) the downward trend was primarily due to the fate of the colony on Bird Rocks. In about 1864, however, a remarkable upward trend got under way in south-west Britain. The first nests were found on the Bull Rock in Co. Cork in 1856 and on Grassholm in Pembroke-shire some time between 1820 and 1860. The colony on the Little Skellig in Kerry was down to about thirty nests in 1880, at a time when the trends in the other colonies was opposite, and after that date also increased; the present situation (1949) is that the Little Skellig is probably the second or third largest gannetry in the world, equal to that at Eldey in Iceland with about twelve thousand nests, and Grassholm is the fourth with eight or nine thousand.

The world population began to recover not long after this trend in the south-west had begun to make itself felt; and more recently has been 'boosted' by the colonization of Shetland and an increase in Iceland. The St. Lawrence colonies have also recovered and new ones have started; in 1834 they held about 67 per cent. of the world population, in 1894 about 8 per cent. and in 1939 about 16 per cent. In 1864 the south-west Britain colonies held about 0.2 per cent. of the world population; in 1894 about 6 per cent.; in 1939 about 19 per cent. The world's largest colony is now that at St. Kilda, which has remained constant, as far as the records show, at fifteen to seventeen thousand nests. We can reach our final conclusions on the numbers of the gannet by bringing up-to-date the remarks of Fisher and Vevers (1943-44) :

The great decrease of the world's gannets in the nineteenth century was primarily due to the activities of man; and the twentieth-

E

century recovery is largely due to the relaxation of his predation, to the control of it, or to positive protective measures. In the history of the gannet man appears in the different roles of mass-destroyer, harvester, conservator and protector. When he has indulged in wanton massacre of gannets, such as at the Bird Rocks, probably at Little Skellig in its early days, the world population has seriously suffered. By thoughtless and heedless killing man has extinguished at least four colonies; Gannet Rock, Grand Manan (1871), Gannet Rock, Yarmouth, Nova Scotia (1883), the Perroquet Islands, N. shore Gulf of St. Lawrence (1887) and Lundy off the Devon coast (1909). He has endangered the colonies at Grassholm, Little Skellig and Bird Rocks at certain periods of their history. By mass destruction man reduced the gannet population of the world by about two-thirds in sixty years.

At certain colonies, however, man has harvested gannets, their eggs, and their young for his own use, apparently without endangering the population. This applies to Ailsa Craig (Firth of Clyde) continuously up to about 1880; to the Bass Rock (Firth of Forth) up to 1885; to St. Kilda up to 1910; to Sule Stack (west of Orkney) intermittently; to Eldey (Iceland) up to 1939; to Sula Sgeir (north of Hebrides), Mykines (Faeroes) and the Westmann Islands (Iceland) up to the present day.

There is no doubt that at the majority of these colonies man has acted as an unconscious conservator. At Mykines and in the Westmanns the inhabitants are conscious conservators, for they never over-crop, and set an upper limit to their bag before killing. It seems true, however, that as Sula Sgeir man has sometimes over-cropped, and only the intervention of bad weather and wars has kept the raiders (from Ness in Lewis) away in some years, and allowed the colony to recover.

So the gannet is now increasing; and there is no indication that it will not continue to do so. In the long run, it is likely to be food-supply that controls the numbers of the gannets, provided man continues to leave them alone. There is no evidence that this supply is stretched in any way, anywhere in the gannet's range, at present.

We append on page 83 a list of the world's gannet colonies, with the approximate numbers of their nests, in 1939, and of the east Atlantic colonies in 1949.

On the Atlantic sea-board man now begins to play the role of conscious conservator, but he has not yet assumed it everywhere;

Group	Colony	Approximate number of nests 1939	1949	Remarks
Armorican	Rouzic, Brittany ..	28	77	*Founded* 1939
	Ortac, Casquets ..	0	225	*Founded* 1940
	Les Etacs, Alderney ..	0	418	*Founded after Ortac*
S.-W.	Grassholm, Pembs. ..	5,875	9,200†	
Britain	Great Saltee, Wexford ..	0	2	
	Bull Rock, Cork ..	575	295	
	Little Skellig, Kerry ..	9,500	12,000	
E. Britain	Bempton, Yorks. ..	4	2	
	Bass Rock	4,374	4,820	
W. Britain	Great Scaur, Wigtownshire	1	100	*Founded* 1939
	Ailsa Craig, Ayrshire ..	5,419	4,947*	
	[Holy Isle, Arran. *12 birds roosting and carrying nest-material* 1949, *no breeding proved*]			
N. Britain,	St. Kilda	16,900	17,035	
Norway	[Rockall. *Up to 15 birds near rock* 1941; *12 carrying nest-material* 1949, *no breeding*]			
&				
Faeroes	Sula Sgeir, Lewis ..	3,970	6,182	
	Sule Stack, Orkney ..	3,490	2,010	
	Noss, Shetland	1,830	3,150	(1946)
	Hermaness, Shetland ..	2,611	3,750	
	Rundø, Norway ..	0	8	*Founded c.*1946
	Mykines, Faeroes ..	1,473	[1,473]	*not counted* 1949
Iceland	Westmann Isles	4,359	5,538	
	Eldey	9,328	11,000	
	Drangey	0	1	*Founded* 1949
	Grímsey	45	0	*Deserted since* 1946
	Rauðinúpur	0	6	*Founded* 1944 *or* 1945
	Skrúður	0	150	*Founded* 1943
	TOTAL EAST ATLANTIC ..	69,782	82,394	
West Atlantic				
	Bird Rocks, Magdalen Is.	1,250		(1934)
	Bonaventure I., Quebec	6,800		
	Gull-cliff Bay, Anticosti I.	496		(1940)
	Cape St. Mary, Newfoundland ..	4,394		
	Bacalieu I., Newfoundland	200		(1941)
	Funk I., Newfoundland	100		(1940)
	TOTAL WEST ATLANTIC ..	13,240		
	WORLD TOTAL (c.1939)	83,022		

*but 6,579 in 1950: a fluctuating colony.
†but *c.*8,000 in 1951 (R.M.L. & P. Scott), *c.*8,500 in 1952 (R.M.L. & D. Surrey-Dane), possibly exaggerated in 1949.

and before we can reach a discussion of his present protection activities we have to consider yet further some aspects of his past predation and exploitation of sea-birds. One special kind of predation was extremely damaging—the trade in plumes. The terrible depopulation and even extinction resulting from it has been vividly described by many writers, particularly in the early publications of the Royal Society for the Protection of Birds in Britain and the Audubon Society in the United States. The miserable business, which still continues to a certain extent in Asia and the Pacific, started in the nineteenth century and in Britain marched closely with the rise of Victorian fashion. Indeed, it no doubt dictated rather than followed any Victorian fashion. At one time it seriously menaced British bird populations—for instance, the persecution of kittiwakes on the big Flamborough colony in the 1860s resulted in a fighting speech by Alfred Newton, the pioneer ornithologist, to the meeting of the British Association for the Advancement of Science in 1868, which resulted, in turn, in the Sea Birds Protection Bill of 1869.

Terns however still came to some of the London sales in the first decade of the present century in alarming numbers from abroad, such as the sooty tern and the wonderful fairy tern, *Gygis*. 14,400 were sold on 14 April 1906; in 1908, 18,000 on 11 February; 16,700 on 14 April; 16,500 on 10 June. It was not until 1922 that the Importation of Plumage (Prohibition) Act was passed and stopped, at least in Britain, this trade in dead birds for human decoration.

In the United States the depredations of plume traders on the Atlantic coast is described in detail by A. C. Bent (1921). Hunters killed vast quantities of terns and took their eggs. On the coast of Virginia in the last decade of the nineteenth century and the first decade of the present century, the large colonies of gull-billed, royal and little terns were virtually annihilated, and similar destruction of terns was recorded in various places from Louisiana and Florida north to the New England states. As Bent points out, the most pitiful tale of destruction is the story of Cobb's Island and other colonies on the Virginian coast. In 1875 the little tern was "astonishingly abundant" all along the Virginian coast, and particularly on Cobb's Island. But their destruction started soon afterwards. As Bent says, "Professional collectors for the millinery trade spent the greater part of the breeding seasons on the island, and killed the innocent birds in almost incredible numbers. The resident fishermen and oystermen also found it a lucrative occupation. As many as 1,200 birds were often killed

Plate Va. Part of the gannetry at Grassholm, a bare windswept island off South Wales. It has increased from about 60 to 8,500 pairs (1952) in a hundred years *(R. M. Lockley)*

Vb. The gannetry on the cliffs of Bonaventure Island in the Gulf of St. Lawrence, Canada
(Allan D. Cruickshank from National Audubon Society)

Plate VI. Brown Pelican, St. Petersburg, Florida, U.S.A.

in a day, and one of the residents who had taken part in the slaughter himself told me that as many as 100,000 terns were sometimes killed in a season."

By 1902 the little tern had gone. Fortunately this island and other places were shortly afterwards recolonised, possibly as a result of the election of Theodore Roosevelt as President of the United States in 1901! As Roger Peterson (1951) writes, "During his term of office, which meant so much to the wild creatures, his pen created 38 federal refuges. Ten years later, when he visited one of these on the coast of Louisiana, he remarked, as a cloud of royal terns arose from their eggs, that this sight alone was worth all the effort."

Of all sea-birds, terns are the most unpredictable in their social breeding habits. The numbers of occupied nest sites, even at ancient and traditional colonies, fluctuate very much more than the numbers at traditional colonies of other sea-birds such as gulls, auks or gannets. Sometimes a very large colony with some thousands of nests may desert in mid-season; sometimes it may establish its headquarters some miles away from the place where it did so in the previous season. A glance at the table will show the reader the fluctuations in occupied nests at the principal Sandwich and common tern colonies in Norfolk. These colonies have been since the early 'twenties under the strictest protection, and it is almost certain that the changes are due to factors outside human control. They are certainly not due to human predation and disturbance, but some of them may be due to fluctuation in food supplies, others to weather; of course, changes in food supplies can be a consequence of weather. Terns appear to be very sensitive to changes in the environment; more so than any other family of sea-birds. Nevertheless, it seems perfectly clear that there has been a really important recovery in the conditions of these sea-birds of the North Atlantic during the present century and that this recovery is due to protection. It is one of the many indications that the bird protection movement which has been active on both sides for more than half a century, has now won appreciable results. We can, for the first time in human history, say that we have improved the number and variety of our wild birds for the aesthetic satisfaction that they give us and for no reason whatsoever connected with commerce or profit.

It is worth giving details of these changes in the fortunes of the terns. The gull-billed tern, for instance, has colonised Florida in the last twenty years, and on the Old World side of the Atlantic has spread from its ancient isolated nucleus in Denmark to Germany and Holland

Tern's Nests between Brancaster and Salthouse, Norfolk, 1920-50
Numbers approximate minima of occupied nests (figures in brackets interpolated)

	SANDWICH TERN				COMMON TERN			
	Salthouse to Cley	Blakeney Point	Scolt Head I.	Total	Salthouse to Cley	Blakeney Point	Scolt Head I.	Total
1830					+	+		
1831, 1838						+		
1847					*all*			
					common			
1851					+			
1898					*left*			
					(rats)			
1901						140		140
1911						*rats*		
1912						350		350
1914		*"some"*				600		600
1916						*bad yr.*		
1920	0	1	0	1	20	?	0	20
1921	0	2	0	2	100	250	0	350
1922	90	9	0	99	610	2000	17	2627
1923	483	100	59	642	200	2000	315	2515
1924	403	300	40	743	420	(700)	600	1720
1925	0	8	653	661	385	700	850	1935
1926	50	100	515	665	90	400	500	990
1927	200	500	21	721	218	400	584	1202
1928	60	1000	75	1135	60	700	300	1060
1929	271	1503	15	1789	75	(700)	382	1157
1930	225	0	500	725		700	700	1400
1931	275	4	203	482	+	1000	500	1500
1932	592	28	204	824	+	1459	550	2009
1933	738	0	38	776		1543	550	2093
1934	827	0	64	891		1962	450	2412
1935	1000	10	37	1047		2177	1347	3524
1936	730	0	114	844		1971	1647	3618
1937	1000	0	214	1214		2231	1440	3671
1938	1000	0	285	1285	+	1923	2470	4393
1939	1000	3	11	1014		2000	2140	4140
1940	1000	15	649	1664		2157	1700	3857
1941	1000	0	446	1446		2000	1700	3700
1942	0	50	1042	1092		1000	1700	2700
1943	0	2	2000	2002		2000	1700	3700
1944	20	3	1000	1023		(1500)	1700	3200
1945	0	1000	400	1400		(1500)	1400	2900
1946	0	2	1900	1902	8	1400	1400	2808
1947	0	30	50	80		1550	1000	2550
1948	0	42	175	217		1500	1000	2500
1949	0	51	474	525	18	1650	1000	2650
1950	0	194	50	244	29	2122	450	2572

Sources : W. Rowan (1915), B. B. Rivière (1930), Marples and Marples (1934), Annual Reports on Bird Protection in Norfolk (Norfolk Naturalists' Trust, published in *Trans.Norf. Nat. Soc.*), and various notes in *Brit. Birds* and the *Zoologist*.
+ a few pairs

in the 1930's, and, within the last few years, to south-east England. These new colonies are not yet well-established, but at least there is a tendency to recovery in a species which once appeared to be declining to extinction. Unfortunately the Caspian tern has not yet returned to the German North Sea coast where it became extinct some time during the first World War. In both Britain and the United States both the common and arctic terns have suffered a good deal from egging, mainly in the nineteenth century and both World Wars, and from the plume trade, though only perhaps slightly from this in Britain. Undoubtedly both have had a general recovery in the present century, though with marked fluctuations. It is doubtful whether, in any year in the present century, there have been many more than seven thousand common terns' nests occupied in England and Wales, and likely that over half of these have been in Norfolk, where a great recovery immediately followed the institution of the coastal sanctuaries in 1920. However, the colony on the Isle of May in the Firth of Forth had, in 1936, nearly as many nests as all the Norfolk sanctuaries put together—about 3,400 against 3,618. There is an even larger colony in Strangford Lough in County Down in Ireland, and the common terns' nests in the whole of this very suitable county may occasionally amount to ten thousand.

The arctic tern does not appear to have increased in England and Wales, as has the common tern, though there is no evidence that it has decreased. This is probably because England is at the southern limit of its world breeding-range, and the limit itself may be moving gradually northwards, as is the case with many arctic and subarctic species, owing to the present climatic amelioration. Certainly of late the arctic tern has become very desultory at its colonies in the Scilly Isles. It is doubtful whether, in the present century, more than three thousand of its nests have been occupied in England and Wales, and likely that more than half of these have been on the Farne Islands. In the rest of Britain it outbreeds the common tern in most parts of Scotland and the exposed part of Ireland.

The roseate tern has made a fine recovery in the British Isles, where the species was first discovered, in 1812, and which now constitutes its European headquarters; its extraordinary breeding distribution appears to be of a relict type (Fig. 16, p. 90). The tendency of such distributions is, of course, to become further restricted. However, the trend has been reversed in Britain. It is doubtful if there were a hundred nests or eight colonies in the whole of Britain in any

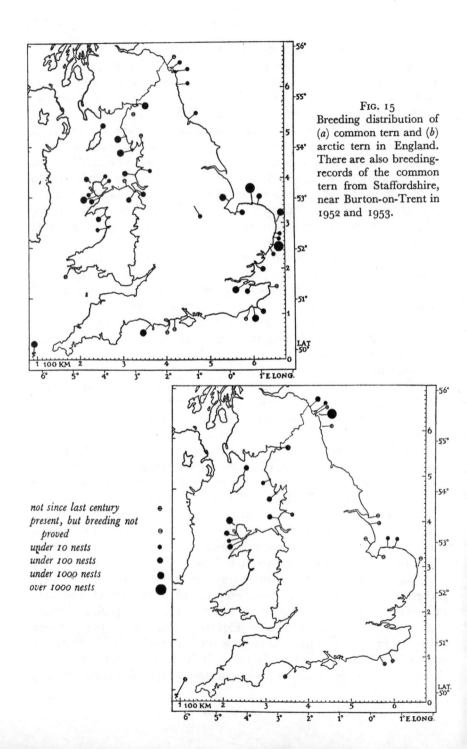

FIG. 15
Breeding distribution of
(*a*) common tern and (*b*)
arctic tern in England.
There are also breeding-
records of the common
tern from Staffordshire,
near Burton-on-Trent in
1952 and 1953.

not since last century
present, but breeding not
     proved
under *10* nests
under *100* nests
under *1000* nests
over *1000* nests

year in the nineteenth century. At the turn of the century it was possible that the only nests in Britain were one or two on the Farne Islands, in Northumberland. At present there are twenty colonies or less, which are not likely to have much more than a thousand occupied nests in any one year, about one-third of which are in Anglesey and at least one-third of which are in County Down. Outside Britain a few hundred pairs of roseate terns breed on islets off the coast of Brittany; and in 1951 R. M. L. and the warden, H. Lomont, of the Réserve zoologique, found two pairs nesting in the Camargue of southern France.

Perhaps the best example of a tern which protection has helped (but whose fluctuation, and desultory breeding, protection has not prevented) is the Sandwich tern. The most spectacular increases in the population of this bird have been in Holland, where at present it is likely that ten times as many nest as in Germany or Britain. Indeed, round 1940 there may have been forty thousand nests on this fairly short coast, which is the culmination of notable increases during the first half of this century, which have been primarily due to protection, in which the Dutch excel. The numbers of the colonies have fluctuated and, as is also true in Germany and Britain, the population has transferred itself from one part of the coast to a neighbouring part in subsequent successful seasons. In Britain it is probable that the Sandwich tern was extinguished at its original haunts near Sandwich by eggers rather than by plume traders. It has never returned. In Norfolk the situation (see table, p. 86) in the sanctuaries provided for terns by the National Trust and the Norfolk Naturalists' Trust shows a triumph for bird protection, which has established the species in large numbers, though it has clearly been unable to control its fluctuation. A colony on the Farne Islands in Northumberland has survived egging by collectors for human food and for oologists' cabinets in the nineteenth century, and while it does not at present attain the numbers it reached in the last century, it seems to have (rather surprisingly) consistently remained at about a thousand nests. In spite of some suitable nesting space being occupied by arctic and other species of terns, the Sandwich tern seems to have started new colonies farther north, for the species seems to be steadily building up its numbers (since 1921) in the Firth of Forth. In Ireland an increase which was noticeable early in the present century may not continue. In Jersey it is numerous in some years; in 1952 the colony of 250 pairs suddenly disappeared after laying eggs.

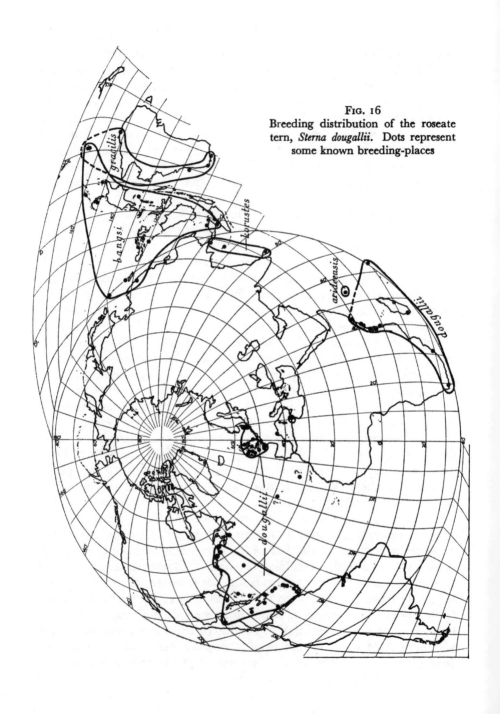

Fig. 16
Breeding distribution of the roseate
tern, *Sterna dougallii*. Dots represent
some known breeding-places

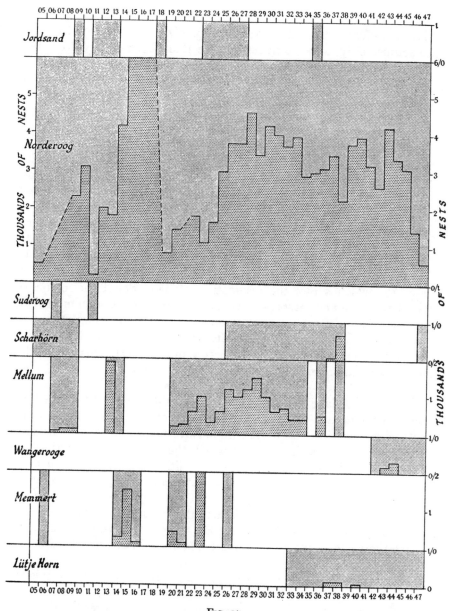

FIG. 17

The populations (occupied nests) of the Sandwich tern colonies of the German North Sea coast (and Jordsand in Denmark). Data mostly from H. Schulz (1947), for years 1905–47. *Dark shading:* population. *Light shading:* station occupied but population not recorded.

We find from the detailed account of Schulz (1947) that since 1819 sixteen different sites have been occupied on the coast of Germany, sometimes only three, and never more than seven at once (or six in the present century). The only colony which has been continuously occupied since that date is on Norderoog in the north Frisian Islands; this has also always (except in one year) been the largest. In 1819 the (? over-) enthusiastic Naumann estimated the numbers breeding on Norderoog as "upwards of half a million!" In the eighteen-seventies it was twice alleged that Norderoog had ten thousand nests; but in the present century estimates which were probably more careful have given a maximum of about six thousand nests in 1915-17. The most recent peak was 4,215 in 1943, and only four times in the last half-century have under a thousand nests been found. At present Norderoog accounts for all but a few hundred of the German Sandwich terns' nests, and the only other regular colonies are on Wangerooge and Lütje Horn. Since 1943 (4,215 nests) the Norderoog colony has decreased, and only 576 sites were occupied in 1947. A glance at Fig. 17, which shows the occupation of Sandwich terneries on the German North Sea coast since 1905, and their population in most years, will persuade the reader at once that Sandwich terns share desultory and unpredictable breeding-habits with the rest of their family, and that along a stretch of coast there is much transference of breeders from one station to another in successive seasons.

*   *   *

So far we have been dealing mostly with cases where greed has blinded the human predator to the consequences of his act, and where conscious acts of altruistic legislation have helped to save the species. However, there are situations in which the human communities have depended, and indeed, still depend, on wild bird populations for much or all of their protein supply, and have entered upon a custom of annual cropping of the colonies which has resulted in no detectable change in the status of these colonies other than can be expected with natural fluctuation. Indeed, there are several cases where, over many years, there has been a general trend of increase in a regularly exploited sea-bird population.

Anybody familiar with the history of St. Kilda or with the existing situation in the Faeroe Islands and Iceland will have discovered a situation completely different from the sorry story of greed and blood-shed associated with the eggers and plume-hunters of Florida, the Carolinas and Virginia, the Asiatic raiders of the Pacific islands, the

Plate VII. Shags make use of the broader cliff ledges: Kittiwakes build in the narrow discontinuous niches (the young are in their first or *tarrock* plumage) (*C. A. Gibson-Hill*)

Plate VIII. Dune-dwelling Sandwich Terns, Holland

Eric Hosking

hungry seamen of the early voyages to the Gulf of St. Lawrence. It is not, of course, inevitable that a resident human community comes into harmonious balance with the sea-birds which he exploits; but besides the places we have mentioned, it is likely that such is also the case in West Greenland, and on Baffin and Bylot Islands, where the Eskimo communities have a long fowling tradition. It is also probable that in some tropical islands the native populations have arrived at an harmonious predation of sea-birds.

There are many accounts of the history of fowling, notably that of H. A. MacPherson (1897). In Britain the two main fowling communities have been the eggers or "climmers" of the Flamborough cliffs in Norfolk, who descend the precipices of Bempton and Speeton on ropes to collect eggs, particularly those of guillemots, and the now extinct community of St. Kilda, which continued its fowling activities until it left the islands in 1930.

The St. Kildans lived very largely on birds. From all the accounts (and there are many) the average St. Kildan ate one bird nearly every day throughout the year. The birds chiefly taken were fulmars, gannets and puffins. In the century 1829-1929, the St. Kildans took an average of 115 fulmars a year per inhabitant (min. 100, max. 130). The greatest total annual catch reliably reported is 12,000 from the years 1829-43, when the human population averaged about 102. Even in 1929, the year before the evacuation, when only about 32 natives remained on the islands, 4,000 fulmars were taken. Most were young, taken between 12 and 26 August when sitting, fat, heavier (and more edible!) than their parents, on their cliff-ledges, but some were adults. The St. Kildans also noosed adults in March, and took a few eggs in mid- and late May. It seems likely that in most years they consumed half the reproductive output of the entire St. Kilda fulmar population.

The gannet colony on Boreray, Stac Lee and Stac an Armin, the great north rocks of St. Kilda, is the largest in the world. In 1939 nearly 17,000 and in 1949 about the same number of nests were estimated to be occupied; about a fifth of all the gannets in the North Atlantic. Martin Martin certainly exaggerated the total crop of gannets taken (22,600 in 1696, he said), and it was the careful N. MacKenzie who showed that before 1829 never more than 5,000 young were taken, and never more than 2,000 from 1829 to 1843. In 1840 the crop was c.1,600 young. But the crop was not only of young; from their arrival on the cliffs the adult gannets were taken, and their eggs; thus 1,100 adult gannets were taken in a single night in June 1847, and in April 1885 (probably before most eggs had been laid) 660 were taken in two nights. The crop of young in 1895 was high—3,200; but only 300 young were taken in 1902. This is the last record of the taking of young. On 14 May 1902 the top of Stac Lee was cleared of gannet eggs. 600 adults were caught in the spring of 1910—the last record we have. St. Kildans thought adult gannets, when arriving fat on the cliffs, and taken in March, were good eating—but not later in the breeding-season. They had a high opinion of the goodness of the eggs.* The "gugas" were held to be excellent, an opinion shared widely in the Lewis (and even in North America, whither salted gugas are sent to Lewisian emigrés at Christmas) and by the writers of this book, who have tasted them in Scotland and the Faeroes.

The Manx shearwater, which nests on Dún and Soay, on a slope of giant talus on Hirta known as the Carn Mór, and probably at the Cambir and other places on Hirta, was not much exploited. Mac-Kenzie (1905) in 1829-43 says the young were relished, and that the eggs and adults were taken; in Dixon's time, in 1884, they were hunted at night; George Murray (unpublished diary) records that on 9 April 1887 shearwaters were taken from their burrows with the aid of dogs. By the turn of the century the St. Kildans were taking shearwaters' eggs for collectors and dealers, but not eating them.

---

*The St. Kildans had somewhat different ideas from the rest of the world about the relative palatability of eggs. H. B. Cott (1948, 1949) submitted a large number of the eggs of wild birds to the Panel of Egg Tasters at the Low Temperature Research Station at Cambridge: they found those of the gannet "relatively unpalatable," thus disagreeing with the St. Kildans. But when, in later experiments (1951, 1952) Cott used hedgehogs and rats as tasters he found gannets' eggs second only in a hierarchy of many species! Certainly the St. Kildans valued gannets' eggs to the extent of making for years annual expeditions in April and May, involving the sensational climbs of Boreray and Stac an Armin, to gather them.

In the eighteenth century, at least, no gannet eggs were taken on Stac Lee, which was left to produce young. These young could then be cropped before those derived from replacement-eggs on the other rocks.

Martin has an amusing passage about the impact of the gannet's egg on the outsiders: "The eggs are found to be of an astringent and windy quality to strangers, but, it seems, are not so to the inhabitants, who are used to eat them from the nest. Our men upon their arrival eating greedily of them become costive and feverish; some had the hemorrhoid veins swelled. . . . They preserve their eggs commonly in their stone pyramids [cletts], scattering the burnt ashes of turf under and about them, to defend them from the air, dryness being their only preservative, and moisture their corruption; they preserve them six, seven or eight months, as above said; and then they become appetizing and loosening, especially those that begin to turn."

The egg of the razorbill, writes MacKenzie, "when fresh is considered very good eating, but the bird even when in condition only fairly so." The razorbill was not important in St. Kilda fowling. Most of its colonies were fairly accessible to the St. Kildans, but they took little of them, save a few basketfuls of eggs a year. Adults were usually stripped of their feathers, and their plucked bodies put to the fields as manure.

The guillemot is much more important. MacKenzie writes "I have seen seventeen baskets full of eggs taken at one time from Stackbiorrach [Stac Biorach, a slender pillar 236 feet high out of the sea between Hirta and Soay], and at another time in the same season fourteen. These baskets hold each about four hundred of these eggs. . . .* These eggs are very good eating when fresh. After they are incubated for a few days most of the egg appears, when boiled, to be changed into a rich thick cream, and in this condition they are also relished. Sometimes eggs, not only of this species but of some others which have not been hatched, are found late in the season. Some of these when cooked look like a piece of sponge cake, have a high gamey flavour, and are esteemed a great delicacy. Others are as bad as the most vivid imagination can depict." The adults were not thought good to eat except when they came in to the rocks, fat, in March and April, when they were caught by an imaginative device, described later (p. 97); they were mostly used as a source of feathers and fertilizer. Many blown eggs were sold to tourists.

More puffins were killed on St. Kilda than any other species of bird. While the St. Kildans' opinion* of its eggs may have been doubtful, or not unanimous, there was no doubt about their attitude to the adult. "The puffin," says John MacGillivray (1842), who visited St. Kilda in 1840, "forms the chief article of food with the St. Kildans during the summer months, and is usually cooked by roasting among the ashes." It was also the primary source of feathers; its feathers commanded a higher price from the laird's factor than those of the fulmar. Often the puffins were captured by women; Sands (1878) describes how on 15 July 1875 a number of young women were left on Soay for three weeks purely to catch puffins for feathers; on 16 July seven more were left on Boreray for the same purpose. Sands also calculated that at least 89,600 puffins were killed in 1876. Connell (1887), on his visit in 1886, may be recording a change of human habit

*These figures are borne out by later accounts, though Dixon's suggestion "the natives gather the eggs literally by boatloads" is an exaggeration.

when he states that "in an overwhelming majority of cases the puffin is killed for its feathers, and the carcass is simply thrown away, going usually to enrich the soil." Certainly when Steele Elliott (1895) visited St. Kilda in 1894 the 4,800 lbs. of feathers produced a year were largely composed of those of puffins, and may have been derived from about 90,000 birds; Sands's estimate of 1876 may have been no exaggeration. However, by 1898 and 1899 (Heathcote, 1900) nothing like 90,000 were being killed, though some thousands were taken every year. Feathers had decreased in value."The St. Kildans eat puffins when they cannot get fulmars," Heathcote wrote. By 1902 feather-taking was finished, and puffins were taken for food only. Wiglesworth (1903) said that the discontinuance of feather-taking has "caused the birds to multiply to such an inordinate extent, that they are doing serious damage to the pasturage by riddling the hillsides with their burrows." This may have been somewhat of an exaggeration; the good grazing-ground of St. Kilda has not been burrowed into yet by a single puffin. The puffin was still being captured for food in 1910 and 1911 (Clarke, 1912b), and probably continued to be so, for this purpose only, until the evacuation. Certainly the men were out killing puffins on 22 April 1927, the day after J. Mathieson (1927) had arrived.

The methods of fowling on St. Kilda were straightforward enough, though one or two of their inventions were ingenious. Manx shearwaters were hunted at night, among the boulders of the Carn Mór and other places; as they landed on the ground and shuffled into their burrows they were easy to take with lights. Puffin-nesting was largely women's work. Dogs helped them find occupied nests under the turf and boulders of the six great puffinries of St. Kilda (the north face of Conachair, the north slopes of Dún, Carn Mór, the sides of

*The St. Kildans appear to have disagreed with the rest of us about the taste of the egg of the puffin. Although the puffin is by far the most abundant bird on St. Kilda (MacKenzie, who was not prone to exaggerate, said "I estimate that there cannot be fewer of them than three millions"—and from Fisher's own experience of the St. Kilda puffin population he is sure he was right), its eggs were not sought like those of the other auks, guillemot and razorbill; yet sought they were, as MacKenzie records, and Connell, Murray and Wiglesworth after him. It is probable that puffin eggs were not collected assiduously because they were usually too deep in burrows; some recorders, like Dixon and Sands, who took evident pride in the completeness of their accounts, do not mention their taking, though they mention the taking of most other eggs; it seems likely that the puffin egg was near the limit of tolerance of even the St. Kildan palate. That this palate was different from ours is clear; tradition and practice had evidently made it so: but even St. Kildans refused to eat the eggs (or the flesh) of the shag, or the flesh of the oystercatcher.

Plate IX. A Guillemot cliff in Shetland. The topmost bird is a bridled individual (note " spectacle " round the eye). The bird (*lower right*) has been splashed with mutings from above

Plate Xa. Fulmars and (*centre*) Great Shearwater, Rockall, June, 1948 (*R. M. Lockley*)

b. A flock of Manx Shearwaters assembling off Skokholm (seen in background)

(*H. M. Salmon*)

the Cambir, Soay and Boreray), each of which is probably larger than any other puffinry in Britain; and they dug and dragged the birds out with a long arm. The men made horsehair nooses stiffened with bits of gannet-quill at the end of tapering bamboo poles from 6 to 15 feet long, which they gently edged over the necks or under the feet of puffins and razorbills sitting about on turf or rocks, and of fulmars, guillemots, and even gannets on their eggs; and snatched the bird to them. Skilled workers could catch several hundreds of birds a day this way. Gannets were stalked asleep before dawn, and seized by the neck. One method of catching guillemots early in the season, when they came to the ledges but had not laid, is described by the accurate MacKenzie: "Two men will go to a likely place and as soon as the birds have left the rocks in the twilight one of the men will lower the other by a rope to the ledges which they have observed to be most thickly peopled. Then he has to wait all night while the birds are away feeding. Just before the earliest dawn he hides himself as close to the edge of the rock as possible, and holds up something white, as a handkerchief, on the rock beside him. The first comer seems to think that this is a still earlier arrival, and settles down beside it. It is at once pounced upon, killed, and held up in a sitting position in order to induce the next comers to settle down beside it. They return in little flocks from half a dozen to a dozen, and out of each the fowler may catch two or three, or if lucky even more. He goes on in this way till it gets so light that no more will settle. Sometimes he may not be successful, but in general he can catch from sixty to seventy." It was usual to try this dodge only once at each favoured ledge; the fowler went the rounds of the traditional stances. Other accounts show that they sometimes covered their heads with a large white sheet, to simulate a whole guano-white ledge rather than the flash-white underparts of a sitting bird.

MacKenzie describes the special St. Kilda puffin-snare or puffin-gin (used for this bird alone): "It consists of about a fathom of stout cord to which hair nooses, about nine inches long, are fastened at intervals of three or four inches. This is stretched out on any boulder or ledge which the birds are at the time frequenting, and fastened at the ends. The nooses along the sides are then carefully opened out to a diameter of about an inch and a half. The birds which have been disturbed are soon back again, and, being restless little fellows, it is not long before some of them have got their feet entangled in the nooses. Three or four are generally caught thus before the snare has to be reset."

H

Sometimes very many more are caught, for the puffin is a very pugnacious little fellow, and when he finds himself caught attacks his
neighbour. In this way a general fight is started, during which many
are caught. On a suitable day a person with four or five of these
snares, which are as many as he can attend to, may kill several
hundreds."

The main killing, of course, was at the autumn collection of young
birds. Their necks broken, the young fulmars were tucked, heads
through belts, round the waists of the fowlers, young and old, men and
women; young gannets were often thrown down to the sea five
hundred feet or more from the heights of Stac Lee or Stac an Armin
to be collected by men in the boats waiting below. It is interesting to
compare the tools of the St. Kilda fowler with those of other North
Atlantic seafowlers. In the Faeroes, is found the *fleygastong*, which
looks like a three-foot lacrosse net on the end of a 12-foot
pole. It is held by the fowler inconspicuously on the ground, at a
traditional catching-place, and swept up skilfully to intercept a flying
puffin or fulmar. Faeroemen also drag puffins from their burrows
with an iron hook on the end of a two-foot stick, the *lundakrók*, and
also dig out burrows with a trowel of traditional design. The *fleyg*
does not appear to have been invented or used at St. Kilda, though
it was in use in Orkney in about 1808; and, quite independently,
the Aleut inhabitants of the Commander Islands, in the North Pacific,
developed a *fleyg*, hooped like a giant butterfly net for catching *Lunda
cirrhata*, the tufted puffin. The nearest the Hebrideans got to the
fleyg was a simple pole, with which fowlers smote or attempted to smite
auks in mid-air, sometimes with fair results; and the nearest the
Faeroeman has got to the St. Kilda puffin-gin (used on land) is a
raft set with hair-nooses, anchored in a fiord to snare auks, decoyed
by stuffed skins; this device appears to be an Iceland invention.
The *lundakrók*, or puffin-gaff, was never used in the puffin-burrows
of St. Kilda, though, as Alex. Ferguson tells us a pointed stick was
used to tear the roof of a burrow shown by a dog to be tenanted.

Egging and young-bird-fowling has also been carried on in Orkney
and Shetland, and in Pembrokeshire, though only desultorily in the
present century. It was never regarded as a very important source
of food. Apart from this the only other traditional fowling in Britain
which may now continue is the annual expedition to the gannet
colony of Sula Sgeir, which is undertaken by the men of Ness in Barvas,
the northernmost parish of the Lewis. The September expedition of

the men of Barvas was made until recently in a 40-foot skeffa or 'sgoth,' a direct descendant of the old Norse galley, the only boat of its type remaining. The men landed on the east side of the island and dragged their boat up its rocky side. They spent about a week among the gannets, living in an ancient stone hut and killing the young ones by clubbing. They took them for human food, dog food and even cattle food in winter, splitting and salting the gugas. It is possible that at certain times, including years of the present century, since the custom of raiding was noted in 1549, the men of Barvas have over-cropped. However, the colony had a good rest during the war and (see p. 83) has considerably increased. We see no reason to depart from the view expressed ten years ago by one of us and H. G. Vevers, which was this: "We are not convinced that absolute protection of this colony is necessary, or indeed desirable in view of the very ancient custom of taking gannets here after a 45-mile journey in an open skeffa from Ness. But we do suggest that future harvesting be consciously planned, and, in view of the recent decline in numbers at this colony, we would propose that no more than a thousand young should be taken in any one year, until further scientific census work justifies an alteration in this number."

In 1952, however, there were signs of an end to Britain's last traditional sea-fowlery (if that is the word). After the war a small boat, the *Mayflower*, with an inboard engine, was substituted for the skeffa. It was too heavy to be dragged up the steep rocky landing, and was precariously moored near the landing-place, where it had to be constantly watched. In 1949 the men got into serious difficulties, and in 1952 the *Mayflower* was lost; the men returning home in a larger boat, the *Mairi Dhonn* from Berneray (Anon, 1952). It would be possible to continue the visits in boats of the size of the *Mairi Dhonn;* but for many years now the harbour at Ness, built at great expense with public funds, has been silted up, and useless for such craft, and the expense of hiring from another parish (Berneray is thirty miles away) is probably prohibitive. So, far from being planned, future harvesting of the Sula Sgeir gannets is likely to be desultory, or to cease altogether after a continuous practice of over four hundred years.

K. Williamson (1948) gives an excellent account of bird fowling in the Faeroe Islands, an important and traditional folk-industry connected with the bird mountains of the northern and western coasts of the islands. In the Faeroes, as in Iceland, fowling has always been combined with farming and fishing, and with a culture and civilisation much more advanced than that of St. Kilda. The St. Kildans could not read, far less write, and as a result what we know of the size of their crops of various species of birds and their eggs comes largely from the miscellaneous writings of a few resident ministers and chance visitors, from whose accounts the picture has to be fitted together like a jig-saw puzzle, of which some pieces have been irrevocably lost. But in the Faeroes and Iceland, at least during the nineteenth and twentieth centuries, wild-fowl figures have been kept; and though no doubt at times and places the inhabitants have given way to various temptations, here to exaggerate and there understate their catches, the figures published by F. Salomonsen (1935) for the Faeroes and the government publication *Hagskýrslur Íslands* for Iceland seem to be reasonably accurate.

In the Faeroes the most important sea-fowl is the puffin, of which half a million are killed in the islands in a good year. Some fowlers working with the *fleyg* have killed 900 birds in a day, and 200-300 per man is quite usual. Williamson, whose important book shows a very proper attitude towards food, describes the cooking and eating of *lundi*, and from our own experience in Iceland and elsewhere we echo his views as to the excellence of the puffin as food, especially when braised in thick gravy and eaten with boiled potatoes sweetened with sugar in the northern style, and jam sauce. The Faeroe men also kill a large number of guillemots, certainly over 60,000 and probably over 100,000 a year, and many razorbills. They also take a vast number of guillemots' eggs—some hundreds of thousands— though they do not take eggs on a large scale from other species. The birds are salted in brine for the winter and the eggs preserved in water-glass. The Faeroe men also snare auks on the sea by noose-rafts (p. 98) and collect young auks on the sea below their cliffs before they grow their primaries and can properly fly.

Since the psittacosis outbreak in the Faeroes young fulmars have been forbidden as an article of food, but before 1936 at least 80,000 young were taken below the cliffs in early September, and some adults were taken as well. There is only one gannetry in the Faeroes, on the Holm of Mykines, and here between 400 and 900 young are usually taken every year, representing approximately half the output of young gannets of the colony. Throughout the literature of fowling it seems to be clear that a traditional established colony of sea-birds can suffer cropping of up to half its annual output of young at the hands of the local fowlers.

Few other species of birds are taken at all importantly in the Faeroes. Few young shearwaters are eaten, a few young kittiwakes, and a few terns' eggs. There is a small eiderdown industry at two places; but as at present conducted the exploitation of eiderdown in the Faeroes and Iceland is a very 'scientific' custom which involves the taking or destruction of no eggs whatsoever, and is therefore not fowling in the strict sense.

In Iceland wild-fowling is still carried on systematically; the fowlers use the *fleyg* (p. 98) (in the Westmann Islands) but rely more on the collection of eggs and the killing of young birds in autumn. The eggs most commonly taken are those of both *Uria* guillemots.

Psittacosis was discovered in the fulmars of Iceland shortly after those of the Faeroes; and the taking of young fulmars has now been forbidden. Previous to the psittacosis outbreak up to nearly 60,000 fulmars were killed in some years in Iceland, but after 1925 it was never more than 50,000, after 1927 not more than 40,000 and after 1933 not more than 30,000. The last annual total before the psittacosis regulations in 1939 was 22,231. Of these by far the most were taken. in the Mýrdalur area of South Iceland, the Westmann Islands and Grímsey. It is rather interesting to note that since the fulmar-fowling stopped there has been a decrease in the population of fulmars in both Grímsey and the Westmann Islands. In both these places the inhabitants have started taking the eggs of fulmars, now that the taking of their young has been prohibited. On St. Kilda it was the general opinion that while fulmar eggs were extremely palatable their taking should be very strictly limited. If a fulmar's egg is taken it does not lay a replacement; its breeding cycle is broken, it goes prematurely into moult and leaves the colony in a week or two. But the taking of a young fulmar from a cliff has no effect upon its parents or their breeding cycle; indeed, they are unlikely to be aware of it, since most fowlers take fulmars when they are fat on the ledges, having already been deserted by their parents, or when they are resting on the water after their first glide down to the sea before they can really fly. It seems reasonable to suppose that a fulmar whose egg is taken might respond to the interference with its breeding cycle sufficiently to move its breeding-quarters in a subsequent year; whereas there is no possibility of response on the part of an adult fulmar to the taking of its well-grown young.

Apart from fulmars it has been the Iceland custom to take very large numbers of puffins, guillemots, razorbills, kittiwakes and gannets.

Gannets have been taken on Eldey off the south-west peninsula, one of the largest gannetries in the world. (This was declared a sanctuary and gannet-taking was forbidden in 1940.) The main annual catch of gannets here between 1910 and 1939 was 3,257, the extremes being 200 and 4,000; the fowlers never took quite half the total annual output of young. On the Westmann Islands gannet-fowling has been known for two-and-a-half centuries, and no doubt has gone on ever since the islands were colonised in the tenth century. Here the total population of nests is now of the order of 5,500. The number of young taken has seldom been more than a quarter of the total output, most being killed on the flat top of the most inaccessible of the breeding cliffs, Súlnasker. In the middle of the 19th century it was alleged that as many as 80,333 puffins were taken yearly in the Westmann Islands, but during the present century the take has seldom exceeded 50,000, and has often been between 20,000 and 30,000. At Grímsey often very large numbers of kittiwakes are taken, however, more than 10,000 in some years, and nearly as many puffins, but only a few hundred guillemots. Very many eggs are taken on Grímsey, particularly those of guillemots, of which about 12,000 are collected in a normal year, and a number of kittiwakes' eggs also.

Since the first accurate figures of 1897, there has been a slow decline in the number killed for food in Iceland. This should be associated with a recent human movement in Iceland from the coastal farms to the towns. Certain parts of Iceland's coast, formerly inhabited by farmer-fishermen are quite deserted, e.g. the northern part of the north-west peninsula. Even in the Westmann Islands, where the fowling tradition is very strong, there has been a slight decline. However, as long as the Icelanders regard fowling as a manly sport, hallowed by generations by tradition, as well as a gainful occupation, fowling will continue on its present lines.

A conclusion from a study of the fowling on St. Kilda, the Faeroes and Iceland is that sea-birds were (and are) a source of cheap and good food, which can be indefinitely enjoyed, provided a calculated harvest be taken from the cliffs which leaves a strong adult population behind. Further, this harvest can be large and yet not materially effect the size of the colony. Experience over some hundreds of years shows that large numbers of eggs* can be taken from those species such as the guillemot which readily lay replacements, and that from all others

*As this book lay in proof the publication began of a most informative summary of egg-exploitation, by Hugh B. Cott (1953).

a crop of fat young can be taken most easily just before the young fly or swim away from the colony. Furthermore it seems that it is safe to take up to half as many young as there are nests in the colony. Of course, this concerns established colonies of great size whose origins are lost in the depths of history, and it is possible that a new colony just starting up, or a colony struggling for existence at the edge of a species' range, cannot stand this kind of human predation. Moreover, there are certain acts which can be dangerous to the population, such as the taking of eggs from species like the fulmar, which do not lay replacements. With these reservations, it seems that man can exploit a community of sea-birds without killing the geese that lay the golden eggs, provided that he restrains his greed and takes less than half that which it would be physically possible for him to take. He may indeed one day need to consider, more seriously than at present, the scientific exploitation of sea-birds for food. The figures we have quoted above may then be not without value for fixing the annual crop which can be gathered without depleting the colonies.

* * *

Man can also, and does, affect the population of sea-birds in ways other than by predation—for instance, by building on, or otherwise altering, sea-birds' breeding sites and by putting waste matter into the sea. Fortunately for sea-birds man has not much use for cliffs, except to put lighthouses on, and as objects of admiration and amenity. Occasionally man quarries a cliff or builds air raid shelters in it, or uses it for target practice. But on the whole his exploitation of a cliffy coast is not usually such as to drive away the sea-birds which nest upon it. However, not all sea-birds nest on cliffs, and those which nest on beaches and marshes, most particularly the terns, have suffered considerably from shortage of nesting sites, due to man's activities in draining marshes for agricultural purposes and in building houses, expanding and developing seaside resorts and in the erection of aerodromes and bombing and artillery ranges. However, we must readily admit that not all coastal aerodromes and bombing ranges have driven the sea-birds away. Sometimes they have driven humans away and increased the numbers of the local nesting sea-birds!

Perhaps of all our British sea-birds the little tern suffers most from human building. The chain of seaside cottages and concrete bungalows that now strings along the back of every likely beach in England, and many in Wales and Scotland, occupies each year yet more of the gravel and sandy stretches occupied by the little terns. This is unfortunately true of the many miles of the coast of Norfolk and Suffolk, along which, fifty years ago, there was an almost continuous scattered colony of little terns; but now they are very few and far between. An interesting comparison of the vulnerability of a shingle or sandy coast and a cliff coast to this advance of man is shown along the coast of Durham and Northumberland. Here the industrial towns and villages, with their huge human populations, run to the very edge of the cliffs. Yet upon the cliffs numbers of sea-birds nest every year and some, like the fulmar, are actually increasing. Of course, there is still human interference, especially by boys and girls making their first tentative experiments in cruelty to animals. But on the whole the cliff birds and the cliff-top men live singularly well together. It is gratifying to note now the shooting of sea-birds at their colonies "for fun," a sport quite widespread in the nineteenth century, has disappeared.

Man's interference with sea-bird population by what he puts into the sea is quite substantial. It can be benign and malevolent. From the sea-bird's point of view man's benign contributions consist mainly of sewage and fish-offal, and, to a certain extent, whale-offal. Not many important main sewers discharge untreated sewage into the sea in the British Isles, but, in the eastern United States, Roger Peterson writes: "The very best spot for gulls is the sewer outlet at 92nd Street in Brooklyn. For several years now the little gull (*Larus minutus*) a tiny European species with smoky-black wing linings, has been seen with the buoyant Bonaparte's gulls, snatching titbits that well up in the sordid flow. Here in the Narrows, where immigrants get their first view of the Statue of Liberty, I have seen both this and another European, the black-headed gull. Curiously enough, the only other place on our whole Atlantic coast where these two rare *Laridae* from the other side can be depended on is also at a sewer outlet, at Newburyport, Massachusetts. There, for at least ten years, the black-headed gull, which looks like a largish Bonaparte's gull with a red bill, has been found off the end of the pipe that dumps its waste into the Merrimac."

Fish-offal has been discharged into the sea at fishing ports and villages ever since large-scale fishing began, and such ports have always had their attendant crowd of gulls—mostly herring-gulls and lesser blackbacks and a few great blackbacks. However, in the last few years the trawlers have been operating at increasing distances from land, have been taking ice with them, and have been gutting and stowing their catch at sea. This has meant that at every trawl there has been a great discharge of unwanted offal, and of unwanted species of fish, squids and other molluscs. Every deep-sea trawler starts from port with a retinue of gulls, some of which may follow for about fifty miles or more to sea; a few occasionally farther. After that, in the deep ocean, fulmars are the principal scavengers in the wake of trawlers which work the north-western and arctic fishing banks. Every time the haul comes up in the coastal belt the gulls resting on the sea gather more closely round the ship, and at every gutting time they scream and fight for offal. The rise of the fishing industry has unquestionably affected the population of the gulls round Britain, and a similar state of affairs has been reported by A. O. Gross (1951) from the northern United States sea-board. In 1900, for instance, the great blackback was practically extinct as a breeding species in England and Wales. In the years round 1930, however, Harrisson and Hurrell (1933) estimated that between 600 and 800 pairs nested in Scilly, about 180 in Pembrokeshire, over 60 in Cornwall, 50 on Lundy, about 45 in the rest of Devon and about 60 in the rest of England and Wales. These figures are probably trebled today; and a parallel increase has taken place also in Ireland and west and north Scotland, where the species has always had a large population. On the United States sea-board before 1916 the great blackback nested nowhere at all. Its farthest breeding place was on the Canadian border of the Bay of Fundy, but in 1906 a pair bred in Maine and in 1928 three pairs certainly did so. By 1931 there were at least ten stations in Maine and one in Massachusetts, and since then it has spread south as far as New York. The U.S. population consisted of some 1,250 pairs in 1944. There are 700 pairs in one bay in Maine alone.

But of all the birds which have been affected by man's dumping of this kind of food into the sea the fulmar has responded most markedly. Both of us independently came to the conclusion that the astonishing spread of the fulmar—the biggest revolution in the numbers of any widely-spread sea-bird (or any bird?)—is primarily connected with modern trawling and probably with its predecessor, North Atlantic whaling. This spread is described in detail in Fisher's *The Fulmar* (1952), and we do not wish to recapitulate the evidence here. Suffice it to say that the spread has been going on now for 200 years, having been first started in south Iceland in the middle of the eighteenth-century, that it has completely changed the bird's distribution in Iceland, the Faeroes and Britain, and that it still continues, no less than thirty colonies or potential colonies being founded annually

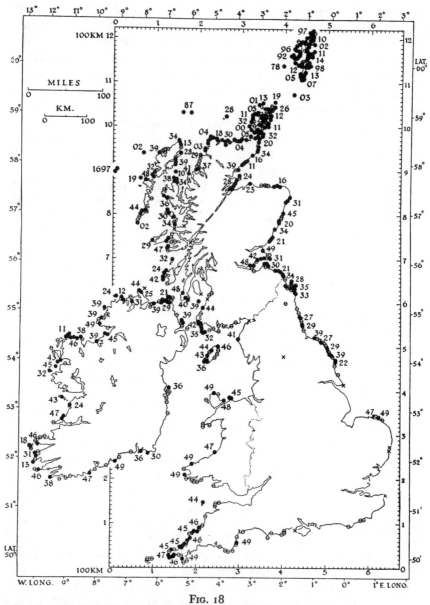

FIG. 18

Sketch map of Britain showing fulmar colonies known by 1949. Breeding colonies black; colonies where fulmars prospecting, but not yet proved to breed, crossed circles. Dates of first breeding at important colonies indicated. Crosses represent places where fulmars have been seen in the breeding season but where they have not yet been proved to be "interested" in establishing a breeding colony (*from Fisher, 1952*)

on the British coast alone. Fig. 18, (opposite) shows the spread of the fulmar in Britain: before 1878 it was known to nest only on St. Kilda. Fulmars congregate round trawlers in enormous numbers, up to more than five thousand at one time. Probably every trawler operating within a few hundred miles of a fulmar colony is visited. Almost invariably, the fulmars outnumber any other kind of bird present at hauling or gutting times. They greedily devour the loose dead fish and bits of fish that come up with the cod end, as well as the guts that are thrown overboard—especially the livers, which are grabbed first. In many parts of the North Atlantic from May to October they are often accompanied by a minority of Tristan great shearwaters and sooty shearwaters.

Man has one entirely malignant effect on sea-bird populations. He casts crude or waste oil into the sea. This oil of course floats on the surface of the water, and a relatively small amount of oil can form a thin film covering some square miles. The volatile oils evaporate, leaving an asphaltic residue which is sticky. When sea-birds swim or dive through this, they quickly get their feathers matted. This reduces the surface tension of the plumage, and the subcutaneous air spaces, to which the birds owe most of their insulation and much of their buoyancy, are filled with oily water. In cold weather the birds rapidly lose heat, which they are unable to replace by hunting and feeding. Most of them die. The oil menace particularly affects the surface swimming guillemots and razorbills, which do most of their feeding over the Continental Shelf, and often close to shipping routes. Puffins and gannets also suffer, but not quite to the same extent. For many years this question of oiling has exercised the bird protection societies, and there have been many international meetings and discussions about it. In 1926, for instance, the United States government was host to an international conference in Washington, but at this there was a division of opinion as to what should be done, and all that resulted was a recommendation that oil should not be discharged within fifty miles from land. Some governments, it is true, passed this recommendation to their shipping companies and navies, and, in some cases, the recommendation was even acted upon, but there was no noticeable diminution in the number of cases of oiling, and during the late thirties and the forties, particularly during the war, oiling has been worse than it has ever been, at least round the coast of Britain. There is no question but that sometimes the waste of sea-bird life through oil pollution is substantial. It is also, of course, a common-

108   SEA-BIRDS

place that the end to which the unfortunate birds come is a particularly
sticky one and horrifying and nauseating to all humane people. At
all recent ornithological congresses, and nearly every international
meeting for bird preservation, the existence of this problem has been
discussed, debated, and hundreds of recommendations have been
made by scores of bodies to scores of governments, many of whom have
given assurances and promises. However, these words have not saved
the sea-birds, who still continue to die in large numbers round our
shores. In Britain we have the Oil in Navigable Waters Act of 1921,
which has been observed as carefully as possible by all shipping
plying to British ports. However, there have been recent occasions
upon which it is obvious that this Act has been grossly ignored, and
during the war a number of tankers were torpedoed and wrecked,
with consequent effects upon the auks. Unfortunately one big discharge
of oil will pollute the sea for a very large area and for a very long time.

It is rather interesting to note that the auks, in particular the
guillemot and razorbill, are among the few common British sea-birds
in which a decrease has occurred during the present century. This
decrease must not be exaggerated, and it has not been noticeable in
all parts of Britain. One of these noticeable decreases is on Ailsa Craig
in the Clyde, which lies on a main shipping route. J. A. Gibson (1951)
thinks that the present population of not more than 5,000 pairs of
guillemots is about one-tenth of what it was forty years ago. In
1937 one of us found 61 auks, most of which were guillemots, and 22
gannets on Ailsa's two-and-a-half miles of coast-line, incapable of
survival, so thickly were they 'oiled'. But the experience of Gibson in
1948 was far more harrowing; on 23 August, along but half a mile
of beach, he counted eight hundred and fifty badly oiled guillemots
ashore and many hundreds floating a little way out at sea. There were
hundreds more round the rest of the coastline of the island—all due
to die. This was nearly a quarter of the breeding population of the
Craig. He illustrates the general decline in the guillemot's fortunes
on Ailsa Craig by the following interesting figures from parts of the
bird-cliffs known as Ashydoo (A) and the Bed o' Grass (B):

	A	B	Total
Average yearly 'bag' of eggs in the years 1905-10	1,080	1,320	2,400
Number of apparently incubating pairs in 1950	240	c.250	c.500

Gibson thinks that the present population (5,381 pairs in 1950) is about a tenth of what it was forty years ago. This would seem to fit the figures from Ashydoo and the Bed o' Grass if, as seems reasonable, the eggers took about half the eggs.

Unfortunately precise figures of the number of auks killed by oiling round the coast of Britain have never been collected. The pronounced decrease of guillemots at Skomer in Pembrokeshire may be due to the present extensive oil-pollution of the Bristol Channel. The Royal Society for the Protection of Birds, just as this chapter was being written, began to collect scientific information on a wide scale, and it is hoped to have some concrete information as to the real extent of the menace in a few years. The remedy—oil-separators on ship and at every port used by oil-carrying ships—is obvious, and well-known, but waits international agreement.

CHAPTER 4

WHAT CONTROLS
THE NUMBERS OF SEA-BIRDS?

A LTHOUGH MAN is so much the most important predator of sea-birds, except in very inaccessible places such as the Antarctic Continent and some of the Subantarctic islands, the existence of other animal predators should not be overlooked. The number and import-ance of these is not great, and the effect of these predators upon the population of their prey is small; but, on the other hand, the effect of the numbers of the prey upon the numbers of the predators may be marked. It is abnormal for a predator to take a crop from its prey which is more than that prey can easily spare. At every important sea-bird station there is normally a small, but often varied community of animals which are predators on the individual members of the main community or their eggs and young. At a typical British island bird rock the predators are all birds. Ravens snap up young that fall from the cliffs or adults which meet with flying accidents (below the cliffs of Ailsa Craig we have seen a raven eviscerating a still living gannet that had been starving for some days with a broken wing). Hooded and carrion-crows nest, like the ravens, on the cliffs of many sea-bird stations, and poach eggs and pick up what they can get. Peregrine falcons also nest on the cliffs and prey upon the inmates. At a peregrine eyrie on Skomer, in 1946, we found two eyasses sitting among the remains of eleven Manx shearwaters and two puffins. Even the short-eared owl may occasionally nest on British islands and prey upon the sea-birds. One of the pair nesting on Skomer used to operate to the neighbouring bird island of Skokholm, where a pellet was found containing the remains of a storm-petrel; and on Skomer the newly-arrived little owls also have persecuted the storm-petrels. But the most important animal predators of sea-birds are other sea-birds. In Shetland the arctic and great skuas of Noss chase terns, kittiwakes and even gannets, to force them to vomit fish, which is then seized by the pursuer. Seldom do these parasites (a truer word for these particular birds than predators) actually kill their prey. However the bonxies, or great skuas, frequently hunt and drown the local kittiwakes, as R. Perry (1948) has observed, dropping on top of them and forcing them down on to the water, often working in couples. The great skuas of Noss and Foula indulge in predation of kittiwakes, as well as guillemots, until the gannets are feeding young, and do not take to parasitism of their main host until then. They also chase great blackbacks and herring-gulls, and make them vomit. The great skuas, like the great blackbacks, watch the cliffs for the young guillemots on their first flights to the sea. Both also take fledgeling kittiwakes and fledgeling herring-gulls. The arctic skuas of Noss get most of their prey by harrying kittiwakes, guillemots and terns over the sea a couple of miles from the island.

The herring-gull is an important predator of other sea-birds, although it has not the aggressive qualities of the great blackback. It is particularly good at robbing gannets of their egg, taking quick advantage of any unusual disturbance in a gannetry, such as the arrival of human beings. Fulmars are much more difficult to dislodge from their eggs than are gannets, but once human investigators have put the fulmars off, the ever-watchful herring-gulls snap the eggs up. The herring-gull is probably the worst egg-robber of the bird-cliffs, and it will take nestlings of any species of gull (including its own), of terns and of the auks.

The lesser blackback, though not quite so aggressive as the herring-gull, has been known to kill adult puffins and Manx shearwaters, and the young of many cliff-breeding birds. The great blackback eats everything so far mentioned. It will smash eggs by taking them up to a height and then dropping them. In general, however, most of of these gulls, predatory though they are, seek their living away from the colony. Often very large colonies of herring-gulls, lesser blackbacks and great blackbacks—sometimes even all three—are situated at the top of a teeming bird-cliff. If all the gulls were to rely only on what they were to get from the bird-cliff the community might collapse. They should be properly described as opportunist predators, who earn their main living elsewhere,—nowadays, as we have already pointed out (p. 104)—very largely as parasites upon the fishing industry of the coast.

In the Arctic the glaucous gull to a large extent takes the place

of the great blackback, and in Greenland the Iceland gull the place
of the herring-gull. Their place in nature seems to be exactly the same,
and their behaviour and function as a member of the cliff-community
is identical.

Other birds not yet mentioned which prey upon sea-birds of the
North Atlantic community are the bald, white-tailed, and even golden
eagles; and sometimes the snowy owl and the eagle-owl. and the gyr-
falcon. The long-tailed skua is not a predator of breeding sea-bird
communities, but pursues terns and kittiwakes at sea to a certain
extent in the off-season. The same is largely true of the pomarine
skua, though this does occasionally take young sea-birds on the
breeding-ground. Of course there are many other bird predators
which have occasionally picked up sea-birds in the course of their
hunting operations. Examples are: the merlin (which has taken a little
tern), common buzzard (which has taken a guillemot and often
young Manx shearwaters), marsh-harrier (a young black-headed gull)
goshawk (a common tern and an arctic (Brünnich's) guillemot)
and the sparrow-hawk (a Leach's petrel and little tern).

Of the mammal predators of the North Atlantic sea-birds quite
a formidable list could be compiled if we were to include every animal
that had ever been seen to eat a sea-bird. The list would certainly admit
the polar bear, the arctic wolf, the arctic fox, the red fox of the Old
World and the red fox of the New World, the otter, the stoat, the
killer-whale, the harp-seal of Newfoundland, and possibly the "black"
rat (*Rattus rattus*), as well as the abundant brown rat (*R. norvegicus*).
It is a commonplace that in Spitsbergen and Greenland, and no
doubt in other parts of the Arctic, the presence of arctic foxes forces
the sea-birds to occupy the more inaccessible ledges of the cliffs;
and they are quite important predators of the more vulnerable occu-
piers of the edges of the colonies. In Britain there are foxes on very
few islands, but the sea-bird stations on the mainland, notably that
at Cló Mór in north Sutherland near Cape Wrath, are harried by foxes.
Indeed, the foxes of Cló Mór have their *cairn* at the top of the most
important bird cliff.

Undoubtedly the only really serious mammal predator of the
North Atlantic sea-birds is the rat, and we believe it is the only sea-
bird predator which can really be said to have made a significant
difference to the status of certain species. It is an introduced species,
not yet in a balanced ecological relationship with its prey where it
comes into contact with certain burrowing sea-birds. To give an

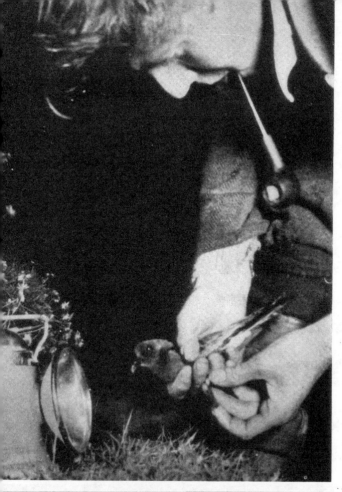

Plate XIa. Ringing a Leach's Petrel, North Rona
(Flashlight photo by Robert Atkinson)

b. The Madeiran Petrel has a slightly forked tail and a conspicuously white rump
(R. M. Lockley)

Plate XIIa. Berlengas Islands, Portugal. A lighthousekeeper holds firmly the powerful North Atlantic Shearwater, *Puffinus kuhlii*, which breeds there, and is freely taken for food

b. Flashlight photograph of Manx Shearwater, Skokholm, Pembrokeshire

Robert Atkinson

example, about a hundred years ago the puffin was by far the most numerous bird on Ailsa Craig in the Clyde. Its numbers were described by many observers up to about 1900 as phenomenal. There were the usual expressions about their darkening the sky. Gibson states (though on what grounds we do not know) that there were probably over a quarter of a million puffins in the 1860's. Unfortunately in 1889, rats got ashore from a wreck. Their effect was not immediate but the decrease of the puffins became noticeable between 1900 and 1910, and serious by 1927—when indeed only a few were to be found. By the 1930's the puffin was practically extinct, and on yearly visits to the island between 1936 and 1942 one of us never saw more than a hundred birds. By 1947 Gibson estimated that there were only thirty birds on the whole island. He puts the decrease down to the combined effects of rats, oil and gulls, though there seems to be no real evidence that any but the first factor has operated importantly. Certainly puffins in the Clyde area do not seem to get oiled in the same way as guillemots and razorbills, and do not appear to have been involved in the appalling oiling disasters of 1937 and 1948. Later Gibson records a considerable recovery for in 1950 he found 246 birds occupying twelve different parts of the island; only one part of the island was occupied in 1947. Rats continue to inhabit the Craig. Equally disastrous histories can be related for other islands, though without so many definite facts. In about 1689 a swarm of rats, which must have been black rats, infested North Rona, which was then inhabited by a small human community. The rats are said to have eaten up all the corn on the island and caused the death of the entire human population (nothing is said about sea-birds).

On Lundy (a Norse word meaning Puffin Island) puffins once bred in "incredible numbers"—at least 100,000 pairs. Rats on this island have reduced the puffins, it is believed, to their present numbers of 400 pairs in 1952. On one of the Shiant islands in the Minch, there is a population of brown rats which, at the time of our visit, invaded the house and kept the ornithologists awake. The big puffin colony in the talus slopes of the Shiants still survives, and is very large, though its size is certainly not up to some of the descriptions of it in the last century. How important the decrease has been, and whether it is due altogether to the rats it is difficult to measure. There are fortunately no rats at some of the finest sea-bird stations in Britain, such as Handa, St. Kilda, Sula Sgeir, North Rona and Skomer. There are rats on Foula, though it is doubtful whether they can get anywhere near the largest puffinry, which is on a broad ledge exactly half-way down the incredible cliff of the Kame.

Occasionally (and certainly not very importantly) fish have been known to prey upon sea-birds. W. E. Glegg (1945, 1947), who has compiled records of aquatic animals preying upon birds, lists the angler-fish as having taken scoter, merganser, cormorant, Manx shearwater, great northern diver, gulls (including the herring-gull), razorbill and guillemots. He also lists the cod as having taken cormorant, Brünnich's guillemot and black guillemot; angel-fish and pike as having taken cormorant; unknown fish as having taken the white-winged black tern, and what were probably fish as having taken the Sandwich tern and the African grey-headed gull.

The ectoparasites of sea-birds are many. They include several highly specialised mites, many mallophaga or biting-lice, ticks and some fleas. There is no evidence whatsoever that any of them significantly control the numbers of their host, nor, indeed, any evidence that any of them carry diseases.*

Very little is known about the endoparasites of sea-birds; they have many species of cestodes, nematodes and trematodes, and some protozoa. Extremely little is known about the bacterial and virus parasites of birds, though it appears that of all the internal parasites these are the only ones likely to affect natural populations. Recently considerable attention has been drawn to the virus diseases of sea-birds by J. A. R. Miles, who has identified a virus epizootic of the Manx shearwater which he calls puffinosis (Miles and Stoker, 1948). This disease kills young Manx shearwaters in the crowded Pembrokeshire colonies; the colony on Skokholm, judging from ringing records, is usually between 10,000 and 15,000 birds and that on Skomer double. In some years "many hundreds" of young Manx shearwaters are found dead, but there is no evidence that the disease materially affects the population. (Surrey-Dane, Miles and Stoker, 1953).

The most important sea-bird disease so far identified is undoubtedly psittacosis (a form of ornithosis) which, in the early 1930's, spread through the vast population of the fulmars nesting in the Faeroes and Iceland. The arguments of R. K. Rasmussen, who first identified the disease, and J. A. R. Miles, who has subsequently studied the problem (Miles and Shrivastav, 1951), are summarised in Fisher's *The Fulmar*

---

*In 1949 Lockley found hundreds of fledgeling puffins dying of excessive blood-sucking by the common red mite (*Dermanyssus gallinae*) on the islet of Burhou, Channel Islands.

(1952), and all that it is necessary to say here is that there is a real possibility that the fulmars may have contracted the psittacosis from a dead parrot or parrots. However, while this disease has killed quite a number of human beings who have split or eaten infected young fulmars in September, there is no evidence that it has made any serious difference to the actual fulmar population. It is not even proved that there is a large mortality among the young fulmars, some at least of which appeared to recover. A strain of ornithosis of another kind has been found in herring-gull, lesser blackback, laughing gull, royal tern and little tern.

From this short survey of the possibilities we find that man most importantly controls the number of sea-birds; but that the only other organisms in a long list of predators and parasites that may also do so in any serious way or to any significant extent are (under special circumstances) rats and possibly a virus or viruses. But it is quite certain that none of the other animals which live on or in sea-birds can possibly be responsible for the changes in sea-bird populations which are clearly going on all the time.

There remain three other factors to investigate; for it is possible that the numbers of sea-birds may be limited by the availability of nest sites, by climate and weather, and by the availability of food.

Before we proceed to a further discussion of these points we must remind the reader of an important principle, and for the first time, state another important principle. The principle already stated (p. 37) is that so carefully established by E. Mayr (1942) and D. Lack (1944)—that in the course of evolution new species of birds originate when forms of the parent species differentiate in geographical isolation and subsequently meet in the same area. The second principle, which we have not so far encountered, was stated by the Russian zoologist G. F. Gause in 1934. It is that two closely related species with identical ecology cannot live together in the same place. Generally speaking throughout the world of animal ecology these two principles have been accepted, though not without some reservations by critical workers such as W. H. Thorpe (1945).

As Lack states, when two such differentiating forms of the same parent-species meet, they will tend to compete ecologically but will eventually reach one of four more stable positions. First, one species may eliminate the other completely (this is likely to happen if they still have the same fundamental ecology). Secondly, the two may withdraw once more to occupy separate but contiguous geographical regions. Thirdly, they may occupy different habitats in the same region. And, fourthly, they may live in the same habitat and region but eat mainly different foods. Lack points out that the last position is often reached when the two species differ markedly in size. His analysis was confined to passerine birds, for which habitat-distinctions are much more clearly marked than they are for sea-birds; and we know of no closely-related species of sea-birds which do, in fact, clearly occupy different habitats in the same region in this way. The occupation of different kinds of nest-site on the breeding-cliffs is very closely marked among sea-birds. Every species appears to have its special niche. Although there remains apparent competition for nest-sites at least between certain species at most sea-bird stations, it is a rule that the denser the population of the station, and the greater the number of species occupying it, the keener and more definite does this nest-site selection become. Among the petrels this may result in a division of the year into separate breeding seasons between species using the same nesting burrow (Lockley, 1952). It would be interesting to collect their parasites.

A similar state of affairs appears to exist with the food of sea-birds. Indeed, the situation gives the impression that there is a kind of non-intervention agreement among the sea-birds by which each has chosen its own particular kind of nest-place and its own particular kind of food so as to avoid competition with the other species. The question is how this state of affairs has come about in the course of evolution.

A full answer seems impossible to give over the question of the differential nest-site selection, at least in the present state of theory, though a very great many facts have been collected and are still being collected about the nest-site shortage on the breeding-grounds of sea-birds.

To the question of the differential feeding habits, a clear answer is suggested by the work of Mayr and Lack. In general terms it is that, unless two forms derived from the same parent-species which meet together on the same area are already at least partly differentiated as regards their feeding-habits, one will eliminate the other from the area. If this is true—and there is every reason from the evidence to believe that it is—then the origin of a species will depend on its possesion of a special pattern of food-preferences. We will find that the population of the species will depend also, in normal circumstances, on the natural supply of the food of that pattern. Indeed, we will discover that only under the interference of quite exceptional agents,

Plate 3. Cormorant colony on the Muckle Green Holm, Orkney

such as man, or exotic species of animals, introduced either consciously or unconsciously by man, or sudden cataclysms of climate, will the fundamental numbers of a species be determined by any other factor than food-supply.

Of course, the food-supply often depends directly on other factors such as the weather; and upon the available food supplies the gradual processes of history and evolutionary change are also working. But, owing to the uniqueness of every species' food-pattern, direct competition with other related species may not be a normal factor in population control! When such direct competition is found, as it is occasionally under peculiar circumstances, it is perhaps the exception that proves the rule.

The first case that we can discover in the literature which precisely states the existence of specific food-patterns among closely related sea-birds is an analysis by the Russian zoologist A. N. Formosov, quoted by the pioneer Gause in his *Struggle for Existence*. In 1923 Formosov examined a mixed colony of terns consisting of many hundreds of each of four species on an island on the west side of the Crimean peninsula. Slightly paraphrasing Formosov's notes, he writes that, "the nests of the terns are situated close to one another and the colony presents a whole system. The entire population of the colony belongs to four species, the Sandwich tern, the common tern, the gull-billed tern and the little tern, and together they chase away predators, e.g. hen-harriers, from the colony. However, as regards the procuring of food there is a sharp difference between them, for every species pursues a definite kind of animal in perfectly definite conditions. Thus the Sandwich terns flies out into the open sea to hunt certain species of fish, the gull-billed tern feeds exclusively on land and can be met in the steppes at a great distance from the sea shore, where it destroys locusts and lizards. The common tern and the little tern catch fish not far away from the shore, sighting them while flying and then falling upon the water and plunging to a small depth. But the light little tern seized the fish in shallow swampy places, whereas the common tern hunts somewhat farther from the shore. In this manner these four similar species of tern living side-by-side upon a single small island differ sharply in all their methods of feeding and procuring food."

However, it is uncommon for all these four species to nest together in the same colony. Usually there is also a fairly marked difference in their selection of nest-sites. For instance, the little tern is more inclined to nest on shingle than the others and the gull-billed tern more near marshy places, though it will nest on sand. At most British colonies where there are common and Sandwich terns together the two species usually nest apart, though it is difficult to detect any particular preference in the type of ground favoured.

So far among closely related sea-birds there have been few studies of difference in feeding-habits, though much is now known in the North Atlantic about the difference in their nesting-site preferences. Such pairs of closely related species as have been carefully analysed show that the principle of Gause is in general correct; they do not have the same ecology and there are marked differences in their food-patterns. D. Lack (1945) points out that if one was to rely on the information given in general works on British birds and by W. E. Collinge (1924-27) one might come to the conclusion that the cormorant and the shag eat mainly the same type of food. Fortunately the economic issues involved (because these species might be thought to compete with fishermen) led to G. A. Steven (1933) carefully investigating the food of these two species round the shores of Cornwall. Steven's investigations made it abundantly clear that the difference was very great. For instance the shag ate more sand-eels than any other prey; the cormorant none. The cormorant ate more flat-fish than any other prey; the shag a very small amount. The shag ate fairly large numbers of sprats and sardines and other small fish, whereas the cormorant appeared only to swallow them by chance. The cormorant, on the other hand, ate great quantities of prawns and shrimps, which the shag appears to swallow only by chance. In general the cormorant fed primarily on animals which live on or close to the bottom of the sea, while the shag fed mainly on free-swimming forms.

Later Lumsden and Haddow (1946) examined the food of the shag in the Clyde area and came to similar conclusions about its preferences for sand-eels, small clupeoids and sprats, sardines etc., though the Clyde birds preferred sand-eels to clupeoids.

A rather wider investigation was made by C. H. Hartley and Fisher in Spitsbergen in 1933. In a fjord in the centre of Spitsbergen they studied the food of the many sea-birds which were feeding in a special food-rich zone at the face of a glacier running into the sea. In spite of the super-abundance of one particular crustacean, *Thysanoessa inermis*, which all but one of the ten sea-birds present ate in large quantities, the food-pattern of each proved to be distinct. Thus, besides *Thysanoessa* the kittiwake seemed particularly fond of a crustacean *Euthemisto libellula;* the fulmar of offal; the arctic tern of a shallow-water crustacean *Mysis oculata;* the glaucous and ivory-gulls of offal; the eider of a crustacean *Gammarus locusta* and lamellibranch molluscs; Brünnich's guillemot of a prawn *Spirontocharis gaimardii;* the black guillemot of *Mysis* and gasteropod molluscs; besides various other shallow-water creatures including butter-fish; and the puffin of fish. Unfortunately we did not sample enough little auks to be quite clear as to their preference, though it appeared to be entirely crustaceans. Of the offal-eaters the fulmar ate a wide range of other organisms besides *Thysanoessa;* the glaucous gull ate a few *Euthemisto;* the ivory-gull ate nothing but *Thysanoessa* and offal; but every one of the species, as far as could be detected, had a different food-spectrum in spite of the abundance of *Thysanoessa.*

It is clear that under conditions of super-abundance, species that would otherwise compete can, at least temporarily, share the same *main* food. To give another example: in north-central Iceland is a large shallow lake, Mývatn, of quite exceptional fertility, in which the hatch of insects in June is one of the marvels of nature. Mývatn is probably the finest duck lake in the world: it supports a population of several tens of thousands of ducks belonging to about ten established species (fourteen have bred by or near the lake in the present century). Almost every indication of differences in nest-site choice and food-spectra between the ducks of Mývatn has disappeared, and in places their nests are placed almost in rows, apparently indiscriminately, in the grass and willow cover at the edge of the lake. All feed apparently on the same supply of chironomid insects. Often they appear to make mistakes and lay eggs in each other's nests. Again: it is a common sight in a large colony of auks to find puffins, guillemots, razorbills feeding together on shoals of sand-eels and small fry (perhaps joined by other sea-birds such as gulls and shearwaters) which swarm inshore during June, July and August in British waters. But it remains probable that even under the special conditions in both examples quoted, some differences in food-spectra persist, as well as the normal differences in feeding actions.

There is, in the wide and scattered literature, already a good deal of information of a qualitative, if not of a quantitative kind, which tells us about differences in the food-patterns of closely related sea-birds; and certainly serves to indicate that in all cases those patterns are different except perhaps under the rare and exceptional conditions of food super-abundance. It is true, however, that no deliberate and quantitative research has so far been done on certain obvious pairs actually in the zones where the two species overlap. Thus no serious work has been done on the food of the arctic and common terns in the fairly wide zones of overlap in both New and Old Worlds, nor is there any detailed investigation of the different foods of the different divers or Leach's and storm-petrels, or of the different tropic-birds and frigate-birds, or, rather surprisingly, of the herring- and lesser black-backed gulls as a straight comparison, or of Brünnich's guillemot and the common guillemot.

In the tropics the three boobies—the blue-faced booby, the brown booby and the red-footed booby—overlap considerably, sharing many of the same breeding-places and feeding-grounds, e.g. round Ascension Island. They differ in ecology quite markedly. Thus, the blue-faced booby nests on flat ground, making only a scrape, the brown booby on the ground but usually on eminences and then with considerable nest-material (it may also perch but not nest on trees), while the red-footed booby nests exclusively on trees and bushes and is limited to breeding on islands which can provide them. While their food habits have not been closely compared it seems clear, from the account of Murphy (1936) that they are different; the blue-faced booby appears to be primarily an eater of small squids, the brown booby an eater of flying-fish and many other species of surface-fish, the red-footed booby primarily a diurnal eater of flying-fish but also a nocturnal feeder on squids.

If we study the skuas, gulls and terns we find perhaps the most complicated food-systems and habitat-selection of any of the sea-birds, and it will be a long time before research has sorted out the real differences which undoubtedly exist between the different species and forms. Two similar species overlap geographically very often, and there are several cases where three similar species overlap, and one case where four do so. In the southern United States, for instance, the common tern overlaps with the closely allied Forster's tern, and in northern North America with the closely allied arctic tern. In many parts of the arctic all three species of the smaller skuas breed in the same general geographical area. In Greenland the glaucous gull overlaps with the very similar Iceland gull or Greenland herring-gull, and with the more closely related, but not so similar, greater blackback. In Iceland the great blackback and glaucous gull overlap, and recently they have been joined in the same general geographical area by the herring-gull and lesser blackback, though so far there is no record of all four species nesting together on the same cliff.

Wherever the ecology of these species has been intensively studied, real differences in food patterns are apparent. Thus, of the three skuas, the pomarine skua remains addicted throughout the breeding-season primarily to the "orthodox" skua life of parasitising and robbing other sea-birds for their food. The arctic skua has the most generalised feeding habits: in certain parts of its range where there are no rodents it lives rather like the pomarine skua, provided the pomarine does not overlap with it: in areas where there are voles, mice or lemmings, it eats quantities of these in the breeding season. The long-tailed skua, while it does parasitise sea-birds to a slight extent in its winter range, seems to have become primarily a rodent-feeder and its breeding range is practically limited to those parts of the world in which rodent food is abundant.

Many overlaps occur in the gulls of Britain and north-western Europe where, at the two ends of a long chain of forms which embraces the whole of the northern hemisphere (see Fig. 4*b*, p. 41) the herring-gull and lesser blackback share a breeding-range, and, at least through most of the year, a feeding-range. What their original food spectra were and that of the other close relation which overlaps with them—the great blackback—might be discovered by the study of populations which have no connection with fishing-ports. Where such independent populations exist, if they do, they have certainly not yet been critically compared. In north-western North America the short-billed gull, which is an eastward extension across the Bering Straits of the common-gull or mew-gull, overlaps with the ring-billed gull. The two birds are fortunately sufficiently different in the zone of overlap to behave as distinct species. As far as we know there has been no precise investigation of their feeding habits. The information collected by Bent (1921) gives us no real clue as the observations were not made in the area of overlap. Both appear to have similar nesting habits, both breeding on the ground and in trees. (Map, fig. 5, p. 44).

From Salomonsen's account of the glaucous and Iceland gull in Greenland it is evident that there is a fairly clear difference in their nest-site selection. The nests of the Iceland gull are placed on narrower ledges, and at the mixed colonies they, "keep at a respectful distance below the glaucous gulls . . . being separated from them by a belt of no-man's-land." The Iceland gull is a fish—and crustacean-eater primarily, and also a scavenger, but it does not take any living bird, and in Salomonsen's opinion the food-competition between the two species is "slight or non-existent." The glaucous gull is a predator of other birds, notably the little auk, at all of whose breeding-places in Greenland there is a dependent community of glaucous gulls. It also takes fish and many crustaceans, thus overlapping with the Iceland gull in the consumption of these foods which often, however, exist in superabundance, notably at the faces of glaciers and near icebergs. Unfortunately no stomach contents of the great blackback have been investigated in Greenland, so it is not possible to make a comparison between this species and the glaucous gull. It is certainly a predator as well as a scavenger in Greenland, as it is in other countries.

As far as we know nobody has ever investigated and compared the food of Brünnich's and the common guillemots in the areas where they overlap. No doubt there is a difference in their spectra even if it is only a subtle one, as with their nest-site selection. For these two very closely-related species breed on the same cliffs and the most constant detectable difference in their habits is that on the whole the Brünnich's guillemots tend to incubate on more sheltered ledges and in cracks, thus taking up the niche occupied by the razorbill, whose distributional range it touches but does not overlap. Its bill is even like that of the razorbill (at least in winter form) and it may occupy the same food niche: the razorbill eats rather less fish and more crustaceans than the common guillemot. The rather scanty studies of the food of the common guillemot indicate that more than half of it is fish, about a third crustaceans and the rest marine molluscs. It seems likely, from the studies in the arctic regions, that Brünnich's guillemot eats a greater proportion of crustaceans, particularly planktonic ones like *Thysanoessa*.

To sum up, then, the evidence shows that Gause was right, and that closely related species living in the same area do not show an identical ecology. It seems logical, from this, to conclude that every species of sea-bird (and, for that matter, every bird) possesses a characteristic food-supply and that while this—its "food-spectrum"—may change in the course of history (as it has done, for instance, with the fulmar) in the long run the numbers of sea-birds depend on their food-factors rather than on other factors in the environment, however important. Probably the populations do not depend on the supply of nest-sites unless this is directly threatened by man; we must record, however, that in the North Atlantic, because of man, many safe breeding-places were not so in the recent past and some species (e.g. great auk and gannet) suffered as a result. With increasing protection safe sites are once more available, and there is now plenty of room for more at most of the North Atlantic sea-bird rookeries.

However, before we finally admit the primary importance of food we must give attention to the question of climatic amelioration in the North Atlantic. In the present century there has been a northward advance of very many species, which seems to be fundamentally due to the effect of the improved weather on the plant life on both land and sea; the birds which have moved north have presumably done so because the most important elements in their food-supply have moved north. These elements are, of course, either the plants themselves (which include, of course, sea-diatoms) or other animals which depend on plants and which stand between plants and birds. The little auk (see p. 60) is becoming extinct in Iceland as a breeding species because the edge of the polar pack-ice on which it seeks its main food is moving annually farther and farther away, carrying with it the particular plankton it is adapted to eat. This is an effect of the climate, but it is felt not directly by the little auk but only through its food. Indeed, there are only two ways in which climate could *directly* affect sea-birds, and neither of them appear to us to be fundamental in the long run.

Every now and then a cataclysm of nature may upset the normal migrations of birds and kill large numbers of them. Some sea-birds are more vulnerable to storms and hurricanes, or sudden changes in temperature, than others. One of the most vulnerable to storms is the little auk, which, under certain irregularities of the weather, seems doomed to "wrecks" or crashes on the coasts of north-west Europe or eastern North America. Many hurricanes originate at irregular intervals in the Caribbean area and occasionally farther up the seaboard to New England. When these take place there is a great deal of loss of sea-bird life. It has been adequately described by Murphy (1936). While the immediate losses of life are sometimes spectacular it seems that, in the long run, they have no fundamental effect on the population of birds, though some species are more vulnerable than others.

It is also possible that birds may be directly prevented from breeding by the weather. It is now clear from the observations of William Rowan (1918), Frances Pitt (1929) and others, that abnormal weather conditions may suddenly stop breeding activity even if birds have arrived at the state of their glands compatible with reproduction. This subject has recently been studied by A. J. Marshall (1949 and unpublished) who examined the effect of the hard winter of 1946-47 on several kinds of small birds. He came to the conclusion that temperature and sunshine play a very important role in timing the breeding seasons of birds, quite apart from the general factors, such as the length of daylight, which zoologists have normally regarded as influencing the breeding season. It appears that the influence of temperature and sunlight, while important, can be regarded more as determining the moment when the trigger is pulled, the cocking of the gun being controlled probably by an internal rhythm, and not, as has been widely supposed, by the hours of daylight. In any case it is doubtful whether climate has ever completely prevented breeding at least in the mature sea-bird, by direct action upon the birds' glands. But climate does often, indirectly, prevent breeding, particularly in the Arctic. It is now commonplace of arctic observation that after late springs and in hard weather some, or even all, of the local bird population fails to breed. In our opinion these non-breeding years are simply due to the bad weather closing down the food-supply. For instance, in very late springs the ice never breaks up in Baffin's Bay and the sea-birds of its cliffs cannot find food within operational range of their breeding colonies. The same state of affairs undoubtedly happens from time to time in east Greenland and Spitsbergen, where the state of the ice fluctuates a great deal. In King Charles Land, east of Spitsbergen, only nine species of sea- and shore-birds were present in 1889 when the ice conditions were bad, whereas 21 species were reported in 1898, when they were good. In spite of the work of Marshall and others it seems to us that successful breeding in the arctic regions depends primarily on whether the adults can find enough food (first for themselves and later for their young) within easy reach or flying distance of the nesting site.

To recapitulate previous argument, we find that sea-bird numbers like all animal numbers, depend primarily on food! So we arrive by analysis at what is, all along, the conclusion which common sense has already indicated! But not all sea-birds are always straining—even in the breeding season—at the limits of their food-supply. We have seen, for instance, that in the last hundred years the numbers of gannets in the North Atlantic have been less influenced by the amount of food available than by being preyed upon by man, who does not behave as a natural predator. Under the present protection the North Atlantic gannet is increasing; it may one day return to equilibrium with its normal food supply, a position which may mean that its numbers will be as high or higher than when man started his ancient

Robert Atkinson

Plate 4. Great blackback at nest; Skokholm, Pembrokeshire

cropping of its colonies. But the balance of populations is a very subtle one, and a lengthy discussion is not called for. We merely wish to draw special attention to the importance of food as a controlling factor, and to suggest that more critical work ought to be done on this neglected subject, and simplest of hypotheses.

CHAPTER 5

SEA-BIRD MOVEMENTS

SINCE SEA-BIRDS cannot nest at sea their life must be a kind of compromise, for during a substantial part of the year, in the slow-breeding species about half, at least one member of the pair has to be in residence at a nest on land which may be some distance—perhaps some hundreds of miles—from the nearest place which provides an assured supply of food. Other sea-birds operate for shorter distances from their base, and the coastal species feed within sight of it. But the pelagic or oceanic types may fly some hundreds of miles and possibly even a thousand before returning to their nest, even when they are incubating eggs; and these birds are very specially adapted to solve the consequent problems,—chiefly those of mobility and endurance.

The oceanic sea-birds have solved these problems of mobility by becoming sailplanes as well as power-craft. This fundamental fact, although pointed out by Wynne-Edwards in 1935 and no doubt familiar to others before him, has been widely overlooked in ornithological circles. Supposing that the oceanic sea-birds relied entirely on powered flight, they would only be able to operate to their goal in calm weather, and only by the consumption of large amounts of energy and, therefore, extra amounts of food. In fact the opposite is the case. It is probable that the oceanic sea-bird would find it difficult to get from land to the middle of the ocean in calm weather, for the motive power of the pelagic sea-bird is provided by the natural winds of the great oceans, deflected upwards from the waves. That is probably why the evolution of the most important group of oceanic sea-birds, the petrels and albatrosses, has taken place in the South Pacific and the neighbourhood of the antarctic continent, for in those seas nature's winds blow hardest and most continuously, and rollers, swells and great waves are permanent features of the surface of the waters. The absence of albatrosses in the North Atlantic may be due to the fact that the equatorial waters of the Atlantic are, on the whole, rather calm and incapable of providing the albatrosses with the lift necessary for them to glide their way through from the south.

Many descriptions of the flight of the tube-nosed birds exist in the literature, and some purport to analyse the motion of these wonderful birds in aerodynamical terms. Most of them dwell in wonder on the effortless flight of these great sea-birds but describe it as flight and overlook the really obvious fact that in ordinary rough weather, apart from the exercising of the control surfaces of the bird's wing and tail and small shifts of its centre of gravity, no important work is done by the bird at all. The oceanic travellers make use primarily of the components of the wind reflected from the banked sides of the waves and swells, and they spend their time making ground by alternating the use of this lift with excursions (by gravitational falls) into the sheltered trough between the crests of the waves, out of the main wind-stream. This is by no means a dead area for it contains various moving air systems which are consequences of the impact of the wind-stream on the irregular surface of the sea. A sea-bird can move forwards dead against the wind, as anyone who has watched a gull at sea will have seen, by using a few wing-beats to gain height, and then gliding on a long plane downwards.

Wind is therefore an advantage from the flying sea-bird's point of view. A sudden calm can strand certain ocean birds in mid-ocean, especially if heavy-laden with food they may have to sit on the water and wait for the wind to get up again. Usually they do not have to wait very long. Most sea-birds can make good use of wind of any force, and a hurricane in mid-Atlantic probably does little damage, if any, to the sea-birds which happen to be there at the time. It is only when sea-birds are caught on a lee shore with no sea-room to manoeuvre that we get many casualties blown inland by storms.

This seems to happen to auks quite often, and most particularly to the little auk or dovekie.

Beyond the rather well-marked boundary of the little auk's normal winter distribution (see Fig. 19, p. 130, derived partly from the excellent paper of Rankin and Duffey, 1948), which brings it closer to the North Sea coast of Britain than most text-books allow, small numbers regularly, and large numbers irregularly, penetrate. On both seaboards of the Atlantic, there are years in which noticeable 'flights' of little auks take place within sight of shore or even overland, and years in which 'wrecks' occur, both locally and over great stretches of coast. In some years there are both flights and wrecks. The evidence

shows that these phenomena of irruption and abundance in lands
beyond the normal winter range are linked with cyclones and gales,
especially, but not necessarily, those which last for some weeks; sometimes a large population has been caught by a sudden gale when
plankton-fishing rather near a lee shore, and elements have been
driven ashore or inland before they could find the sea-room necessary
to escape to one flank or the other. One thing seems certain about the
little auk irruptions: they are *quite* irregular, and do not reflect any
changes in population, as far as can be seen. There is no sign of any
periodic cycle of abundance in the numbers of any North Atlantic
sea-bird, except perhaps skuas.

A dovekie wreck on the U.S. seaboard is not necessarily associated
with a little auk wreck in Britain, though when weather conditions
are extraordinary right across the Atlantic they may coincide. When
wrecks occur the light, small-winged little birds turn up in all sorts of
places: on reservoirs, lakes, ponds, duck-ponds, rivers, sewage-farms,
flooded gutters; in greenhouses, down chimneys, in porches, back
yards, pigsties, gardens, roads, turnip-fields; and are caught by
foxes, cats, dogs, opossums, raccoons, gulls, ravens, crows, and boys.
During the 1911-12 wreck of the little auk a doctor in Finsbury met
one entering his surgery door; it snapped at anyone who tried to
handle it. The ornithological machine has been sensitive enough to
detect all important flights and crashes in Britain only since about 1841,
though it is known that there were flights and great abundance in
Orkney in 1802-03 or 1803-04 (the records state 'winter of 1803,' which
is a common kind of ambiguity which has frustrated many a bird
historian) and 1811-12. Since 1841 we list the British, and some of
the eastern U.S. flights and wrecks as follows:

Little auk flights and wrecks, Britain and U.S. (italics) 1841-1950
(Years omitted are those in which nothing special was reported.)

'Winter' of
1841-42*   Big influx, flights and wrecks in October and November, east and south
            England, east Ireland.
1845-46   Local wreck in the Moray area of Scotland.
1846-47   Unusually abundant Orkney, and minor flight Aberdeenshire.
1848-49*   Great influx, flights and wrecks in December, Norfolk and Suffolk.
1860-61   *Some inland New England.*
1861-62*   Great influx, flights and wrecks in November, east England; many
            north Scotland January, after gale.
1863-64   Large flights, autumn, Durham and Yorkshire.

1866-67	Large flights Tweed area Scotland, and small influx west Scotland (Oban).
1867-68	Modest influx and flights west Scotland (Oban, Clyde).
1868-69	Flights Tweed area Scotland.
1871-72	*"Inundation" of Maine and Massachusetts.* "Wonderful irruption" of Tay area Scotland.
1874-75	"Very numerous" December and January, Devon.
1876-77	Abundant Tweed area, December.
1878-79*	*Many on Maine coast after December storm.* Very big flights and crashes in east Scotland and east England after November gale.
1881-82	"Uncommonly fruitful year" in Tay area Scotland.
1882-83	"Pretty numerous" in Northumberland.
1884-85	Flights in north England, November. A modest invasion of western Scotland in January.
1889-90	Flight off Yorkshire coast, January-February.
1891-92	*Notable flight Massachusetts, November.*
1893-94	Wrecks Ireland and Solway area after November gale.
1894-95*	Perhaps the greatest flights and wrecks in Britain, during and after fierce easterly gales in January and February; wrecks most noticeable from Tweed to Suffolk, but also noted Moray area in north-east Scotland, and in Ireland (see W. E. Clarke, 1895, etc.). Wrecks in Scotland, illustrated Fig. 20, p. 132.
1896-97	Minor February flight and some wrecks in Tweed and Forth.
1899-1900*	Substantial flights and wrecks in February and March from Dee to Yorkshire, and in Solway.
1900-01	Flights on various parts of east coast from Shetland to Suffolk, Jan.-March; biggest, with wrecks, in Norfolk February-March.
1901-02	*Abundant mid-November, Maine.*
1902-03	*Many December, Maine.*
1904-05	Flights November to February, Forth and Tay.
1908-09	Flight Fair Isle January-February; Tay area February-March.
1909-10	Flights Ireland January, and a few England.
1910-11	Substantial flights in Britain (particularly Norfolk and Suffolk) in November (extending also to Germany).
1911-12*	Great flights and wrecks in Britain in January and February; England, Scotland and Wales.
1912-13	Flights Norfolk November and January, and Scotland in February after south-east gale (see W. E. Clarke, 1912, etc.).
1913-14	*Many December, Maine.*
1914-15	Unusual number southerly records Oct.-Nov. (Channel Is., Cornwall, Scilly); flights and wrecks on both east and west coasts of Scotland and Orkney in December and January.
1915-16	Flights in Scotland and Isle of Man after storms in February and March.
1916-17	Flights in December in south-east England.
1917-18	*Flights mid-November, Maine.*
1921-22	A crash in Orkney in February.
1923-24	Flights (but no wrecks) east England.
1928-29*	Flights south-east England (including Norfolk) late November, numbers wrecked.

K

1929-30   Sudden wreck in south-east England 28 December to 1 January; little auk found alive in Round Pond, Kensington Gardens, central London.

1930-31   *Small invasion, November-December, of New Jersey and Virginia.*

1931-32   *Invasions, November-January, of Maine, reaching Massachusetts.*

1932-33   *Probably the greatest flight and wreck on the American seaboard in historical times. Influx November from Canada to Florida, some reaching Cuba (Murphy and Vogt, 1933), after unusual easterly winds.*

1936-37   *Flights and wrecks on U.S. seaboard, December-January though not as many as in 1932-33 (A. Sprunt, 1938).*

1939-40   *Small invasion of North Carolina, November to February.*

1942-43   Some numbers Yorkshire, November. Small flights and wrecks Devon and Cornwall, December and February.

1945-46   *Flight early December, Maine.*

1946-47   Rather unusual numbers on coast east Scotland and north-east England, January to April.

1947-48   Flights, north-east England, particularly November.

1948-49*   Marked flights, but relatively few wrecks throughout year, coasts Scotland, north England, Ireland.

1949-50*   Wrecks in Channel Islands, south-west England, west Wales, and south and west Ireland in February; flights Yorkshire February to May (see D. E. Sergeant, 1952) (Fig. 21, p. 134).

1950-51   Small wrecks in south England, January. *Notable flights and wrecks on New England coast.*

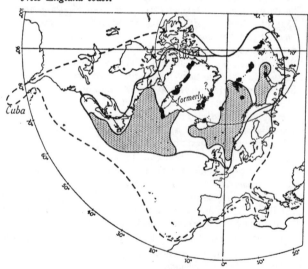

FIG. 19

The distribution of the little auk, *Plotus alle*. *Black:* breeding-stations. *Shades:* normal winter sea-range. *Outer runbroken line:* extent of summer sea-range and more fluctuating winter range. *Broken line:* extreme limit of sporadic records.

These marked * constitute notable invasions of Britain, outstanding compared with those of neighbouring years. The intervals between them however are irregular : 7, 13, 17, 16, 5, 12, 17 and 20 years.

The extreme limits to which the little auk can get, or can be carried by weather, are shown on Fig. 19, opposite. Strays have penetrated the Mediterranean as far as Italy, Sicily and Malta, and one has reputedly been seen in Egypt; and some have quite often reached the Canaries and Azores. In some winters there is quite an invasion of the unfrozen parts of the Baltic.

In order to carry on a sailing life upon the ocean it is obviously necessary for a sea-bird to be adapted to operate for a considerable time from base, even though, in ordinary rough weather, it may be able to sail very swiftly and make perhaps twenty or thirty miles an hour. Some sea-birds, and particularly the tube-nosed birds, in their early years before they make their first journeys to breeding cliffs, spend certainly two and up to seven years at sea without visiting land at all, possibly even without a sight of it. They are therefore adapted to drinking salt water and many have been recorded as doing so (shearwaters, petrels, auks and gulls).

Another adaptation of the birds to this kind of life is the power to go for long periods without food. It is known that the tube-nosed birds (and also the puffin and gannet) can survive, certainly for a week and possibly for very much longer, in this way. Indeed, in many species the adults only relieve each other at the nest at intervals of from four to seven days, and the young of some can be neglected in the burrow or nest for about a week without any apparent ill-effects or delay in the normal fledging period.

Between the inshore, or coastal sea-bird, that spends its life within sight of land, and often within sight of its breeding-place, and the fully oceanic bird, there are many intermediate states. We think it best, however, to adhere to the simple classification into the three main types for which Wynne-Edwards (1930) is originally responsible. The categories are inshore (or coastal), offshore (or marine), and pelagic (or oceanic). According to Wynne-Edwards inshore species include the cormorant and shag, the scoters, eiders and other sea-ducks, most of the smaller species of *Larus* gulls and, at certain seasons, all terns. These are the species which feed almost entirely within sight of the shore, and we think that to them could certainly be added the black guillemot, the divers in winter, and the red-footed and blue-

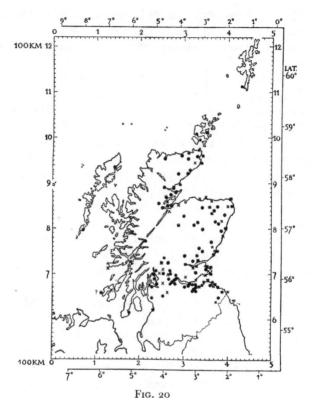

FIG. 20

A famous little auk wreck in Scotland, that of 1894-95 *replotted from*
W. E. Clarke (1895):

●: *one;*   ×: *several;*   ✳: *many*

faced boobies of the tropics, though these last two occasionally work a
little farther afield.

Wynne-Edward's offshore birds include the gannet, all the auks
except the little auk, and two *Larus* gulls, the lesser blackback and the
herring-gull. We would suggest that the black guillemot is perhaps
more coastal and that the puffin is somewhere between an offshore and
a pelagic species. Offshore birds, by definition, are those which obtain
their food within the continental shelf which, in the Atlantic, is,
generally speaking, marked by the 100-fathom line and is at most
200 miles from land. Of course, birds do not know where the 100-
fathom line is, but it coincides practically with the edge of human
fishing-grounds and the food changes very quickly beyond this point.

R. M. Lockley

Plate XIIIa. The all-black Bulwer's Petrel (adult) breeds numerously in the Desertas, Madeira

b. Bulwer's Petrel day-old chick, Desertas, Madeira

R. M. Lockley

Plate XIVa. Deserted by its parents: the young Manx Shearwater at ten weeks'
old, about to leave the burrow

b. Deserted by its parents: the young Fulmar at seven weeks' old

Of the marine birds the great blackback does not usually venture as far out as the lesser blackback and herring-gulls. (We have seen a few lesser blackback and herring-gulls at Rockall, which is 191 miles west of the St. Kilda islands and nearly 300 miles north-west of Ireland; it is however "land" and it lies on a fishing bank of its own.) In the parts of the North Atlantic most familiar to British and American ornithologists the most typical inhabitants of the marine or offshore zone are the razorbill, guillemot, lesser blackback, herring-gull, puffin and gannet; in the tropics the brown booby. The last three of these—the puffin, gannet and brown booby—are perhaps more oceanic than the others and more inclined to be found also in the next zone, which Wynne-Edwards names pelagic but which we shall generally here call oceanic.

This zone contains some all-the-year-round birds, and some seasonal birds. The Manx shearwater, which is also very much an inhabitant of the offshore zone, is found here in greater numbers than early workers have recognised, and can also certainly be classified as an oceanic bird. Among the important seasonal birds are the arctic tern, which makes a twice-yearly crossing of the North Atlantic, the four species of skuas, which also make twice-yearly seasonal crossings, and the two species of ocean-wintering phalaropes. The all-the-year-rounders, i.e. species which use the open ocean at all times when they are not actually engaged in breeding and return to it when they are off-duty, even during the breeding-season, include almost all the tube-nosed birds; particularly in the North Atlantic, Leach's petrel, the storm-petrel, the fulmar, the Tristan great shearwater, the North Atlantic shearwater, the sooty shearwater, Bulwer's petrel, the frigate-petrels and the gadfly petrels. The only oceanic gull is the kittiwake. The little auk might fall into this category, but it has a food-connection with the ice-front which necessitates a rather special definition of its distribution. In general, as Wynne-Edwards points out, each of the three chief families of northern sea-birds is the main possessor of one óf these three zones. The gulls largely possess the inshore zone, the auks largely the offshore zone, the tubenoses the oceanic zone.

During the present century a number of ornithologists have crossed the North Atlantic and plotted accurately the sea-birds which they encountered, checking their position with the ship's log. Recently E. M. Nicholson (1950,1951) has made a classification of the whole of of the North Atlantic into ten-degree blocks, for which he has provided a practical and easily memorable nomenclature (Fig. 55, p. 291).

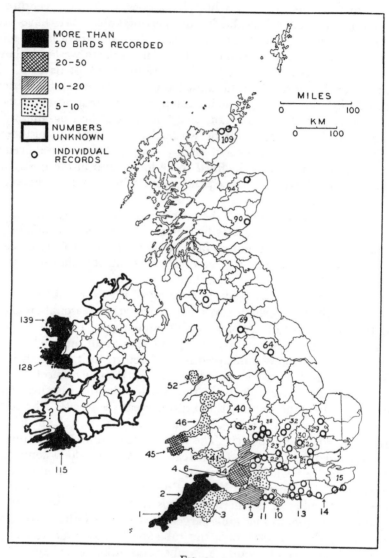

Fig. 21

A little auk wreck mainly in England, Wales and Eire, that of 1949-50
from D. E. Sergeant (1952)

This most helpful piece of work has been widely accepted throughout the ornithological world and there is no doubt that we are beginning to understand the distribution of birds in these waters, and beginning to see that the hidden topography of the sea, which we have analysed in our first chapter, is reflected in the distribution of sea-birds, which has, for most species, a well-marked pattern, with seasonal changes of an orderly kind. A recent important follow-up to Wynne-Edwards's pioneer work on the distribution of sea-birds at sea, is the paper by Rankin and Duffey, published in 1948, based on many transects made by them when they were on operational duties in the Royal Navy during the last world war. A pioneer investigator of the sea distribution of the North Atlantic sea-birds was the late Poul Jespersen (1924, 1929, 1930) whose excursions were further into the tropics than those of other workers. It is now possible to make preliminary analyses and maps as a result of these and other investigations which show not so much a fortuitous distribution of observers as a real distribution of the observed. Derived from all the available literature, and from certain unpublished notes of Eric Duffey, one of us has made six maps showing the distribution of the fulmar at sea on a two-monthly basis. Every observation of at least one certain fulmar was plotted as accurately as possible. The result (Fisher, 1952) shows not only the distribution of the fulmar through the seasons but the amount of information on a sea-bird that is now generally available.

While nearly all the inshore sea-birds are either resident or migratory it seems necessary that the word "dispersive" should be used to describe at least some of the offshore and most of the pelagic species. This word is not a contradiction of the word "migratory," because many species are undoubtedly both dispersive and migratory, if we use migratory to mean "making a regular journey in a particular direction," and dispersive to mean "scattering in no particular direction." In the early days of marine ornithology the word dispersive was applied to many species. Quite early in the present century, when the ringing recoveries of the guillemots began to mount up, it became clear that a large number of British breeding birds made northward journeys at the end of their breeding season, often north-eastwards to the coast of Norway, instead of the expected southward journeys. It was discovered, too, that even the inshore coastal terns, particularly the young, sometimes made northward journeys, the first journeys of their lives. Gannets, too, were found by ringing returns to go north, south, east and west of their gannetries. It was thought

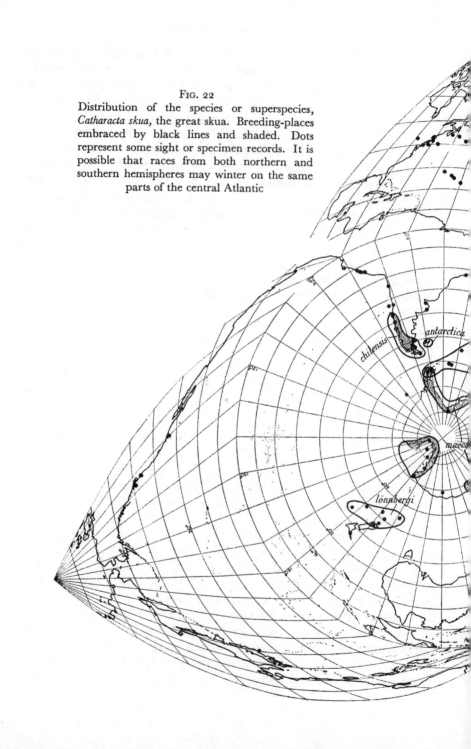

FIG. 22
Distribution of the species or superspecies, *Catharacta skua,* the great skua. Breeding-places embraced by black lines and shaded. Dots represent some sight or specimen records. It is possible that races from both northern and southern hemispheres may winter on the same parts of the central Atlantic

skua

subspecies
uncertain

rgi (clarkei)

lönnbergi (intercedens)

skua

that these dispersive birds simply voyaged in no particular direction until they found adequate supplies of food. Some of the Norway recoveries however may have been due to the equinoctial gales from south-west.

It is now known that a proportion of our gull population simply attaches itself to the inshore and shallow sea fishing fleet and follows it throughout the winter wherever it goes. (This does not apply so much to the lesser blackback, which is a more truly migratory species— p. 250.) Gannets, which are also partly parasitic on the fishing fleet, stay round the British coast when they are adult; they do not normally feed within sight of their gannetry and from the ringing returns can be shown sometimes to wander quite close to other gannetries. The adults especially are truly dispersive. It was thought that the fulmars, Leach's and storm-petrels were dispersive because they disappeared into the ocean when their breeding season was over, and were seen to be scattered fairly evenly over certain parts of it. Unfortunately we have as yet learned little from marking storm- and Leach's petrels, but the first important results from marking fulmars have now come to hand and they show that some at least of the young fulmars from West Greenland and from St. Kilda go to the Newfoundland Banks within a few months of fledging. This must be regarded as a migration, and it would certainly appear that the young fulmar, like the young gannet, is migratory, even if its parent is dispersive.

The gannet is seldom seen beyond the Continental shelf—i.e. the hundred-fathom line. The many ringing recovery records analysed by Thomson (1939) show that the marked winter movement of gannets south from Britain along the Biscay, Portugal and West African coasts is composed of adults and young, and that it is predominantly the young (particularly those in their first year) that go on to Africa; they reach Senegal. The Abbé Parquin (Mayaud, 1947) came across a huge concentration of gannet flocks on 16 January 1940 off the coast of Morocco from Casablanca to Mogador. This "he estimated at more than 100,000 individuals," which approaches half the world population! Gannets have been seen, in numbers that cannot in all cases be regarded as casual, in the Adriatic, and even off Egypt and Palestine.

To the north the disperal of the gannet sometimes reaches distances of a thousand miles or more from its breeding-colonies. It visits the coast of Norway up to the Lofotens (often in winter) and casually to Varanger Fjord and beyond. It has been seen fishing near Bear

Island (Bertram and Lack, 1933): one was seen at Jan Mayen on 21 July 1900 (G.Kolthoff, 1901). There are only four certain gannet records for Greenland (Hørring and Salomonsen, 1941), three from the south-west coast and one from Scoresby Sound on the east side. Nevertheless the gannet does appear to penetrate Davis Straits a little distance, also sometimes Hudson's Strait, for the Eskimos of Ungava see it occasionally (B. Hantzsch, 1928) and T. H. Manning (1952) saw, in August 1947, three or four birds that he believed to be gannets at the mouth of the Shagamu River, south-west Hudson's Bay. We have one extraordinary (hitherto unpublished) record from the Canadian Arctic beyond Davis Strait, from Jones Sound which enters Baffin's Bay as far north as 75°N. Here, on 23 August 1937, while excavating the old Eskimo village at Cape Hardy on the north coast of Devon Island, T. C. Lethbridge and his companions (who were all familiar with the species) saw several gannets flying in line quite close to them.

The West Atlantic breeding birds do not disperse in quite the same way as the East Atlantic birds in winter, for the St. Lawrence population appears to go south for the winter, adults and young together. None goes north: there is no record whatever of any gannets along the Atlantic coast of Labrador from the Straits of Belle Isle to Davis Strait (O. L. Austin, 1932), which suggests that the birds seen in Greenland and the Canadian Arctic may have dispersed there from Iceland or from some other East Atlantic headquarters. In winter gannets are more common off Virginia than off Cape Cod; the birds range far south into the Caribbean, regularly to Florida and Cuba and into the Gulf of Mexico, occasionally as far as the Mexican coast, and reputedly to Trinidad. So the West Atlantic gannet is a true migrant. The guillemot and even more so the razorbill, like the young gannet, are migratory: both enter the Mediterranean and penetrate eastwards as far as Italy and the Italian islands.

The sea-birds which make the greatest journeys of all are the great and sooty shearwaters which visit us from the southern hemisphere and our own northern-hemisphere-breeding Manx shearwaters, arctic terns, skuas and phalaropes. All cross the open ocean at the Equator on their way to their objectives in the southern hemisphere. Lately it has been proved that the Manx shearwater makes a diagonal migration, from the British Isles to South America (region of Buenos Aires and Rio de Janeiro, where two individuals ringed at Skokholm have been recovered). Crossing the line of the shearwater migration is the well-marked diagonal fly-way of the arctic tern between New-foundland and North-West Africa, which may involve a very large proportion of the population of this tern in the eastern part of North America. The arctic tern's migrations, indeed, are not only rather complicated, but certainly more spectacular than those of any other sea-bird; the little bird probably travels farther in the course of its year than any animal in the world, except perhaps some whales. Its travels are worth describing in some detail.

It was previously thought by some workers, e.g. Seebohm (1885), that, in spite of its circumpolar breeding-distribution, the arctic tern had "not yet discovered the existence of the Pacific Ocean." Certainly there seem to be rather few records on the eastern coast of the Pacific, and practically none on the west side south of Kamchatka. But this is probably because the arctic tern's passage is largely at sea; stragglers have indeed been recorded in the Hawaiian islands and in the North Island of New Zealand. The passage is detectable off and along the California coast, and quite a number are found offshore along the coasts of Peru and Chile. Even allowing for the relative numbers of observers (there are practically none at sea in the Pacific), it seems clear that the Atlantic passage is the greater, however. In late summer and autumn very many are seen crossing the North Atlantic trans-ocean shipping routes, and most, though not all, are passing at that time from north-west to south-east. It would seem that many of the arctic terns that breed in the north-west corner of the Atlantic, and round the arctic waters that communicate with it, pass on a slant to make their passage on the east side of the Atlantic. The (now famous) ringing recoveries of arctic terns marked in Labrador (on the Red Islands in Turnavik Bay) by O. L. Austin bear this out. One, marked as young on 22 July 1927, was recovered at la Rochelle in France on 1 October 1927; the other, marked on 23 July 1928, was found dead at Margate, fifteen miles south-west of Port Shepstone, in Natal on the south-east coast of Africa, on 14 November 1929—it has flown at least nine thousand miles in ninety days. A tern ringed on Eastern Egg Rock in Maine on 3 July 1913 and recovered at the mouth of the river Niger in August 1917 is now known to be an arctic tern (not a common tern as was originally recorded). Three birds marked as young at Machias Seal Island, belonging to New Brunswick but on the borders of Maine, have been recovered across the Atlantic (O. Hawksley, 1949). One marked on 20 July 1935 was captured near St. Nazaire in France on 8 October of the same year. One marked on 5 July 1947 was found

Plate *XVa.* Brown Booby, Fort Jefferson, Dry Tortugas, Florida, U.S.A.

(*Roger T. Peterson*)

b. Blue-faced Boobies, Dry Tortugas, Florida, U.S.A.

(*Roger T. Peterson*)

Plate XVIa. Mutual display of mated Gannets continues throughout the breeding season (Grassholm)

b. The feeding process in the gannetry (Grassholm)

on 10 November 1948 near Wilderness in Eastern Cape Province, South Africa. One marked on 18 July 1948 was picked up dead towards the end of September of the same year on the hills near Kylestrome in West Sutherland, Scotland.

Two of the young arctic terns hatched in Disko Bay, West Greenland, have been recovered. One ringed in July 1947 was collected a year later on the shore of James Bay, Ontario, where it was occupying a small ternery as a non-breeder. The other, ringed on 7 August 1949, was recovered in Gloucestershire on 20 October of the same year. One British nestling marked in Northern Ireland on 13 June 1941 was recovered at Lobito, Angola, in the south-west of Africa in February 1942.

The latest West Greenland arctic tern recovery involves the longest journey of any bird ever recorded by ringing. A juvenile ringed at Ikamiut in the Christianshåb district on 8 July 1951 was recovered newly dead in Durban Harbour, Natal, South Africa, on 30 October of the same year. It had flown over eleven thousand miles in less than three months after first taking wing.

These add up to an Atlantic crossing of at least some of the North American elements, and to a northward penetration into the Indian Ocean once the birds have rounded the Cape (Fig. 23, p. 142). But though we now know that some of these corner-turners reach Madagascar, we are also now quite sure that large numbers continue from the south Atlantic on to the Antarctic; and that some, also, do not cross the Atlantic first, but pass down, and off, the coasts of Brazil and the Argentine to this goal. Many ornithologists have been, quite properly, hesitant about accepting the arctic tern records in the Antarctic—particularly in view of the chance of confusion of sight (and even some specimen) records with the two southern breeding species, *Sterna vittata*, the antarctic tern, and *S. hirundinacea*, the South American tern. However, the facts are now accepted by such critical workers as R. C. Murphy, and have been abundantly augmented in the season 1946-47 by W. H. Bierman, an experienced ornithologist who was ship's surgeon to the Dutch whaling-ship *Willem Barendsz*. (Bierman and Voous, 1950). Some of the certain observations of arctic terns round the Antarctic Continent, and in the oceans and lands between it and the breeding-grounds of this extraordinary bird, are plotted on fig. 22. The birds particularly inhabit the pack-ice and the neighbourhood of bergs, and feed in the 'leads' and near the bergs, where whale-krill (particularly *Euphausia*) is plentiful, in much the same way as they do in the Arctic.

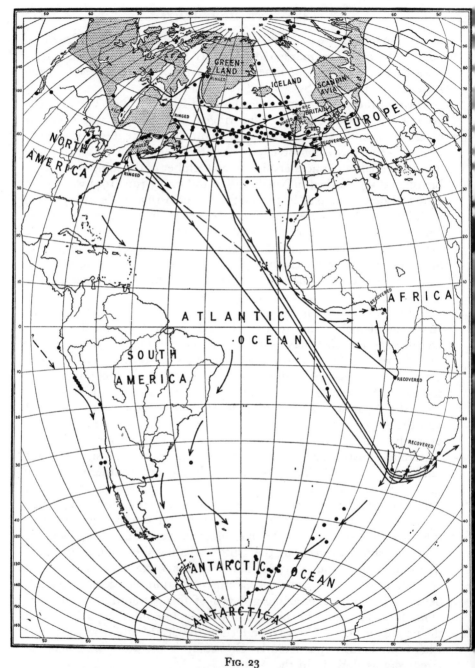

FIG. 23

Distribution and Atlantic migration of the arctic tern, *Sterna paradisaea*
Dark shading: breeding-distribution. Dots: some certain sight or specimen
records. Lines connecting ringing: to recovery places do not of course
necessarily represent actual routes taken

From the British Isles the arctic tern is totally absent from December (usually November) to March, while it is engaged on this great southward visit. When on passage through Britain it moves usually by coastal routes; and some Baltic and Frisian birds (by ringing records) join up with the passage on the coast of eastern England. In some years arctic terns join the marked inland passage of common terns along the English river-valleys. But beyond Britain most of the passage becomes oceanic, and the records in inland Europe and the eastern Mediterranean are very scanty.

The four skuas, which in the winter are generally parasitic on other sea-birds, also (like the arctic tern) make long journeys which involve entering and crossing the open oceans. To understand their migrations it is necessary to consider also their breeding-distribution in some detail. The largest of them, the bonxie or great skua, *Catharacta skua*, is one of the few birds with a bipolar distribution. We think it likely that this interesting species (or superspecies) originated in the north, and colonised the south where it evolved into a bird of more gull-like form and habits than the other skuas; and that the presence of a breeding-outpost in the North Atlantic is possibly quite a recent development, and probably derived from the main subantarctic and antarctic population.

Most authorities consider all the bonxies to be of one species; but it is possible, as Murphy and others point out, that two of the southern forms, hitherto classed as the subspecies *C. skua maccormicki* and *C. skua lönnbergi*, may breed on the same islands in the South Shetlands, in which case they should be regarded as separate species, even if they are overlapping end-members of a subspecies chain (see p. 39). If the world's bonxies do not all belong to one species, they certainly form one superspecies; and the differences between the northern *C. skua skua* and the Falkland Islands and Chilean races of the antarctic skua, *C. skua antarctica,* and *C. skua chilensis* are not great. The distribution of the bonxies, on their breeding-grounds and at sea, is shown in Fig. 22 (p. 136). It will be seen that southern skuas cross the equator in the Pacific, and nearly reach it in the Indian Ocean: those which travel up the eastern shore of the Pacific as far as the United States and even British Columbia are *C. skua chilensis;* one of the great skuas taken in Japan has been positively identified as the south polar skua *C. skua maccormicki*—not of the race *lönnbergi* which breeds south of New Zealand and thus much nearer Japan. This form (*lönnbergi*) has not so far actually been found in the Pacific north of the North Island of New Zealand, and may be more sedentary in ranging-habits than the south polar skua. The skuas seen at sea in the Atlantic south of the equator have been identified on the west side as belonging to the Falklands race *antarctica;* on the east side the affinities of the Tristan-Gough breeding-population are obscure (they most closely resemble *lönnbergi,* it seems) and the identity of the race commonly observed off the west coast of South Africa is unknown. as is the form noticed chasing terns in the Seychelles in the northern Indian Ocean.

There is so far no formal proof that the southern bonxies of today penetrate to the North Atlantic, though they must have done so on occasion if the theory of the antarctic origin of the British-Iceland population be the correct one. Bonxies have been seen between the equator and the West Indies in April and May, off the West African coast south of the Cape Verde Islands in November, January and February, and in the central part of the Sargasso Sea between October and December (not in any other month). But whether these are southern or northern is not certain, as none has been collected. North of these latitudes bonxies spread widely over the sea, parasitising gulls and terns, from New York to the Straits of Gibraltar, and there is no doubt that they are northern bonxies; a bird ringed at Hermaness, Shetland, has been recovered near Boston (Massachusetts), and birds from Noss, also in Shetland, have been recovered in Spain and Portugal. Bonxies haunt American waters through the summer, for instance the fishing-grounds of Nantucket and the Newfoundland Banks; but the suggestion that these may—because of the season when they are seen—be southern birds must be resisted. Indeed, they wander far at all seasons, for their breeding-grounds are confined to south Iceland, the Faeroe Islands, Shetland and the island of Hoy in Orkney, while foraging birds are often seen west, north and east to Labrador, Greenland, Jan Mayen, Bear Island, Spitsbergen, and have been observed as far as Novaya Zemlya. A few birds enter the Mediterranean, though they are not regular in any part of it east of Gibraltar.

Outside the Iceland-Britain area, there are only rumours of North Atlantic bonxie colonies. Ludwig Kumlien (1879), in his exploration of Baffin Island, supposed the presence of a colony on Lady Franklin Island, off the south-east corner of Baffin Island; but there is no modern evidence of a colony anywhere in this area, or—as has also been rumoured—in south Greenland.

In south-east Iceland the great ice-cap of Vatnajökull drains into

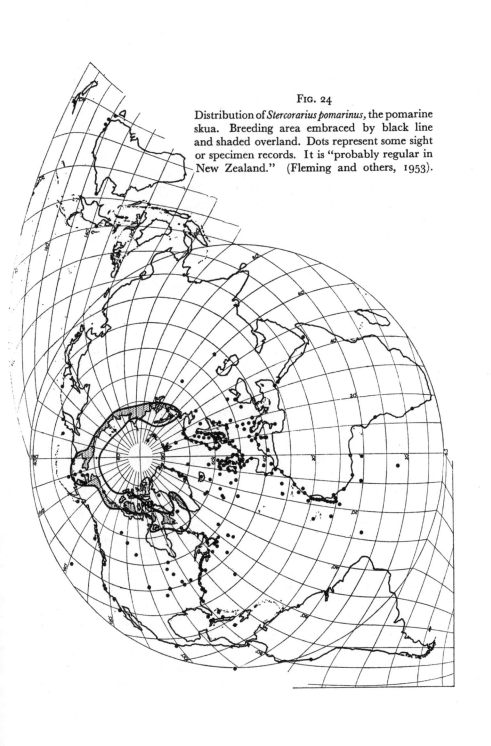

FIG. 24
Distribution of *Stercorarius pomarinus*, the pomarine skua. Breeding area embraced by black line and shaded overland. Dots represent some sight or specimen records. It is "probably regular in New Zealand." (Fleming and others, 1953).

a maze of rivers, of which many short ones lie between it and the sea, flowing erratically, depending on the temperature and melting (sometimes also on volcanic eruptions), through great, flat, wide aprons of morainic lava-sand, in places ten miles wide. These aprons of sand are the chief breeding-habitat of the bonxie in Iceland; its headquarters is on the sand-waste Breiðamerkursandur, and there are many on the larger Skeiðararsandur, and some on the little waste of Steina-sandur. Other parts of Iceland have a few breeding great skuas, but not many nest on moorland resembling their typical habitat in Shet-land. In the Faeroes and Britain the present situation is that annually there are just over a hundred nests in the Faeroes, distributed over eight islands, the vast majority being on Streymoy: about a thousand nests in Shetland, distributed over nine islands, the vast majority being on Foula, Unst, Yell, Hascosay and Noss: and over twenty nests on Hoy in Orkney. It seems unlikely that there are over ten thousand living northern bonxies in the world; yet the bird is so conspicuous that it features very frequently in at-sea observations and transects of the North Atlantic.

The pomarine skua (we prefer this name to pomatorhine skua), *Stercorarius pomarinus*, has the most restricted distribution (Fig. 24, p. 145) of the three smaller species. Its breeding-range is typically arctic, and confined to tundra countries, and it is quite absent from the arctic sector between West Greenland and Novaya Zemlya, except for what appear to be casual breeding-records from the Mur-mansk coast and Kanin Peninsula in European Siberia, and Franz Josef Land. It is doubtful whether it breeds anywhere in Labrador; it is probably only irregular in Alaska south of the Arctic Circle, and nobody seems to know anything about its status in Kamchatka (a part of the Palearctic from which little information about birds seems to be available).

It is now possible to derive an indication of the off-season distri-bution of pomarine skuas from a plot of recorded observations of birds on land at sea. What must clearly be quite a considerable proportion of the world population enters the North Atlantic *via* the Norwegian Sea, and migrates along the shores of Britain (particularly the eastern shores), as well as more directly to mid-ocean. Pomarines reach the Nova Scotia and U.S. seaboard; and pass along the western North Atlantic shore as far as Florida, the Bahamas and North Cuba; and there are records from the Sargasso Sea, and one from Dutch Guiana. On the eastern side there seems to be a small, but fairly regular, overland passage to the Caspian, Black Sea and Mediterranean; and along the east Atlantic shore, and some distance off it, they travel in numbers to the tropical West African coast in the neighbourhood of the Rio de Oro and Cape Verde. Here there is a significant concentration of pomarine skuas, remarked upon by many different observers; and some go farther, towards the Gulf of Guinea and even beyond, for there are records from Walvis Bay in South Africa and from St. Helena.

In the Indian Ocean the pomarine skua has, as far as we can find, only been recorded from Burma. In the Pacific it coasts along the American side to Mexico, has reached the equator at the Galapagos Islands and crossed it to Peru. On the Asiatic side it is found in the Kuriles, off Japan and possibly off northern New Guinea; and it has reached northern and eastern Australia; one straggler is recorded from North Island, New Zealand.

The arctic skua, *Stercorarius parasiticus*, has much the widest breeding-distribution of all skuas, extending from the High Arctic to the moors of northern Scotland, and the forest zone of northern Europe, Asia, and America. Comments on the map (Fig. 25, p. 148) can be confined to particular areas; the arctic skua is probably the only skua that breeds regularly in Labrador, though much has still to be discovered about its exact distribution on that coast. In Greenland it breeds on three well-defined coastal strips: the southern part of the west coast; the Thule district at the entrance to Smith Sound; and the east coast between Scoresby Sound and Hochstetter's Foreland; not, apparently, elsewhere. It is the only skua which breeds regularly on Jan Mayen. In Europe its southern limit was formerly Denmark; it still breeds on the fells and coastal moors of Norway south to its southern tip, Lindesnes, but is relatively rare in Sweden—even in arctic Swedish Lapland, where the long-tailed skua is commoner. It breeds, however, in western Finland and on the Åland islands in the Baltic. It is abundant on the moors and sands of Iceland, and on all the islands of the Faeroes. In Britain it now breeds regularly in Shetland, Orkney, Caithness, the Outer Hebrides and the Inner Hebridean island of Coll. In Shetland it is widespread, nesting in at least three parts of Mainland, and on Mousa, Noss, Yell, Fetlar, Hascosay, Unst, Foula and the Fair Isle. In Orkney it breeds in Hoy, and has bred in Papa Westray since about 1925; it formerly bred in Eday and Sanday. The Caithness and Coll colonies are small and fluctuating, and the Outer Hebridean birds are widely scattered over the maze

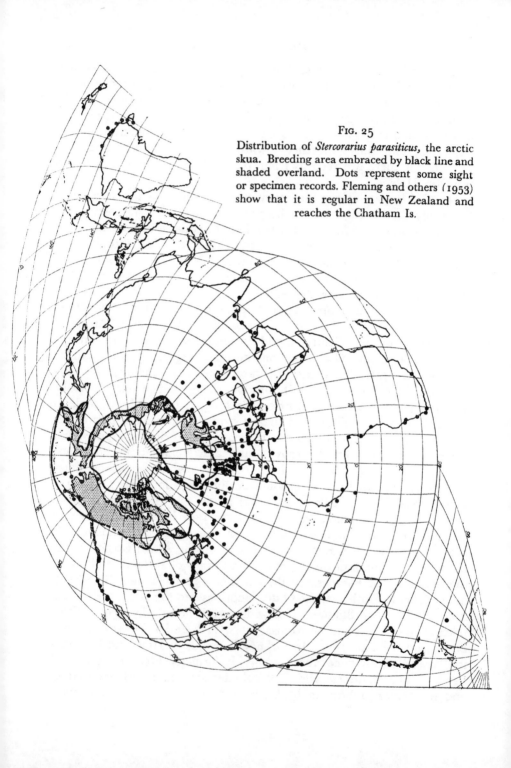

FIG. 25

Distribution of *Stercorarius parasiticus,* the arctic skua. Breeding area embraced by black line and shaded overland. Dots represent some sight or specimen records. Fleming and others (1953) show that it is regular in New Zealand and reaches the Chatham Is.

of land and water from Lewis to South Uist. When Thomas Pennant travelled on his famous tours in Scotland he found arctic skuas nesting on Islay and Jura in 1772; but they have bred since only sporadically on these islands, e.g. on Jura in 1890 and 1939 and on Islay in 1922. At least one pair bred regularly in Sutherland until the end of the last century, but now it is sporadic there. It has nested sporadically also in Tiree (1891), Argyll (c.1931) and West Inverness (1928-33).

At sea the arctic skua has been called "the unfailing attendant of the arctic tern," and follows this and other species across the equator in both Atlantic and Pacific. The plot (Fig. 25, opposite) of at-sea records in the North Atlantic, as compared with other ocean areas, reflects the distribution of observers rather than that of skuas; but there is no doubt that the arctic skua passes to its winter waters by ocean passages. It reaches the Straits of Magellan by the Pacific and probably also by the Atlantic, has been recorded from St. Paul Rocks and St. Helena, and reaches the Cape in Africa. It is recorded from tropical West Africa, though it does not appear to concentrate around and south of Cape Verde as does the pomarine skua. It passes along the U.S. seaboard to the Mexican Gulf, North Cuba, the Bahamas and the Sargasso Sea, and has been recorded from the Grenadines in the West Indies. It passes commonly along both east and west British shores, and to a certain extent also overland in Europe to the Mediterranean-Caspian line; and some elements reach the southern Red Sea, the Persian Gulf, and the Mexican coast. West Pacific birds reach New Guinea, Australia, New Zealand and Chatham Island.

The breeding-distribution of the long-tailed skua, *Stercorarius longicaudus* is not the most restricted, but its at-sea distribution is the most mysterious (Fig. 26 p. 150). Its population is much smaller than that of the arctic skua, and probably smaller than that of the pomarine skua. Its nesting distribution is wide through the arctic, but scattered and over vast regions (see map) sporadic; it extends south of the Arctic Circle to the Dovre Fjeld area, or even farther south in Norway. It breeds south to Nunivak Island in Alaska, to York Factory in Hudson's Bay, probably *not* to northern Labrador and Iceland; the evidence is unsatisfactory from these areas. It does not breed in south Greenland, or on Bear Island and many other arctic islands; in general it nests only where there are small rodents available, particularly lemmings, though it does not *need* these, for it has successfully nested on Jan Mayen (once, in 1900) and several times in Spitsbergen (e.g. 1931), where there are no rodents. One of us was stooped at by a

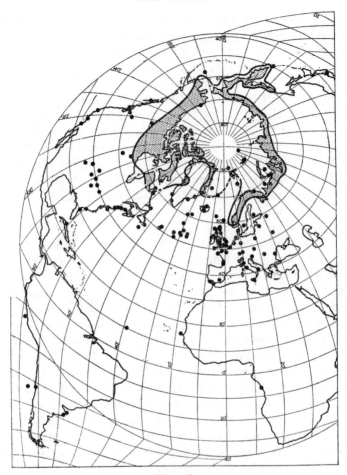

FIG. 26

Distribution of *Stercorarius longicaudus*, the long-tailed skua. Breeding area
embraced by black line and shaded overland. Dots represent some sight or
specimen records

long-tailed skua in Spitsbergen in 1933, while he was looking for
arctic skuas' nests, but though the bird was clearly defending a territory
its nest was not found.

Like the other skuas, the long-tailed skua passes to its Atlantic
winter waters by ocean routes, though it is often seen off British shores,
and a strong element passes south down the North Sea and through
the Channel. Whether the inland records in Europe indicate a real

(small) overland passage to the Mediterranean, or are merely casual, is not yet clear. In the Atlantic the species reaches the Sargasso Sea (Jespersen, 1930), has been seen in mid-ocean between the Amazons and Cape Verde, and has once only (as far as we can discover) been seen off tropical West Africa—four together near the Cape Verde Islands on 8 May 1947 (Bierman and Voous, 1950). The only observations of this species in the southern hemisphere derive from Murphy (1936), who records long-tailed skuas off Peru, Chile and Argentina between October and December, and Wetmore (1926) who found them harrying Trudeau's terns, *Sterna trudeaui*, off the Buenos Aires coast of Argentina in December. We can find no record whatever of this species from the Indian Ocean, Australasia, or the West Pacific south of Japan; on the east Pacific shore long-tailed skuas—perhaps on their way to Chile—pass along the coasts of British Columbia, the western United States, and Mexico. But the winter quarters of this interesting species remain generally mysterious. It is possible that the long-tailed skuas scatter more widely than the others, and do not usually gather in numbers over special waters.

We cannot leave the subject of sea-bird movements without a glance at what are perhaps the most interesting and specialised to all the secondary sea-birds—the phalaropes, the only waders that spend part of their lives as true sea-birds.

There are actually three kinds of phalaropes, but Wilson's phalarope, *Steganopus tricolor*, is never a bird of the open sea. The others, which are both known in Britain, winter in the wide ocean, where they hunt and swim for surface-plankton; an adaptation which continues to astonish those who meet them under such circumstances. The larger of the two, the grey phalarope, *Phalaropus fulicarius* (known in North America as the red phalarope) is a pan-arctic breeder which has been recorded as nesting at the highest possible latitudes all round the mainland and islands of the Polar Basin; in fact it has been found breeding in all those lands nearest the Pole save Svernayà Zemlya off Siberia and the islands north and west of Melville Island in the Canadian Arctic; and might be found on these if they were well explored. The southern boundaries of its breeding-distribution do not extend far beyond the coastal tundras of Greenland, the Canadian North-West, Yukon, Alaska and Asiatic Siberia; it is not found breeding in Alaska far south of the mouth of the Yukon, or in Hudson's Bay (except on its north-western shore), or in Labrador, or on the European arctic mainland; indeed in Siberia-in-Europe it breeds only very doubtfully on Kolguev and Waigatz, though certainly, and in places abundantly, on Novaya Zemlya, Franz Josef Land and Spitsbergen. It nests in small numbers, and perhaps not every year, on Bear Island, and has a stable and fairly large breeding population in south Iceland; it occasionally breeds in other parts of Iceland. It has not been proved to nest on Jan Mayen.

The breeding-range of the red-necked phalarope, *Phalaropus lobatus*, known in America as the northern phalarope, is actually less northerly than that of the grey phalarope, though it nests in many parts of the High Arctic. Its range stops short of Devon and Ellesmere Islands in the Canadian Arctic, of the northern two-fifths of Greenland, and of most of the islands of the Eurasian half of the Polar Basin, though it breeds in Novaya Zemlya, Kolguev and Waigatz, and has occasionally bred in Spitsbergen. It is not on the breeding-list for Bear Island or Jan Mayen. Iceland is an headquarters of it; thousands nest on the eutrophic oasis-lake of Mývatn in the north, and these tame, pretty birds of Odin nest even on a public lake in the middle of Reykjavík, Iceland's capital. The southern limits of the creature's breeding-range are not easy to define, for the outposts are very scattered; it is clear that there are some in north-west Ireland, in the Hebrides, and in Orkney, Shetland and the Faeroes; but the situation is obscure in Russia, where elements may reach the Kirghiz Steppes, and do reach northern Sakhalin. In North America the red-necked phalarope breeds in Newfoundland Labrador, but not in Newfoundland, reaches its farthest south as a nesting species in James Bay, and has scattered outposts in the interior of the North-West, Yukon and Alaska. But the main breeding-grounds are along the coastal tundras of the edge of the Polar Basin, and by the mouths of the great north-flowing rivers.

The winter-quarters of the two sea-phalaropes have until recently been little known, and they are still somewhat mysterious. The present extent of our knowledge is plotted on Figs 27 and 28 (pp. 154, 155). In the west Pacific we know that the grey phalarope reaches Japan, but whether flocks winter in the South China Sea or other Pacific waters to the south of Japan and east of the Philippines is quite unknown. The red-necked phalarope definitely enters those waters, and flocks have been seen off North Borneo, northern New Guinea, and further south among the East Indies in the Banda Sea. Phalarope red-necked is recorded from Malaya,* and two from New Zealand;

*J. Delacour (1947) says the red-necked phalarope "winters in the seas south of Malaysia"—presumably therefore in the eastern part of the Indian Ocean.

four grey phalaropes have also been found in New Zealand—the only West Pacific records south of Japan.

In the east Pacific both species travel down the western seaboard of the United States, and have been recorded as stragglers to Hawaii. The red-necked phalarope appears to have a winter sea-headquarters off the coast of Peru, though elements certainly carry on to Patagonia and have been found inland in Bolivia and Argentina. The grey phalarope appears to disperse more over the ocean, having been found in the Galapagos Islands, and having been seen by Poul Jespersen (1933) many times on a voyage from Panama to the Marquesas. A headquarters appears to be off the coast of Chile, farther south than that of the red-necked phalarope. The species has been seen on the other side of South America up the River Plate, and probably in the Falkland Islands.

On the west side of the Atlantic the situation seems really mysterious. Ludlow Griscom (1939) who has studied the migrations of both species off Cape Cod, Massachusetts, for a number of years, comments that more red-necked (northern) phalaropes use this route than grey (red) phalaropes. However, he has seen a thousand grey phalaropes in a day (19 April 1938), moving north at a time some weeks before the normal movement of red-necks. Up to a quarter of a million red-necks gather in early August between Eastport and Grand Manan in the Bay of Fundy, and flocks of a thousand or more are occasionally seen off the Massachusetts coast. But farther south the phalaropes disappear into limbo; both species are recorded as far as Florida, and there are a few records of both on or near the north shore of the Gulf of Mexico. From the entire West Indies and the Caribbean Sea there is *not one record* of either species of phalarope. Do the West Atlantic phalaropes mainly winter off the New England coast? Probably not. Do they only straggle farther south? Or do they cross to West Mexico and pursue their way to western South America? Or what?

In the open North Atlantic away from the coast phalaropes have been encountered at sea in many transects, notably those of Jespersen, Mayr, Wynne-Edwards, Rankin and Duffey. None of the observers has felt sure enough to decide which species he was observing, though it seems clear that at least some, if not all, were grey: the records have been plotted on the grey phalarope's map. The red-necked phalarope has been recorded once from Bermuda and once from the Azores, but otherwise was unknown from the central and eastern Atlantic south

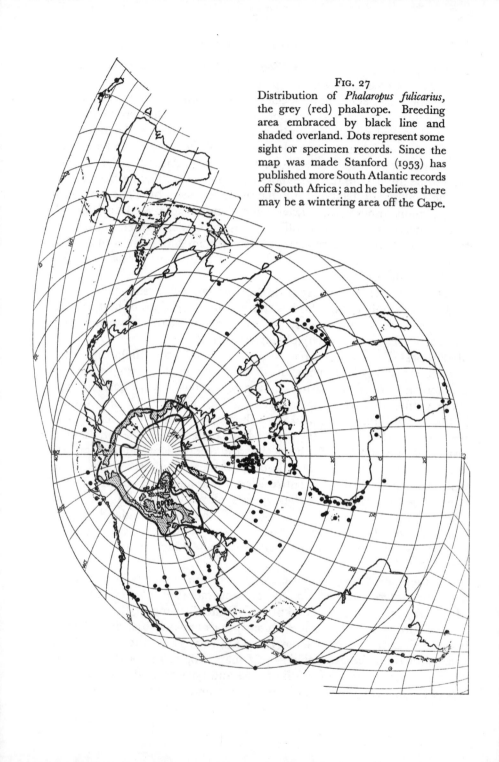

FIG. 27
Distribution of *Phalaropus fulicarius,*
the grey (red) phalarope. Breeding
area embraced by black line and
shaded overland. Dots represent some
sight or specimen records. Since the
map was made Stanford (1953) has
published more South Atlantic records
off South Africa; and he believes there
may be a wintering area off the Cape.

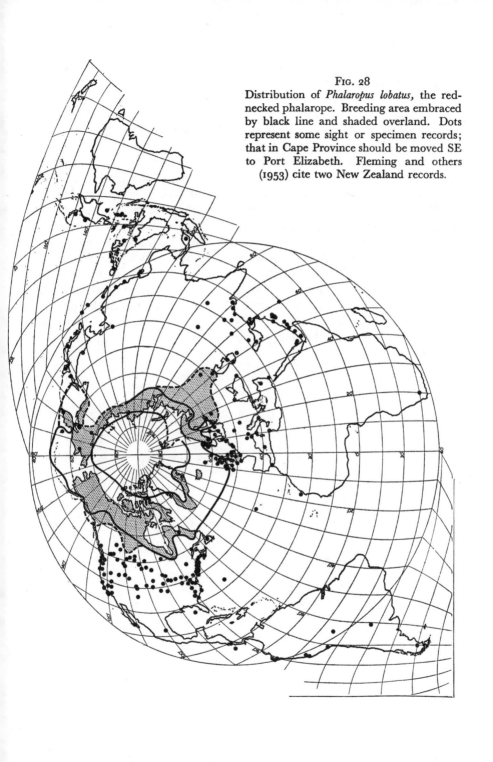

FIG. 28

Distribution of *Phalaropus lobatus*, the red-necked phalarope. Breeding area embraced by black line and shaded overland. Dots represent some sight or specimen records; that in Cape Province should be moved SE to Port Elizabeth. Fleming and others (1953) cite two New Zealand records.

of the Straits of Gibraltar until 17 March 1930, when from the research ship *Dana* Å. V. Tåning (1933) saw small flocks in a sea-area also occupied by grey phalaropes off the Rio de Oro coast of West Africa. But it is the grey phalarope (as P. F. Holmes (1939) particularly shows) that appears to have a regular wintering area off the coast of subtropical and tropical West Africa, from Madeira and the Canaries to the Cape Verde Islands and beyond; indeed some elements clearly carry on to the Cape in South Africa, probably *via* the Gulf of Guinea and the Cameroons; there are a few inland records in South Africa.

The remaining sea-area known to be inhabited by the two phalaropes in the winter is that part of the Indian Ocean that stretches from the Gulf of Aden to north-west India, and which includes the entrances of the Red Sea and the Persian Gulf. This concentration of phalaropes is discussed by R. Meinertzhagen (1935) and several others: probably both species approach it from the Eurasian arctic breeding-grounds mostly overland; the records of red-necks suggest so, though some elements of both species pass through the Mediterranean. However, neither has yet been recorded from Egypt.

CHAPTER 6

NAVIGATION BY SEA-BIRDS

WE HAVE SEEN sea-birds, especially the tubenoses, in the Atlantic many hundreds, often well over a thousand miles, from the nearest continent, and sometimes several thousand miles from their breeding grounds. As the open sea to a man without instruments of navigation is a seemingly trackless desert, we marvel at the ability of the sea-bird to fly home to a remote island or cliff many weeks' journey from its wintering grounds. Thus the arctic tern crosses almost from pole to pole, from the Antarctic to Greenland. The great and sooty shear-waters breed on islands in the extreme South Atlantic bordering the Antarctic, but winter in the North Atlantic (thus enjoying perpetual summer) as far as the east coast of North America, Greenland, Iceland and the west coast of Europe. Wilson's petrel, breeding along the edge of the Antarctic Continent, performs one of the longest migrations known, one of about 7,000 miles each way. During most of this journey from the south polar sea to the Newfoundland Banks or to the Bay of Biscay or the seas between, it may never see the land, yet this small fragile-looking bird is able to return to the same nesting hole and mate at approximately the same date each year of its adult life. It may be argued that if Wilson's petrel continued to fly south it would be bound to strike the Antarctic Continent and so have a landmark to guide it to its breeding island or shore in the nearby seas. But how does the great shearwater, breeding exclusively on the Tristan da Cunha islands, and migrating six thousand miles northwards in the southern winter, find its home islands, which are 1,500 miles from the nearest land, whence, as Wynne-Edwards points out, they subtend an arc of only 15 minutes. It is possible that Tristan normally provides a bigger target than that, for it projects some thousands of feet into the sky and for most of the time produces a cloud-mass which is high and spreads for many miles. And it is possible that great oceanic islands, such as Tristan, even if their actual area is fairly small, may produce minute changes in the surface and topography of the sea which may be detectable many scores of miles away by birds.

Many experiments have been made with sea-birds with the object of discovering the physical nature of the mechanism of homing birds. Visual memory can serve where there are familiar land or sea marks, and birds experimentally released within sight of these do orientate themselves and fly home very quickly. But where they successfully return when released far from home and in country or upon seas which they are presumed never to have visited before, visual memory as an aid is out of the question. The classical experiments with noddy and sooty terns carried out by Watson and Lashley (1915) are well known. Breeding adults from the Tortugas Islands, Gulf of Mexico, were sent by ship for distances of more than 850 miles, and returned from points far to the north of their normal distributional range. Griffin summarised these and other homing experiments which included terns, gulls, petrels and shearwaters; he concluded that some birds return home by a process of exploration in search of familiar visual landmarks. A gull released over the land and followed in an airplane flew at random until it sighted the ocean, towards which it then headed directly, although this particular part of the sea was neither the nearest salt water to the point of release nor the direction in which its nesting ground lay. Griffin and Hock (1948) took gannets from Bonaventure in the Gulf of St. Lawrence, released them over a hundred miles from the coast and followed them by air, sometimes for more than a hundred miles. The paths taken by the birds consisted of fairly long "legs" with sudden sharp turns, and somewhat resembled a cubist's idea of a spiral search, though the most simple explanation of this search is that it was quite at random. About sixty per cent. of the gannets released eventually reached home at a speed of about a hundred miles a day; those followed by air homed equally with a group of control birds that were not followed.

Two Manx shearwaters which returned to Skokholm after release at Venice have provided an early example of a sea-bird returning from an almost land-locked sea which it never normally visits (Lockley, 1942). A significant fact about this release was that one of the shearwaters, instead of heading for the open sea (Venice is 3,700 miles by sea from Skokholm, and a bird taking the sea-route would have to begin by flying in a direction directly opposite to that of Skokholm), rose up into the air and flew inland westwards in the direction of the sun, which was at that moment sinking behind the Italian Alps!

By airline Venice is only 930 miles from Skokholm; and one bird got back in 14 days. At the time of this experiment this instantaneous correct orientation on release in fine weather was regarded as remarkable, but thought to be accidental; as were also the correct orientations of some other shearwaters released in the Alps. However the latest work by G. V. T. Matthews with shearwaters from Skokholm has confirmed that there is an immediate initial orientation of this species when released inland in fine weather; returns to Skokholm were at high speed (from Cambridge, 230 land miles in $6\frac{3}{4}$, 8, 8, and $8\frac{1}{2}$ hours, from Birmingham, 156 miles and London, 225 miles, in $17\frac{1}{2}$ hours). In heavily overcast weather birds released at Cambridge showed an initial random scatter and none returned until the third night (Matthews, 1952). Finally the latest shearwater test by Dr. Matthews, arranged by one of the writers, has created a world record for a ringed bird used in a homing experiment. A Skokholm shearwater, conveyed by our friend Rosario Mazzeo to Boston by air and released on 3 June 1952 at the edge of the airport which fringes the sea there, returned to its nest burrow at Skokholm on 16 June. It covered the 3,200 (land) miles across the Atlantic in $12\frac{1}{2}$ days, thus averaging 250 miles a day, or more than 10 miles an hour. Even swallows (128 miles a day) and terns (139 miles a day) used in earlier tests have not equalled this speed. For a reason which is discussed below it is possible that this Boston-Skokholm shearwater may not have travelled at night; in any case we must allow it at least four hours average a day for feeding, preening and resting, and we must also allow for time lost as a result of its normal swinging deviating flight which makes its surface speed probably a third less than its flight-speed. It is clear that this bird had not time to spare for random searching, and yet the Manx shearwater does not visit the North American coast except as a very rare straggler. It was a fine clear morning when it was released at Boston and it immediatly flew eastwards in the direction of the open Atlantic—and Skokholm. This initial correct orientation cannot be explained satisfactorily by stating that it was accidental, or that a sea-bird would naturally fly away from the land; our shearwater at Venice turned inland towards high mountains, and Matthews' shearwaters in London and Cambridge flew at first further inland (in order to reach Skokholm quickly) rather than eastwards to the nearest sea. Initial orientation almost (in some instances quite) on the right compass bearing in fine weather and unknown territory can only be explained by the possession by the shearwater of an orientation mechanism which is quite independent of topographical 'knowledge' or memory; and the fact that the mechanism breaks down in cloudy weather suggests very strongly that orientation is by the sun. Kramer (1952) found that the highly accurate orientation faculty in his caged starlings vanished if the sun was hidden: when tests were made with an artificial sun (lamp) indoors, they orientated as if the lamp were the sun.

The sun-navigation theory, while it disposes of earlier hypotheses of kinaesthetic memory and sensitivity to the earth's magnetic field or Corioli's force (which depends on the velocity of movement of points on the earth's surface relative to its axis and which therefore varies with latitude), does not explain night-migration, which is a well-known phenomenon, although not commonly reported of sea-birds. Most sea-birds in fact rest at night, either on land or sea. The activity of fulmars, watched by us from a trawler, showed considerable diminuution at night. Manx and other shearwaters assemble in rafts on the sea in sight of their breeding-grounds *before* sunset, although they often do not land until two hours after sunset. In heavy overcast conditions many night-migrants appear confused and may descend in their greatest numbers on the coastal bird observatories, there to rest—and this is sometimes erroneously referred to as a "good migration." But it is on clear moonlit nights that the best migration occurs— at least for the migrants, which can navigate onwards without a halt, and without striking the lanterns of lighthouses, because they see the outlines of the land and the astronomical signs clearly.

Sun or astronomical navigation seems to be the most satisfactory explanation so far; and more research into night-migration may reveal that the migrant is guided by moon, stars, pre-glow and after-glow which may assist it to keep on a course already begun before the sun or its glow has left the sky. It should be remembered that night-migrants only fly for a comparatively short period, for not more than half the night—unless they are caught, being land-birds, over the sea, when they must continue flying to the nearest land, often some cape or island where there may be a migration observation station. Research may also show that the sea-bird is more lost and helpless in misty weather than was formerly believed; and that stories of homing through dense fog are largely fictitious. Sea-birds are in fact confused in heavy mist, and are then easily caught at the nest by the use of a powerful torch; on such nights shearwaters will accidentally strike objects over the breeding ground during flight, including light-

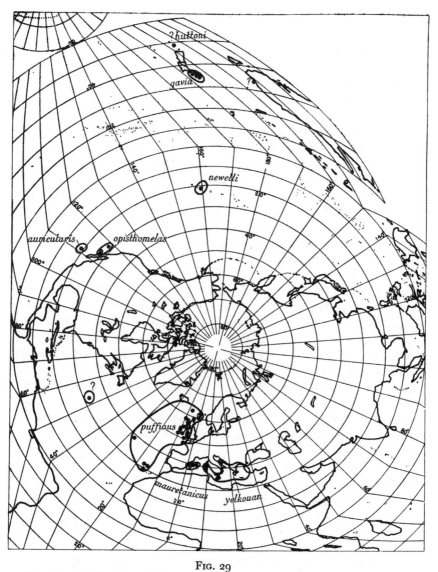

FIG. 29

Breeding distribution of the Manx shearwater species (or superspecies)
Puffinus puffinus. *P.p. yelkouan* also nests on the island Riou, near Marseilles;
and *P.p. gavia* as far far south as Cook Strait.

M

houses, rocks, and the observer himself—but never on fairly clear or clear nights.

The Manx shearwater is loudest and most vociferous at its breeding island on dark nights and when there is dense mist. This, we believe, is partly explained by the fact that the incoming bird, unable to recognise immediately the environment of its burrow in thick weather, screams almost continuously so as to attract a response from its mate on duty in the burrow, who answers and so guides the arriving bird. Glauert (1946) believes this to be the explanation in the case of the little shearwater (*Puffinus assimilis*), in Western Australia where on Eclipse Island these birds called loudly on dark nights and almost not at all on moonlit nights. There was the same amount of activity under both conditions; the little shearwater on Eclipse Island has no predatory enemies. But on other islands where adult shearwaters and petrels are slain by resident gulls and hawks and owls* there is notably less activity on fine clear nights, as well as almost complete silence from the few incoming birds. Obviously if the mate of the bird is already at the nest and answers the cry of the homecoming bird on a dark night there is direct guidance. But why should the incoming bird scream on a dark night, when (e.g. early in the season) there is no mate to reply? We put forward the suggestion, cautiously and merely as a possible line of investigation: that just as some animals (e.g. bats) are extremely sensitive to the echoes of sound-waves and are able to judge accurately the short distance they are in flight from objects they cannot see; so the homing sea-bird, on a dark night, may do so by receiving back from the rocks and cliffs and uneven surface of the breeding-ground echoes, perhaps of its voice† even its own wing-beats.

To return to long-distance homing and migration, it would now appear that the tubenoses navigate great distances over the sea with the aid of the sun and a time-sense which enables them to compensate for the diurnal movement of the sun; as well as, after crossing the Equator at the equinox, a return to early summer. Having once made the annual migration both ways (we have referred to an arctic tern, ringed as a juvenile 8 July 1951 in the Christianshåb district of West Greenland which travelled over eleven thousand miles across

---

* At Skokholm and Skomer little owls prey upon storm-petrels.

† As this book lay in page-proof we heard of the successful proof by D. R. Griffin and W. H. Phelps Jr. that the oil-bird *Steatornis caripensis* of the Venezuela caves navigates in darkness by echo-sounding, like bats.

the Equator and was recovered at Durban, Natal, on 30 October 1951 —average rate, about 100 miles a day for 114 days!), the individual has presumably become acquainted with what is, to man, an almost trackless route. As to the young non-breeding adult of *over a year old* it will presumably have the older more experienced adults to travel with. Rowan (1952) suggests that great shearwaters form rafts on the sea close to the breeding islands at the end of the season in preparation for departure in flocks for the northerly migration. But what of the fledgeling of those species such as the petrels and the puffins, which is deserted by its parents a week or two before it leaves the land, and travels solitarily to the sea? It may be observed making its way alone into the ocean up to fifty miles or so from the breeding-ground, as we have ourselves recorded. What happens to it in the next few days no one seems to have observed accurately, but it can receive no guidance from the adults in those early weeks—they are far at sea, and in moult. Probably, like the fledgeling gannet, it soon overtakes the adult flocks or at least passes through their extended wintering range, and, guided by an instinctive orientation, proceeds to a nursery or wintering-ground of juveniles, perhaps hundreds of miles beyond that of the adults. We would cite the case of a Manx shearwater, ringed as a juvenile at Skokholm on 10 September 1951, which was reported from Rio de Janeiro on 20 November 1951, thus confirming what we had long suspected: that the Manx shearwaters which are known to visit South America include young birds from Europe. This particular juvenile had covered 5,050 nautical miles in a maximum of 71 days (which is 71 miles a day), a striking performance for so young a bird. Another ringed Manx shearwater has been recovered in the South Atlantic; an adult marked on Skokholm in July 1947 reached a point 200 miles south of Buenos Aires in the autumn of 1952. So the old shearwaters can migrate as far south as the young ones. But the concentration of fulmars on the Newfoundland Banks, about fifteen hundred miles from the nearest breeding station, may be a young fulmar nursery. Fisher (1952) shows that the four marked birds recovered there were all first year (juvenile) birds, two from Greenland and two from St. Kilda.

This must be a short chapter, because our knowledge of the mechanism of orientation is so limited. To sum up: it seems that sea-birds may navigate like human beings do at sea. Although without mechanical aids, they find their way by learning the chart; by knowing the time (it is becoming clear that most birds have an accurate time-sense); by dead reckoning, probably in terms of flying-time rather than distance covered; by observing the sun and stars and their position in relation to the horizon. They may exploit other signs, such as the set of the currents, temperatures, and the presence of animals of their own or other kinds. We know that birds can make the mistakes that human navigators make, such as getting adrift and wrecked. And we know that they can, by instinctive orientation and navigation, without instruments, do things that humans cannot do.

That is the present state of our knowledge.

CHAPTER 7

SOCIAL AND SEXUAL BEHAVIOUR

BEFORE WE describe their exciting and varied life-histories we ought to review the present state of our knowledge of the social and sexual behaviour of sea-birds, from which a general pattern emerges which enables us to understand the meaning of their fascinating, and often very peculiar, specific ceremonies and displays.

After normal 'maintenance activities' (as they have to be called) the life of the sea-bird is centred round its reproduction, without which the species cannot continue. From these two activities all sociality (gregariousness, flocking or living together) arises; and sexual behaviour is the most important aspect of social behaviour.

Pair-formation requires the location of a partner, the attainment of which in the first place involves the breaking down of certain safeguards and habits with which the individual protects itself during the non-breeding period, and the establishment of a state of intimacy between male and female. The mechanism or behaviour by which the individual ring-fence is maintained on the one hand, and by which it is altered in order to secure the sexual bond on the other hand, is a remarkable phenomenon, popularly known as display.

In sea-birds, which are monogamous, display is mutual. The unilateral display and courtship behaviour of polygamous land-birds (such as the ruff, blackcock and jungle-fowl) hardly concerns this chapter as comparative material. Polygamy is usually associated with a brief but brilliant display or tournament between conspicuously adorned males, which, after mating, leave all the work of incubation and brooding to the dull-coloured females. The polygamist is an egoist occupied solely with the three m's: mating, moulting and maintenance. The male sea-bird, a monogamist, is by human standards a model husband, taking equal responsibility with his mate for nest-making, incubation, and rearing duties. Darwin (1871) overlooked the significance of mutual display when promulgating his theory of sexual selection; it was Selous (1905, 1905-06) who pioneered the general concept of unilateral versus mutual display, to be followed by Huxley (1914) who, with his papers on the striking courtship of the great crested grebe, introduced its importance to professional biology.

The mutual ceremonies of the sea-birds are hardly less remarkable than those of the grebes. They are prolonged throughout the summer, long after mating has taken place and the young have hatched, but their function is a useful one: mutual display serves as an emotional bond to keep the monogamous pair united so long as parental cares continue. This interesting biological device is of course of no value to the polygamous land-birds, in which the male takes absolutely no interest in the family. It is evident, then, that the relation of the sexes to the young and to each other determines the type of courtship display as well as the degree of development of the external sexual characters (colour and plumage) in male and female. Sexually faithful husbands resemble their wives so closely as a rule that the observer often cannot distinguish between the sexes of sea-birds in the field— for even the act of coition is sometimes reversed. Mutual display— leading to mutual stimulation—is advantageous where there is such outward uniformity.

It is interesting to trace the origins of sexual display. In courtship all sea-birds make use of the bill in rubbing, fencing, scissorsing, fondling or preening motions; in doing so they are unconsciously copying the familiar movements of feeding and being fed as chicks. Gaping is a characteristic of some sea-bird courtship; it too is derived from gaping when being fed in the nest. Threat attitudes, involving the use of the bill, the raising of neck-feathers, and often wing-play, can be traced to the behaviour of the growing chick when it first defends itself from its nest-mates (as when securing food at feeding-time) or other rivals or enemies; these threat attitudes become incorporated in, or adapted to, the courtship display.

How early in its existence the young sea-bird receives the first indelible impressions of the voice and behaviour, including the mutual display, of its parents we do not know—probably the precocious gull, tern and skua chick does so as soon as it hatches. Lorenz (1935) has shown that by taking the place and duties of the parent wild goose at the moment of hatching he transferred to himself the allegiance of the gosling, including its responses of sexual behaviour which develop at the appropriate age. This imprinting of parental influence is the first step in the socialising of the chick, which proceeds rapidly during the close contact of the rearing period as it receives affection, protection, and guidance from the adult. Every action of feeding and preening of the young by the parents strengthens the family (social) bond—an experience to be of value later in the bird's life. The chick learns to associate food and protection with others of its kind. Gradually it learns to recognise individuals, first of all, its parents; although it may not distinguish their sex at this stage it probably recognises them as individuals by their individual behaviour, as for example when the male gull feeds the female who in turn feeds the chick.

So far it has learned to associate its parent's bill with the pleasant sensations of feeding and grooming. How does it acquire knowledge of danger, for soon it must learn that only its parents are not its enemies? Danger is usually indicated by the warning-notes and flight-actions of the adult, the chick's response to which seems to be at first due to instinct, or maturation of instinct, rather than to any process of learning. Young gulls, though precocious and born with their eyes open and able to walk, do not crouch or hide on a warning signal until they are two or three days old. Young gannets, born blind and naked and with a more embryonic brain than the gull chick, do not strike at intruders (when, with warning cries, the adults leave the nest) until their eyes are open and they are covered with the first down. As the brain develops however, learning is mingled with maturation of instinct, and adaptability to new situations is acquired.

At fledging time the young sea-bird discovers that its parents are growing indifferent to its food-begging advances, and will ultimately repulse them, or will abandon the chick completely (tubenoses, gannets and puffins). In some species of social gulls the adults not only become hostile but, unless the young bird retreats, will actively attack and kill it. Thus sociality, which is not proved to be innate (no hormone for gregariousness has been demonstrated in studies of the endocrine organ of a bird), receives its first serious check, and the family bond is broken. To minimise the attacks of the adults the juvenile sea-bird learns to keep at least one body's length (striking distance) from a neighbour; and a pattern of behaviour is acquired which enables the bird not only to retreat at the aggressive display of the adult, but to employ the same threat signals to drive away birds younger or weaker than itself. By this device—usually a lowering of the head, pointing of the bill (mouth sometimes open) and raising of the neck-feathers—it is able to take its place in the community.

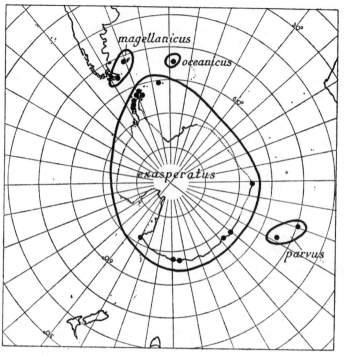

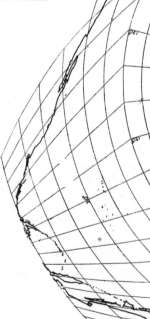

FIG. 30

Distribution of sight and specimen records of Wilson's
petrel, *Oceanites oceanicus*, replotted from B.B. Roberts
(1940). Inset, breeding distribution; dots here represent
some known breeding stations. A recent paper of Murphy
and Snyder (1952) indicates that *magellanicus* should
probably be united under *parvus* and *exasperatus* under
oceanicus.

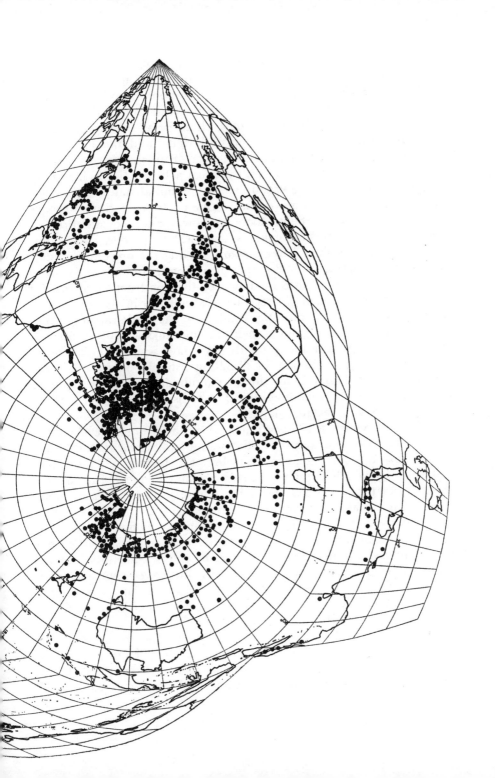

Threat display in fact is now a very important part of the behaviour of the newly independent bird if it is to secure an advantageous position in the winter flock. In the congregations of gulls which feed in farm fields, at rubbish-tips, by sewers, rivers and harbours, and which roost on reservoirs and islands, there is, as in domestic hens, a definite order of precedence, or peck-right, and the flock is so organised that the most dominant bird takes up the best feeding or roosting position, and maintains it by threat actions. In this hierarchy the inexperienced juvenile usually has a low initial status, as in communities of men. It will move towards the centre as it grows stronger and more experienced. Some flocks are however composed entirely of juveniles, as those of some gannets, shearwaters, petrels, and puffins which, deserted by their parents before leaving the breeding ground, perform long migrations, and gather at wintering grounds beyond the range of the adults. Little is known of the construction of pelagic flocks; probably a form of precedence is built up in the same way, both specifically and inter-specifically, in the wide-ranging tube-noses, skuas, terns, and gannets, pelicans, and auks when they become concentrated at rich fishing grounds. We have watched great shear-waters displaying at fulmars in disputing fish-offal at the side of a trawler at Rockall, and fulmar dominated fulmar in the same scramble for food, using the characteristic threat display of lowered head, opened wings and cackling noises.

When the young sea-bird, stimulated by the seasonal development of its breeding organs, returns to the nesting ground for the first time, it has now to overcome two obstacles: the barrier of "individual distance" by which it maintained its position in the flock, and the difficulty of procuring a mate of the opposite sex—if it is to breed successfully. These obstacles are so formidable that the inexperienced bird may never overcome them in the summer of its first return to the land. Its behaviour may remain appetitive, never reaching the stage of consummation: it arrives, establishes or enters a territory, displays and flirts with a bird of the opposite sex, but never copulates (or it copulates too late to breed successfully). However this behaviour is not without its function: from this experience it will be better equipped to initiate successful breeding in succeeding years.

The male (terns and gulls) is usually the first to arrive at the breeding ground, or at least to occupy a prospective nest-site or pre-territory. He calls loudly as if seeking to attract a partner. But at first he behaves aggressively towards any bird, male or female, which responds; he uses the threat display—the only social behaviour or reaction he is, by use, familiar with. As the sexes are so alike it has been suggested that, if he is inexperienced and attempting to breed for the first time, the male may not know the sex of the responding bird, but must find out by a closer acquaintance, by trial and error. His behaviour suggests this: the male tern or gull threatens, even attacks, the newcomer. If the arrival is male he will fly away or engage in a dispute for the territory; if female she will stay, and by her refusal to fight indicate her readiness to pair. She may remain quietly near him, watching his threat display, or responding with similar movements, but without being aggressive. Her behaviour acts as a releaser or signal that elicits the beginning of the love-bond. Threat-display wanes in favour of mutual attitudes of appeasement, expressed by turning away (upwards or aside) the conspicuous bill and head (gannets, cormorants, gulls, terns, skuas, auks). Sex-recognition has taken place, and with it begins mate-recognition.

In the love-ceremonies that follow the barrier of individual distance is gradually broken down. Yet although the head, with all its apparatus of intimidation—coloured bill and gape, facial adornments, raised neck-feathers, is turned away in the appeasing movements, in order to become intimate the bills, and in order to copulate the bodies, must be brought together. The female gull, skua and tern indulge in a food-begging ceremony in which she crouches in a supplicatory attitude before the male, her bill towards his, her mouth open, thus unconsciously imitating her behaviour as a chick. Females of other species—gannets, cormorants, tubenoses and auks—touch bills with their males in head-shaking, scissoring, and clashing movements, ceremonies likewise derived from the chick stage. Stimulating contact has been made, and soon coition follows, usually in the nest, and the barrier between female and male temporarily disappears. The mated pair now stand or sit (or fly) side by side. The male of the more mobile species (gull, skua, tern, puffin) establishes a somewhat larger "mated female distance" or sexual territory around his mate and the nest-site, from which he drives away or intimidates all other males. For this purpose the familiar threat display is used. She will also attack—other females. On their territory the pair are invincible; moral right is stronger than physical might in defence of the home.

After pairing the love-ceremonies do not cease. The establishment of the family bond is imperative if the young are to be reared by joint effort. The pleasurable ceremonies are continued after coition has ceased, and throughout incubation and rearing. Gannets clash bills, puffins rub beaks, shearwaters yodel and interlock bills, gulls and terns beg for food, throughout the summer, until at last the urge wanes with the fledging of the young and the onset of the moult and migration. Mutual display late in the season may be of a playful or recreational significance, an outlet for surplus energy.

There are other interesting, and some quaint, ceremonies. Thus at the nest relief, after the greeting display of billing and harsh cries is over, gulls and gannets will add material to the nest if prevented from brooding by the refusal of a mate to leave the eggs. This is a 'displacement activity', and it takes various forms. All nest-making sea-birds toy with material, placing it over the shoulder, or throwing it in the air and even swallowing it (gannets and gulls), while puffins, which do not make more than a slight lining to the nest (sometimes no lining), aimlessly pick up, carry and drop grass, feathers and stones.

Does mate-recognition last for more than one summer, that is to say, do sea-birds pair for life? By his behaviour and voice the mature female recognises a male calling her to a nest-site; by his voice and his occupation of the familiar nest-site she probably finds the identical mate of last spring. To that extent the monogamic sea-birds may be said to be faithful so long as both shall live; proof has been forthcoming in recent studies of ringed shearwaters, penguins, guillemots and razorbills. Even so, before the love-bond is re-affirmed in the spring the same ritual of threat—followed by appeasement—gestures is carried out; just as it is, in more or less degree, at every reunion of the pair at the nest throughout the summer. Yet the sequence now is bivalent—it has become less a display serving its original purposes than a ritualised greeting between mated pairs. Elements of two main drives in the life of the bird can be detected in the love-ceremonies: thus the frenzied billing of gannets and nose-rubbing of puffins seem to exhibit something of the desires of both self-preservation and reproduction inextricably mixed. Fighting and love-making behaviour are nearly akin, as hate is to love; both are highly stimulating. The winter habit of keeping at a safe distance from a neighbour seems to be latent in every sea-bird, and the arrival of even its mate at the nest tests the nervous organisation of a bird severely, so that its first reactions may be mixed, with the self-preservation drive on top. This is demonstrated by the actions of a herring-gull if its mate's return is sudden—according to the mood of the bird at home it may move away or attack, until full recognition occurs and the ceremonies of greeting take place.

The opening of wings alerts a neighbour or partner; in the herring-gull this action releases the attack drive, and it may stab at its mate's wings, or even its own. Even when recognition takes place at a distance (gulls and puffins can recognise their mates by sight ten metres away, either in the air or on the ground) display takes place as the pair come together. Often the untoward movement of one of the partners as the pair sit or stand near the nest will start the other, or neighbours, displaying or calling or both. Any movement within the colony is stimulating.

This stimulation, relating as it does to numbers, brings us to consider the relations of the individual, and the pair to the breeding flock, and what advantages there are in social nesting. Perhaps the first thing to note is what determines the density of the breeding flock. In spite of the availability of apparently suitable territory near by, the social sea-birds prefer to crowd together in a specific and fixed density pattern. As examples, gannets, increasing from 60 to 16,000 breeding adults in less than one hundred years at Grassholm, Wales, have never varied the positioning of their nests one yard apart, and today they occupy only two of the twenty-two acres of ground suitable for expansion; and guillemots, which formerly occupied completely a wide ledge two or three hundred yards long on the neighbouring island of Skomer, as they decreased in recent years, instead of spreading out thinly over the ancient breeding ledge continued to crowd together, leaving large gaps which have become grown over with the nitrogen-loving chickweed. The innate sociality of sea-birds is such that a diminishing colony contracts towards the centre in the same fixed pattern that an increasing colony expands; and the pattern is deter-mined by the minimum territorial requirements of the breeding pair—in the gannet a three feet radius from the nest-centre, in the guillemot about twelve inches between each brooding bird. The attraction towards the centre of population (evidence of sociality in its highest form) is not unique to sea-birds; it is a protective device, common to many social animals. The breeding flock is composed of a core of old adults in the best positions at the centre, surrounded by a bulk of middle-aged members, and an outer skin of inexperienced young birds. The greatest mortality occurs at the perimeters where the young birds, detached, inexperienced, often wandering solitarily and far on migrations, are most exposed to outside dangers. Until they return and begin moving in towards the centre, they do not become units in the main flock; but once they have re-established themselves in the flock they will continue year by year moving towards the centre as the old birds die and leave vacant places. In the centre lies the greatest safety for the individual.

The smaller the flock the greater the exposure of the individual to peripheral dangers until, when a colony of only one or two pairs is reached, the core is wide open to those dangers. Conversely there is protection in numbers—and there is also stimulation. It is well known that in certain species (the budgerigar is quoted as a classic example) two or three pairs together breed and produce more young per adult than one pair breeding alone. Darling has suggested that there is a threshold below which a social species breeds irregularly or fails to breed, although he admits that this concept must be applied warily, since the numerical threshold varies with the environmental complex. Stimulation and protection in breeding by isolated pairs of a social sea-bird may, however, come from related or unrelated species using the same breeding ground; thus two pairs of gannets have bred successfully for many years, although without increasing their breeding numbers there, in the centre of a large colony of guillemots (Saltee Islands); and the reverse is recorded—a few pairs of guillemots breeding successfully within a large colony of gannets (Grassholm, and also Alderney). It is generally accepted that small colonies of guillemots and razorbills, gulls and other sea-birds produce fewer young per head of breeding adult than large colonies. It has been suggested that this may be because small colonies are composed of younger birds; if this were invariably so then it would argue that individuals, as they grow older, move from the small colonies to the large! This, however, is not the case; we have known small colonies of shearwaters, and of guillemots and razorbills at Skokholm which have existed for decades (within a few hundred yards or less of large colonies) with their hard core of old ringed breeders. Their breeding success has been variable, fair in the shearwaters, poor in the guillemots; but habit compels them to stick to the old site, whatever the success. Single pairs of guillemots and razorbills have generally had no breeding success. It is true however that small *new* colonies of sea-birds are invariably composed of young birds, which are always the colonists, and they take several years (and sometimes fail in the end) to build up a permanent breeding core. The fulmars which are spreading to new sites in western Europe are probably all young birds which have not bred before; also, for years Great Saltee Island was visited by immature Manx shearwaters before breeding took place there recently.

How does the advantageous stimulation of the large flock work?

When in a flock a sentinel bird sees an enemy and flees, or flies to attack it, the rest of the flock instantly heed the signal (a cry of warning, a display of wing or tail pattern, or merely the opening of the wings, or all of these signs together), and they too rise in the air. Thus a mood of uniform alertness is elicited in every member of the flock at the first notice of danger, and this is an advantage of numbers which has obvious survival value. So swift is the bird's reaction to warning and other signals that the flock may appear to act with complete synchronisation; but the mood is not really instantaneous, it is acquired by each bird individually copying another, and in the largest flocks the mood is seen to pass through the birds in a wave.

So-called synchronised flights also occur for no apparent reason, initiated in the same way by a leader or dominant or nervous bird, such as the "dreads" and panic flights of terns. Other combined operations, such as the joy-wheels of puffins and other auks, the mass diving of guillemots, the nocturnal circling flights of petrels, and the summer assemblies of gulls and oyster-catchers in favourite spots away from the nesting sites, seem to have a sexual significance. They may be caused by a temporary re-assertion of the flocking instinct (Tinbergen, 1951); their function seems to be that of sustaining a high emotive tone, for they are set in motion by the most exuberant individual in the flock, whose example and mood is so infectious that it is rapidly mimicked by the whole community. Herring-gulls will automatically preen in unison, copying a leader, as sub-consciously as man may copy another man yawning.

In a colony of sea-birds the most mature adults are the first to take up territory and breed in the spring; their display and pre-coitional activities set the pace for the less mature members of the community. Their example acts as a stimulus, with psychological and physiological effect on their neighbours; their first matings promote the hormonic development and the ripening of ova in neighbouring pairs. Their mood elicits a like mood in the others, and the sexual rhythm of the whole colony is quickened as the emotive tone rises. Occasionally, if their females are not ready, the stimulated males may even attempt adulterous matings (gulls, puffins, albatrosses). Usually however, the males are occupied in inducing their own mates to copulate within the nest-site territory, and their display and behaviour has the effect of synchronising the female sexual rhythm with theirs. All this intensive stimulation results in earlier and more uniform breeding in the large flock.

The advantages are obvious: the shorter the period of exposure of the eggs and chicks to possible predators the better the chance of survival. On the question of predation, however, we should note that the individual in the large flock is not necessarily able to defend itself better than the individual in the small flock, except that quantitatively the individual is safer in the crowd. Although sea-birds are sociable they are essentially selfish and non-co-operative outside the family circle; tales of flocks of sea-birds attacking an enemy in formation must be discredited. At most single or a pair of skuas, terns or gulls will mob an intruder, and only provided it is trespassing near their nests; skuas will also employ the broken-wing trick (injury-feigning) to lure an enemy away. These two responses, as distraction displays, are only advantageous in species which are comparatively nimble on land and in the air, and which can easily escape from an enemy; they are entirely instinctive actions, but often have a successful result, especially in drawing mammals from the vicinity of the nest. But gannets, petrels and auks—birds clumsy on land—have no distraction display; when threatened by a predator they remain, at the best, prepared to do battle, or they take flight. Combined operations by sea-birds against a common enemy are quite unknown—otherwise man would not be able to show himself in a large sea-bird colony with no greater hurt than an occasional tap on the head, or a shirt soiled with droppings! However, large colonies of sea-birds are rarely established, and certainly cannot be maintained, except on isolated islands and in other situations where there is minimum interference from terrestrial enemies.

To recapitulate, the advantage of the large breeding flock lies principally in social stimulation leading to synchronised breeding and so to an earlier and shorter and therefore more successful nesting season. This stimulation may have its source in the greater numbers of experienced breeders in the large flock. There is also the quantitative effect that the individual is safer from normal predation in a crowd; and there is greater alertness against attack because there are more individuals on the watch for enemies.

Some of these advantages apply in the winter flock, which is principally engaged in the maintenance activities of feeding and safe-roosting; there are the protection and vigilance of numbers, and, besides, the advantage of many pairs of eyes discovering new sources of food supply. If food happens to be scarce the flock spreads far and wide in its search, but does not disintegrate completely.

Individuals keep within sight of each other and when food is found and the discoverer drops down and remains feeding for some time, the nearest birds quickly note this behaviour and are drawn to the food; in this way the whole flock becomes concentrated upon a rich supply until it is exhausted. The flock then disperses, resuming the widespread search for a new supply of food, but maintaining its former coherent but extended pattern.

CHAPTER 8

THE TUBENOSES

OF ALL THE BIRDS which frequent the North Atlantic Ocean, the petrels or, as they are known today to ornithologists, the tube-noses, appear to be the most perfectly adapted to its frequent wild moods and heavy storms. A chapter on their life-histories would be incomplete, therefore, without a full discussion on the pelagic phases —little understood until recently—of the petrel's year. Only those who have seen from a ship at sea the fragile-looking storm-petrel or the long-winged shearwater or the more gull-like fulmar ride out a whole winter gale can realise, and admire and respect fully, this perfection of adaptation to the extreme conditions of environment. The more savage the gale, in fact, the more easily do these graceful birds seem to ride upon the salty air, and skim the heaving surface of the sea with more perfect mastery. Sustained by the winds, they are able to glide nearer to ships, and the human observer is able to study them. But formerly the superstitious mariner regarded the appearance of the small petrels close to the ship as an ill omen, accompanied as they were by storms.

The perfection of oceanic flight is seen best among the largest petrels, the true albatrosses, which, in the Atlantic, are confined principally to the southern hemisphere and rarely wander north of the equator. The structure of the very long slender wing of the albatross, with its long humeral bones and strong rigid primaries, makes normal wing-beating, such as that of the storm-petrel, difficult, and progression is almost entirely by gliding. The flight of the shearwater is similar. A considerable air-speed is a requisite of continuous gliding; albatrosses and shearwaters overtake, sail and soar around a fast-moving steamer without difficulty, and are seen to beat their wings seldom, and chiefly when, turning or mounting, they stall and lose momentum for a second or two.

The observer sees that they are able to accompany a ship without overtaking it too quickly only when it is steaming against the wind because their 'ground' speed is then reduced by the speed of the wind, but they move too fast when a ship is steaming with the wind and must then make a series of ellipses far out to port and starboard if they would keep with the ship. In calm weather these long-winged petrels manoeuvre in all directions and their true flight-speed, estimated to reach at least sixty miles an hour, is then more easily gauged.

The flight track is always slightly curved, and although the albatross is seen to fly more often on a level keel than the smaller shearwater, both proceed by careering from side to side, rising up ten or twenty feet at the end of each movement to gain height (momentum is thereby lost) for the powerful downward plunge that shall carry the bird skimming at speed low over the surface of the sea. The observer sees first the dark back of the bird turned to him, and one wing-tip all but touching the crest or side or trough of the swell, then the bird rises, perhaps with one, or two, wing beats, swings slowly over, and presents the (usually) white belly to view as it glides gracefully onwards on the other tack. Once they have settled on a dead calm sea the albatrosses and the larger shearwaters have some difficulty in rising from the surface. When approached quickly in a boat, they flap awkwardly for a long distance over the surface, paddling with their legs, and may settle again without having got on the wing at all. If they are full fed they often lighten themselves by disgorging food. But in rough weather they easily launch themselves by opening their wings into the wind from the top of a wave, and are airborne immediately. On land they need a long run to take off in fine weather if they cannot drop into the air from a cliff or high rock, or unless a strong wind is blowing.

The flight of the shorter-winged fulmars is similar, but the gliding periods are shorter, and turning and banking manoeuvres are achieved within a narrower compass, the wings being broader and the primaries rather more flexible than those of the albatrosses and shearwaters.

Very different is the flight at sea of the storm-petrels and frigate-petrels, which is best described as an erratic bat-like flitting, with brief intervals of gliding. It has been called swallow-like, but it lacks the directness of the swallow's flight, though it is almost as fast, and the wings are more expanded and the whole motion more light and wavering. In rough as in calm weather these little petrels follow the undulations of swell and wave, keeping within a few inches of the heaving surface, with an astonishing nicety. It is only when feeding

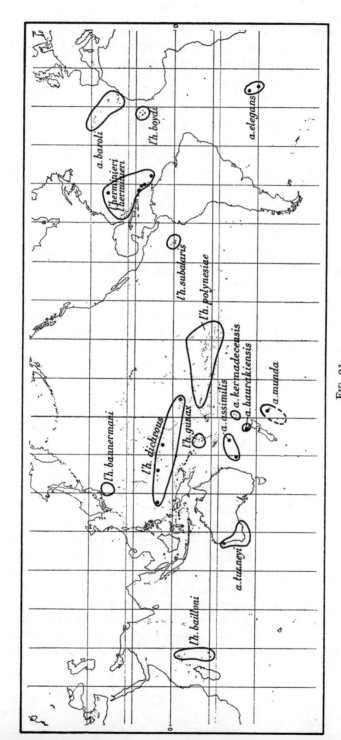

FIG. 31

Breeding distribution of the species-pair, the little shearwater, *Puffinus assimilis* and Audubon's shearwater, *P. l'herminieri*. Since this map was made it has been suggested that *assimilis* may breed on the Solanders, S. New Zealand, and that the race here and on Chatham I. (*munda*), is unifiable with *elegans*.

or searching for food that they hover, dropping their webbed feet to the surface, and paddling upon it lightly as if walking, and sometimes diving for a moment. The word petrel (according to most dictionaries) is derived from St. Peter who walked the waves. The frigate- and Wilson's petrels use their long legs more often for this purpose and have an even more erratic flight. But these dainty petrels also dive well; we have seen storm-petrels at their best in wild weather off the Rockall Bank feeding and diving in the heavy swell. They would skim the marbled slopes of the sea, hesitate for a fraction of a second as they sighted food, then plunge under the surface for perhaps one, two or three seconds, scarcely folding their wings; and emerging with the same ease, wings swiftly spread, and every feather perfectly dry. Murphy (1918) describes how Wilson's petrels dived to a depth of several times their length, leaping forth dry and light-winged from the water into the air.

All tubenoses are good divers, but do not remain long under water or dive deep. Their food is obtained near or on the surface.

The little shearwaters, which are intermediate in size between the storm-petrels and the Manx shearwater, have an intermediate flight described by P. R. Lowe as consisting of "four or five beats and then a short glide and so on."

There is no doubt but that the small sea-birds generally, and the petrels in particular, are able to help themselves in storms by avoiding those parts of the surface of the sea where the wind is most concentrated, that is, the crest of the wave or swell. They follow the trough of the wave, keeping closely to the windward slope where the water's surface is much less disturbed and there is a good upward air current to sustain them. B. Roberts (1940) repeatedly watched Wilson's petrel feeding and gliding on these windward slopes, but if the birds rose more than a few inches from the water they were instantly blown away downwind. It is when the storm shifts suddenly through 90° and blows parallel to the swell that small birds find no definite troughs in which to shelter, and so become exhausted by constant wing-beating over the confused water. As a result in changeable gales many are blown inland, or drowned and washed ashore.

Roberts refers to the problem which has confronted all observers of pelagic birds—the inference that petrels in stormy latitudes have few opportunites to sleep or rest during the six months of continuous winter storms. But other birds apparently do without sleep for certain periods (as on migration), while immature swifts which in summer are

seen to fly into the sky at dusk, do not return to roosting places: it
now seems possible that these night-flying swifts doze or sleep on the
wing.

This, then, is the familiar picture of the petrels for the majority
of people who only see these most pelagic of birds at sea. Able to
sustain life in the stormiest zones farthest from land, and fitted to live
without true sleep for days on the wing, the mysterious petrels have
recently been the subject of intensive research on the remote islands
where they breed. Their life histories are strange and interesting and
many problems in them are unsolved.

The old breeding birds are the first to return home in early spring,
both because their reproductive organs are active before those of their
young sons and daughters, and because they are experienced migrants
familiar with the annual migration route. The urge to breed hastens
their departure from the wintering area, an urge which in some species
may prevent the older adults from reaching the extremity of that area,
and fully mature birds may remain within a day or so by air (say
five hundred miles) of home throughout the winter. Once the adult
tubenose has bred successfully it probably remains faithful to the same
site for the rest of its life provided it can obtain a mate to share "home"
with it.

Territory (that is, nest-site-finding) is not therefore a novel or
serious problem for the adult, which has only to occupy and defend
the site already established in previous summers. To do this most
successfully however it must return early, or the nest-site may be
pirated by newcomers. Ringing has proved that both male and
female petrel return to the familiar nest-site; and this is true for other
sea-birds.

This would suggest that petrels pair for life. If so, it may be asked,
do they remain together on their migrations? It may be significant,
that, generally speaking, petrels are not usually seen in pairs at sea, but
more often singly or in flocks. But Richdale (1950) is convinced that
the royal albatross, *Diomedea epomophora,* pair associate with each
other at sea during the non-breeding year, and he proves that they
return to the nesting area together. These albatrosses spend over
a year in one breeding season and therefore have a short non-breeding
year alternating with the over-long breeding season. Roberts and
Lockley both consider that in the other petrels there is joint ownership
of the nest-burrow or -site by a pair which meet there at the beginning
of each season. There is no evidence among the smaller petrels and

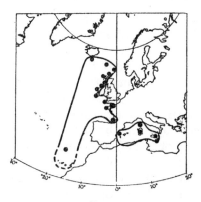

FIG. 32
Breeding distribution of the storm-
petrel, *Hydrobates pelagicus*

shearwaters of any other lasting mutual bond, but, as mentioned in the previous chapter, because the pair meet and mate at the familiar focal point of the nest, so long as both shall live they remain faithful for life. This was found to be the case with a few exceptions over many years with the Manx shearwater and the storm-petrel, and over two years with the Wilson's petrel.

Nest-occupation by all species of petrels begins well ahead of the laying of the single egg. Thus fulmars arrive in November and December but do not lay until 5 May, normally not until after 12 May; Manx shearwaters first arrive in February but do not begin laying until the end of April; great shearwaters arrive in August and lay in November; storm-petrels come to land at the end of April and lay in June; Wilson's petrels are at least three weeks in preparing the nesting burrow while the winter snows have scarcely left the land; and the little shearwater in Western Australia apparently returns in January but does not lay until the end of June. The exceptionally early return of the fulmar and the little shearwater in the largest colonies may be fundamentally associated with the pressure of great numbers of experienced adults in severe competition for the best nest sites; it is paralleled in the case of other sociable birds, e.g. the common guillemot which returns (large colonies only) five months before laying begins. Where colonies are of a smaller size the return is correspondingly later in all these species, and many other sociable birds, including the fulmar (Fisher, 1952). Nest-site pressure, however (it should be added) is only one of many population-controlling factors.

With the early return of the established breeders courtship activities begin. They are not at first either prolonged or passionate but rather preliminary. The Manx and little shearwaters and the fulmars on arrival rest much and appear to sleep a good deal in the first few days. Nor do they visit their territories regularly. The first arrivals may be males—among albatrosses this is certainly the case. The night-active petrels and shearwaters may miss one or two nights, and the day-fulmars may skip a day or two, and at first may stay only for a few hours on land. Male albatrosses may desert the colony for a few days at laying-time. But gradually, as the colony becomes fuller with later arrivals, those in possession of territory are less and less willing to leave it, until at least one or other of the pair remains constantly on duty. Courtship and defence of territory are now in full swing.

As might be expected the awkwardness of these oceanic birds on land (their feet are placed too far to the rear of the body to make an upright stance possible, except in the albatrosses) prevents a very elaborate display. But clashing and scissorsing of bills is part of the ceremonial. The courtship of the nocturnal petrels has been difficult to observe: but it is not difficult to hear the accompanying noises, which must be very nearly the most weird in nature. The shearwaters make indescribable crowing and screaming calls, and the storm- and fork-tailed petrels have squeaking and purring notes. The fulmar sings a curious cackling song, opening wide its dark purple mouth towards its mate, and waving its head from side to side and up and down, without moving its body much or opening its wings, as it sits on a cliff-ledge. In the excitement oil may be passed between the courting birds. Because fulmars nest in the open their display has been more observed than that of other tubenoses. It probably is typical for all these primitive, small-brained birds. Display is mutual, and may take place between more than two birds (Manx and little shearwaters, fulmar, storm-petrel), "visiting" by unemployed birds being a habit of the courtship period of the tubenoses up to the time of the laying of the single egg.

Alone of the North Atlantic tubenoses the fulmar does not burrow, although it will appropriate the entrance to the burrow of other birds or rabbits. This may be associated with the fact that the fulmar is powerful enough to be able to drive away almost every avian territorial competitor (Fisher, 1952). Normally it inhabits steep cliffs above the zone of the kittiwakes and guillemots, where its increase is said to have pushed out the herring-gulls. It has also been accused of driving cormorants, shags, guillemots and razorbills from the ledges; but there may have been a confusion of sequence and consequence, for the fulmars may simply have taken advantage of space vacated when these species were decreasing. On some islands the fulmar also nests on the ground, on screes, on ruins and on occupied buildings; it has become very plastic in its nest-site selection.

The comparative tameness and fearlessness of the fulmar is believed to be due not to its famous oil-spitting ability but to the fact that it is not heavily preyed upon by any animals save man. H. Kritzler (1948) says "the fulmar brain probably contains no innate mechanism whereby its owner is apt to respond distrustfully with regard to human beings ... when food is available they are incapable of associating the manner in which it is presented—with possible hazard to themselves." Certainly fulmars are easily caught in a hand-net when attracted to the side of a trawler by fish offal; their desire for food overcomes the little fear they have of man. But it must be noted that fishermen, in general, seldom molest the fulmar at sea, regarding it superstitiously: there is a popular belief that each "molly" (fulmar) is the reincarnation of a dead seaman who formerly fished in that region. So man is not normally a predator taking adult fulmars; he collects principally the fledgelings (in Greenland; and formerly in Iceland, the Faeroes and St. Kilda). As to other large enemies, the arctic fox may kill a few young fulmars; though no other predator is important. Quite a number of casual predators have been listed by Fisher (1952). The great skua cannot drive the fulmar off its nest, although gulls (glaucous especially) will take a fulmar's egg or small chick if this is left unprotected; but, as we have shown, except when disturbed by man, one or other of the adults always remains with the egg. When approached by an enemy, the adult fulmar instinctively spits forth oil for a distance of two or three feet, and although deliberate aim is unlikely, the effect is much the same since the fulmar ejects as it faces the intruder. The young fulmar is capable of spitting oil while still in the egg—through the pipped shell; and it spits at its parents instinctively for a few days after hatching, until it has recognised them as its friends. Birds, no less than humans, dislike being plastered with this extremely foul-smelling oil.*

Some of the larger shearwaters exhibit the same fearlessness. The powerful North Atlantic shearwater (*Puffinus diomedea borealis*) is less nocturnal and less of a burrower than the smallest shearwaters, especially where it is not molested by man. On the Great Salvage Islands, where they are carefully protected so that the young ones can be collected for food when deserted by their parents, these shearwaters breed in almost any large crevice; both in large dark caves and in

---

*Really an excretion as well as a secretion, from the alimentary system, of excess fat and Vitamin A. All tubenoses vomit, but the fulmar seems to have been most successful in turning the habit to defensive purposes, by throwing the oil towards the intruder.

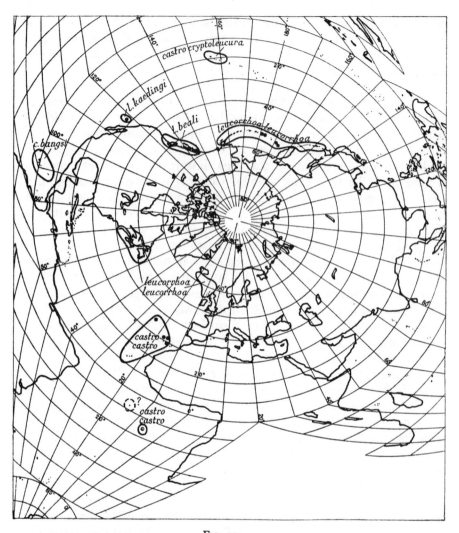

FIG. 33

Breeding distribution of the fork-tailed petrel species–pair, *Oceanodroma leucorhoa* (Leach's petrel) and *O. castro* (Madeiran fork-tailed petrel in Atlantic)

shallow openings in the volcanic rock into which the sun may shine upon the sitting birds. Soon after midday these great shearwaters begin to assemble in vast numbers on the sea close to their island, and long before sunset there is an exciting scene in the air as the flocks begin to rise and come inland, circling overhead in thousands. But where much persecuted by fishermen, as in the Berlengas Islands off Portugal, and the Desertas off Madeira, this shearwater is nocturnal. On Nightingale Island, Tristan da Cunha, Rowan (1952) found the great shearwater (*P. gravis*) partly diurnal.

With comparatively few other tubenoses is it possible to witness this magnificent gathering of birds waiting to come to land. The rafts of tens of thousands of Manx shearwaters off Skokholm and Skomer in British waters are well known, but assemblies at sea of tube-noses are more generally associated with a concentration of food, as at whaling stations and trawling grounds. Many hundreds of fulmars at one time may be seen on the water close to St. Kilda, and up to 5,000 may gather around one trawler at Rockall. J. T. Nichols (Bent, 1922) recorded over one thousand Wilson's petrels in sight at one time from the coast of Long Island on 30 June 1913.

The courtship of the smaller petrels—Wilson's, Bulwer's, storm-, Leach's, Madeiran and frigate-petrels, visiting their burrows at night—has not been easy to study. Like the albatrosses of New Zealand, storm-petrels at Skokholm (Lockley, 1932), Madeiran petrels on the Desertas (Lockley, 1942) and Leach's petrels at North Rona (Ainslie and Atkinson, 1937) have a circling flight over the nesting burrows that appears to be partly a ceremonial dance, accompanied by excited call-notes, very soft, of the storm- and Madeiran petrels, but by a pleasant, almost musical, eight-syllabled cry of Leach's petrel. Wilson's petrel has a similar night-flight, which Roberts considers is an important part of their courtship, and utters a harsh call, generally as the bird alights near its burrow when it chatters to its mate underground and is answered. This night flying is characteristic of Bulwer's petrel, but it is silent and not so prolonged, the incoming birds seeming to circle for a short period as if orientating. As these circling flights become localised the petrels drop down to their burrows and begin the night's activities of burrowing, mating and incubating. Burrowing by petrels and shearwaters is carried out by both sexes. The bill is used as a pickaxe and the loose material thrown under the breast; the webbed feet then drag and scatter it backwards down and out of the burrow, as the bird lies now on one side and now on the other.

Quite hard earth and sandy rock is, by degrees, excavated with these feeble tools.

Information has now been gathered to give a fairly comprehensive picture of the incubation and fledging periods of the tubenoses. Coition takes place at or near the nest. Only one egg* is laid, and if this is taken, even when fresh, another is not laid that year; except in the case of some of the large albatrosses which, although normally laying only one egg in two years, nevertheless lay a second egg in the same year if the first be taken fresh (Matthews, 1929). Deliberate nest building, except by the large albatrosses, is usually absent or at most fortuitous or haphazard. Manx shearwaters will carry feathers, dead bracken stalks, bluebell bulbs, roots, grass, etc., from near the burrow entrance or from the burrow walls and this accumulates in the form of a ring of debris around the egg or chick in the nest chamber. The chick, too, may pull material in towards the nest from the burrow walls. Fulmars and North Atlantic great shearwaters will pick up and arrange small stones around the egg. In the Berlengas and on Great Salvage Island Lockley found the North Atlantic shearwater had built quite substantial platforms of small stones, and he surprised one adult entering its cave with a stone in its bill.

Incubation is by both sexes, though possibly the female sits altogether rather more than half the period. Several observers of burrow-nesting species have recorded that, in the first week after laying, the egg may be left unattended by day, but we are inclined to believe that this absence is often the result of fright due to the handling of the adult when its ring number is being checked. Once it is frightened in this way the adult may not return for more than twenty-four hours, but this can be now explained by the fact that petrels share the incubation period by taking shifts, generally of two or, three, but sometimes of four and up to ten days at a time; and that of some if not all species the off-duty bird does not usually return each night until the end of its "legitimate holiday" is at hand. This incubation by long shifts of several days has been conclusively proved in the case of the North Atlantic great, the Manx and the little shear-waters, storm-petrel, Wilson's, Leach's and Bulwer's petrels, the frigate-petrel, and the fulmar. There is no evidence that the incoming bird feeds the fasting bird, or that the male ever feeds the female or vice versa at any stage (we except the oil-feeding of courting ful-mars); and every indication that once incubation has begun the adults

*A very small percentage of fulmars (probably about one per cent) lay two eggs.

only meet at the nest for a few hours during the change-over. The incoming bird is usually plump and glossy from the exercise and feeding at sea, while the outgoing bird with an empty stomach is light to handle, stained with long contact with the earth and dirt of the burrow, and anxious to escape to sea in order to break its fast. The fulmar incubates in spells of up to four days (Richter, 1937).

The following are the available records of the average incubation and fledging periods of the petrels:

	Incubation	Fledging
MANX SHEARWATER (Lockley, 1942)	51	72
LITTLE SHEARWATER (Glauert, 1946)	53	72
GREAT SHEARWATER (Rowan, 1952)	about 55	about 84
STORM-PETREL (Lockley, 1932)	38	61
LEACH'S PETREL (Gross, 1935)	42	50
WILSON'S PETREL (Roberts, 1940)	43	52?
FRIGATE-PETREL (Richdale, 1943)	48?	58
FULMAR (Fisher, 1952)	53	48

These figures show that the petrels have much longer incubation and fledging periods than other birds of comparable size.

The chick is free of the egg forty to eighty hours after chipping. The empty shell is usually ignored, and may be trampled into the nest. The chick is covered with down; it is small, often blind (storm- and Wilson's petrels) and so weak-necked that it cannot hold up its head at first, but rests with the bill touching the ground. One parent usually broods it continuously for about seven days, in its incubation-patch, as if it were an egg. During the first forty-eight hours it is fed frequently, small doses at a time, by the brooding adult, but later the number of meals is reduced. The semi-liquid oily food is regurgitated and at first held in the throat of the adult, whence it is "dribbled" down to the feeble chick reaching upwards with its bill. As the chick grows stronger it learns to feed more vigorously; the growing bill becomes too awkward to insert wholly into the mouth of the adult. The amount of food rapidly increases with each meal, and the chick now "inserts its bill crosswise into the parent's with its gape pressed firmly against that of the adult. The chick's lower mandible, which is shaped like a trough, is pushed up against the top of the tongue of the adult bird, the tip being well below the chick's bill. The parent now reduces the opening of its throat . . . and semi-liquid is forced through, in fire-hose fashion, into the chick's trough, which has an upslope, and down the neck. While the chick is feeding its lower throat and mandible keep vibrating rapidly. The small opening of the parent's throat seems to act as a strainer allowing, as a rule, only semi-digested food to pass, and I have often seen an adult re-swallow larger portions of food which cannot get through. . . . Before it is possible to feed the chick again, the vomiting process must be repeated." (Richdale, 1939, on the royal albatross).

The North Atlantic petrels are primarily plankton-feeders. Fisher (1952, pp. 409-32) gives a comprehensive list of the foods found in fulmars' stomachs; it includes remains of birds' carcases, carrion of bear, walrus, seal and whale, molluscs (cephalopod beaks and lenses are found universally in petrel stomachs), crustaceans, and coelenterates especially. All petrels greedily eat oily matter and fat, especially that from live and dead whales.

Fulmars have greatly increased in the North Atlantic during the last two hundred years, and, as discussed in a preceding chapter (p. 105), this increase is almost certainly related in the first century to the offal supplied by northern whaling (in which right whales were flensed at ship's side), and in the second century to the continuous vast output of fish offal thrown into the sea by the modern fleets of power-driven trawlers and fishing boats in deep water of the Continental Shelf; this waste is greedily devoured by fulmars which attend the trawling grounds in their thousands today, and every day throughout the year.

Planktonic crustacea are responsible for the red, orange or yellow colour of the oil which petrels eject when disturbed. This waxy oil, like cod-liver oil, is rich in vitamin A; it also contains vitamin D, and is similar in character to the oil from the preen-glands of birds.* Its composition is different from that of the oil of the marine organisms on which petrels feed, and it is certainly (Matthews, 1949, 1950) a stomach gland secretion and not an indigestible residue of food. It is generally believed that the very young chick at first is fed wholly on this clear oil (Roberts, 1940, p. 168), but as it grows older the crop of the young bird is found to contain more solid food, including recognisable portions of cephalopoda, crustacea, small fishes, etc. Vegetable débris is often present in small quantities, especially in the stomach of the adult, such as grass, sorrel and other plant scraps, evidently picked up on the breeding ground.

*Fisher (1952) has no doubt that the tubular nostrils are an anatomical adaptation for preening, since they are found only on birds which produce stomach-oil; and that there is a discharge of oil through the nostrils in preening operations. Certainly after vomiting oil through the mouth, fulmar and storm-petrel will be found to have oil exuding from the nostrils.

When first hatched the chick's body-temperature is about 10°C below that of the adult. It therefore needs the warmth of its parent's body (about 38.8°C in the case of Wilson's petrel), until its own temperature-regulating mechanism, aided by a plentiful down, is developed; this occurs towards the end of the first week, when it 'emerges' from its parent's incubation-patch; whereupon, it is abandoned by the day and not ever brooded by the adult again, although occasionally an adult will remain by day in the nest, sitting *beside* the chick quite late in the rearing period.

Wilson's, Leach's and storm-petrel chicks, born in cool latitudes, are feeble and blind when born and develop slowly. The chick of Bulwer's petrel, on the contrary, born in the warm latitudes, has its eyes open and is extremely active. It grows rapidly. It has no bald spot on the crown as have the storm- and frigate-petrels.

After the first week, then, the regular attention (one might justifiably say, the στοργή of the parents for the new-born) which the chick has received suffers a gradual change. It was first fed a few hours after hatching and again several times during the first twenty-four hours (Richdale, 1943, p. 113, on the frigate-petrel), so long as the adult, with ample reserves of "oil" in its crop, was there to brood and care for it. But once (aided by good feeding) it has reached the homiothermic stage it is left alone by day. The adults (of some species at least) now go farther to sea, seeking solid food, and do not return at all on some nights. Ringing of breeding Manx shearwaters has shown (Lockley, 1942) that the adults, with mates on eggs at Skokholm, may travel as far south as the Spanish coast, six hundred miles distant, to feed (principally on sardines—they are shot or caught by Basque sardine fishermen); this voyage of one thousand two hundred miles there and back could not be accomplished in less than two days, and, allowing time for feeding, probably longer. Incidentally the value of this patient ringing of several thousands of these birds on their remote breeding island was never more obvious than in the proof of this amazing journey of the breeding shearwaters.

During the latter half of the eight to ten weeks of the fledging period, feeding becomes more and more intermittent. During a moonlit period several nights may elapse without the Manx shearwater chick being visited. The burrows of Wilson's petrel are often blocked by snow, for several days, but even when clear of snow they are not regularly visited; and the unfed nestlings lose weight. The chick of Leach's petrel is fed irregularly; it has even been suggested that the adults may visit the colony without feeding it (Ainslie and Atkinson). This supposition was intended to explain the excessively large number of adults present in relation to the number of young birds which were fed; but we believe that this increase is explained more satisfactorily by inferring that at that time (July-August) on North Rona there was, as in other petrel colonies in midsummer, the usual influx of yearling or "sweethearting" birds. Irregular feeding begins quite early in the frigate-petrel (Richdale) and also the little shearwater (Glauert says "normally the chick is fed every second night for the first fortnight"). Intervals of two to three days between feeding is recorded of the storm-petrel (Lockley, 1932).

The nestling is eventually abandoned before fledging. This at least happens to the young of the Manx, little and great shearwaters; and there is very strong evidence that those of the storm- and Leach's petrels and fulmar are forsaken in like manner. The "starvation theory", of abandoned fasting nestlings, has also for long been widely stated to apply to the largest of the tubenoses, the albatrosses; but recently Richdale (1952) has shown that the royal albatross *Diomedea epomophora* has no starvation period, and he summarises evidence to show that other species, including the wandering albatross *D. exulans*, have little, if any. The same may apply to at least one of the smaller petrels, for Roberts (1940) suggests that the Wilson's petrel is not abandoned and may be fed even after it is fully fledged. However, it does seem to be a fact that among all tubenoses intensively studied, apart from albatrosses and Wilson's petrel, the young is positively deserted at the end of the fledging period and stays on its nest for a time much longer than the normal interval of parental inattention, being then fat and as heavy as or slightly heavier than an adult. For the great shearwater the period between the last feed and the flight to the sea is about a month. For the Manx shearwater it is ten to twelve days and for the little shearwater eight to thirteen days. At the end of this period of starvation the subcutaneous and body-cavity fat is greatly reduced by absorption into the blood stream and apparently is partly used up in hardening and setting the feathers.

When there is room to do so the abandoned chick exercises its wings much during this period. Thus young fulmars are seen to flap their wings as they sit on ledges in September, and even flutter from one ledge to another; while the few remaining adult fulmars, taking no interest in them, visit and gape and enjoy themselves elsewhere on the ledges. Abandoned Manx shearwater fledgelings come out from their burrows at night and stretch and exercise for an hour or two, and then return to the safety of the burrow. So does the young mutton-bird, *Pterodroma macroptera*, which emerges from the burrows after dark and ambles "about in an aimless fashion over tree-stumps and other obstacles. They often return again to the burrow before daylight, but sometimes take wing." (Falla, 1934). Those shearwaters which are born in burrows in the centre of islands where predators are numerous (as at Skokholm) may not reach the sea in one night. If the weather be calm, the young bird is quite unable to rise off level ground, and can only flutter down inclines. Unless it can find shelter before dawn, therefore, it will probably be killed by gull or hawk. But on other large islands, where there are no predators, the fledgeling journeys safely by easy stages to the sea. Where shearwaters breed in holes on steep cliffs, as in the Faeroes and Iceland, the take-off is only a matter of fluttering downwards, and the young bird, once airborne in a good breeze, flies well by instinct. Normally, however, the young shearwater flutters to the sea and makes its way into the ocean by vigorous swimming. When attacked at sea by a predator it dives deep, swimming for a long distance under water. It may be aided on its first flight by autumn breezes ruffling the sea and thus assisting it to take off. Yet numbers of young petrels, shearwaters and other newly fledged sea-birds get caught inshore in severe equinoctial gales and are drowned in the breakers or carried far inland. The westerly gales regularly experienced off the west coast of the British Isles in the autumn result in such a crop of inland records of Manx shearwaters and storm-petrels that the late T. A. Coward erroneously inferred that there was a regular migration overland. A study of meteorological records, however, has proved that these occurrences are always preceded by severe westerly gales.

It is difficult to see how the chicks of some of the smaller petrels, nesting deep among boulders and cliff débris, can find space in which to exercise and strengthen their wings before going to sea. It is remarkable that the storm-petrel at this stage, with tufts of down still adhering to its plumage, when taken from a rock crevice and dropped towards the sea, avoids the water and will fly—though it has apparently never fully stretched its wings before—making for the horizon low over the sea. As long as the observer can watch it, it continues on the wing. Well may we wonder at the astonishing vitality of these frail looking petrels—storm-, Leach's, Wilson's, Bulwer's and frigate-petrels. On land they are much more nimble than the heavier shearwaters.

So far the breeding of shearwaters inland has been little studied. Manx shearwaters breed on mountains in sight of the sea in Scotland (islands of Rhum, at over 2,000 feet, and Eigg, over 1,000 feet high) and in Madeira (over 4,000 feet high). Cool windy conditions akin to those of the islands exist there, and presumably the nesting and rearing procedure are similar. We can suppose that when the deserted youngster is ready to fly it has only to scramble down the mountainside until some sheer cliff or rock enables it to become airborne.

The young bird has flown. When will it return to the colony? How long does it remain solitary at sea? These questions are difficult to answer. Rowan (1952), computing the population of great shearwaters at four million breeding adults on Nightingale Island, Tristan da Cunha, considers that the vast numbers of *Puffinus gravis* still in north Atlantic waters when the breeding season begins in the south may be explained by the supposition that these absentees are immature non-breeders. The great shearwater begins visiting its burrow late in August, the egg is laid early in November; but from August to November inclusive this species is common in the eastern north Atlantic. These non-breeders probably approach Tristan, as Manx shearwater non-breeders approach and visit Skokholm, towards the middle of the nesting season, making in fact a trial landing in preparation for the years of regular breeding ahead. At any rate it seems clear that the adolescent shearwaters move more or less independently of the mature adults in their first year. They may, in the case of *gravis* which is a large bird, spend two or more years of vagabondage at sea, like the albatrosses, and as Fisher suggested (1952) like the fulmar.

The marking of individual Wilson's petrels over two years in Graham Land, of Manx shearwaters over a period of sixteen years at Skokholm, and of albatrosses in New Zealand have shown that the young bird does not return to the exact site or colony in which it was born and reared, although it does normally return to breed on or near the same island. As it is deserted before it is fledged it has no family ties, and must establish for itself a niche in the colony when it is old enough to reproduce. It may even have to fight for possession of such a territory in an overcrowded breeding-ground, or it may go elsewhere and colonise a new site. Single birds have been seen endeavouring to enter burrows occupied by mated pairs, and Rowan records (1952) a great shearwater which suffered bleeding and disarrangement of plumage in its persistent attempts to enter a burrow in which a pair were noisily courting.

The arrival of unattached and inexperienced birds at the colony, usually late in summer, is (as we have already pointed out) of biological value to the species, since it enables these immatures to "practise" for the following years when, with their breeding organs fully developed, they will present themselves in better time to secure territory and mates. The term "sweethearting" has been appropriately applied to the behaviour of these non-breeding shearwaters and petrels which sit about in pairs in the colony, often occupying some hole or platform quite inadequate for proper nesting. They are only playing at house-keeping and are gone after a few hours. An examination of the ovaries and testes of these pairs of non-breeding adults has shown that they are little developed and have never been used for breeding (Lockley, 1942); these midsummer visitants were of course not confused with the chicks, which were at that time freshly hatched. The visits of the immatures cease some time before the fledgelings are grown and old enough to leave the breeding-ground; Rowan (1952) has disposed of Wilkins' observations that the great shearwaters occupying burrows at the end of the season were adults, by proving that they must have been fully plumaged fledgelings deserted and waiting the psychological moment for departure to the sea.

The cycle is complete. We come back to where we started from—the fledgeling, alone and unguided except by its inherited instinct, overtakes the adults which are now deep in moult at sea, and may go on to winter in waters several hundred miles beyond. In the following year it may not return to the place where it was born. It may spend its first "adult" summer entirely at sea, which would mean that it would not return to the land for nearly two years; probably three or four years would be nearer the truth. After a few years of wandering at sea, for instance, the fulmar develops an incubation patch and a drive to sit on a nest-site, but cannot lay or fertilise an egg for another four to five years. Probably not until it is 7, 8, or 9 years old does the fulmar breed, and then it does so regularly each summer or so long as it is healthy and able to find a mate (Fisher, 1952). New, eggless colonies of fulmars, and of Manx shearwaters (Lockley, 1942) have been recorded during the breeding season; these virgin colonies are composed of inexperienced and sexually immature birds.

Recent ringing results (Skokholm Bird Observatory Reports for 1946 to 1951) have indicated that among the Manx shearwaters there is an interchange of non-breeding individuals between the islands of Skomer and Skokholm, two miles distant, each carrying many thousands of pairs, and also between Skokholm and Lundy (forty-three miles distant), which has only a small colony. This interchange would have the effect of ensuring specific uniformity in the shearwater population of the Bristol Channel islands, which in fact is the case. Further ringing is desirable to discover if there is an interchange of young shearwaters of the Pembrokeshire islands with those of the Isles of Scilly and the Irish breeding colonies, for it is only by such evidence that the wanderings of the immature individual, and the extent of its community, may be known.

G. Harper Hall

Plate XVIIa. Braking, preparing to land, Bonaventure

   b. Adult Gannet in attitude adopted when about to take flight from a crowded colony
(at Grassholm)

R. M. Lockley

Plate XVIIIa. (above). At Grassholm. A Gannet arrives with a beakload of dried grass—stolen from a neighbour's nest ; *b,* Gannet about 10 days old ; *c,* Gannet in its first (immature) plumage about to leave the nest (*Photographs by R. M. Lockley*)

CHAPTER 9

THE PELICANS

A LTHOUGH DIFFERING outwardly from each other much in form, size and habits, the fish-eating pelicans comprise a natural order (*Pelecaniformes*), ranging over all seas and zones, which is quite distinct from other sea-bird orders. They are powerful swimmers and divers, having all four toes directed forwards and connected by strong webs. The inner edge of the third toe is pectinated, forming a tooth-comb which is used for scratching the plumage for lice and other parasites. In temperate and sub-arctic latitudes of the North Atlantic the gannet and the cormorants (including the shag) are the familiar representatives. The pelicans, darters, boobies, frigate- and tropic-birds are confined principally to the tropics.

The powers of flight vary: the cormorants, birds which spend more time resting on land than swimming or flying, and migrate little, are rather slow and laboured in flight, while the more pelagic gannet is fast and powerful. The frigate- and tropic-birds can sustain an apparently effortless aerial manoeuvring that is nearest perfection. This air mastery, and the great assemblies at the breeding cliffs and islands, make the pelican tribe the most spectacular among sea-birds. It has been estimated that 100,000 brown pelicans are in sight at once on the guano islands off the coast of Peru. On San Martin Island, California, about 350,000 nests of the double-crested cormorant were estimated by H. W. Wright (1913). In North Atlantic waters, e.g. Bonaventure in the Gulf of St. Lawrence, Eldey near Iceland, St. Kilda in Scotland, Little Skellig in Ireland, and Grassholm in Wales, thousands of white-plumaged gannets are in the air together, performing a magnificent revolving circle above their densely packed nesting rock.

Although the pelican tribe are all, more or less, colonial nesters, they are not always sociable away from the breeding colony, with the exception of the true pelicans. They are more often seen at sea singly or in small parties; but they may roost communally. In flight there are no very closely co-ordinated movements as in flocks of shearwaters, waders and starlings. But when a shoal of fish is sighted numbers come together in one spot and there may be all the appearance of co-ordinated action. The little black cormorant (*Phalacrocorax sulcirostris*) and the white pelican (*Pelecanus erythrorhynchos*) have a communal method of fishing. They gather in large companies and fly in long columns until a shoal is encountered; the leading birds wheel round, settle on the water, and proceed to concentrate the shoal by an ever-narrowing circling movement—*diagram A* (Serventy, 1939). The guanay cormorant (*P. bougainvillii*) actually appears to send out scouts, which indicate prey as vultures do.

FIG. 34
Path of fishing cormorants; A: after Serventy (1939); B: after Steven (1933)

Steven (1933) observed that a single shag rounded up a shoal of sand-eels, then fed as it swam through the centre of concentration—*diagram B*. Taverner (1934) says that double-crested cormorants (*P. auritus*) will spread themselves across the mouth of a bay, and make a drive towards a common centre. The scene becomes more and more animated as the fish are congested in shallow water. The divings become shorter and more rapid, and more fish are tossed and swallowed in hurried haste for the next beakful. At last the surviving fish make a despairing rush through the ranks of their enemies. The birds then form lines again along another section of the water to repeat the operation. Some of these rafts may consist of 1,800 to 2,000 individuals.

Where cormorants and pelicans fish together the more agile cormorants will steal fish in front of the open scoop-like bill of the pelicans which are greedily filling their huge pouches; and the brown pelican has a pouch capacity of $3\frac{1}{2}$ gallons. The man-o'-war bird *Fregata magnificens*, which is expert at snatching fish from the mouth of the overloaded pelican, can fish on its own account, plunging downwards from a great height, but because it prefers not to wet its non-oily plumage it deftly scoops its prey from the surface. Most of its food, however, is obtained parasitically by robbing other birds, skua-like, on the wing. Its powers of flight are truly magnificent—the normal floating progress by easy beats of the half-open wings suggests a great reserve of power, which is proved when it easily overtakes the fast-flying boobies.

Gannets, boobies and tropic-birds dive for their food; they live principally on surface-swimming fish (mackerel, herring, pollack, garfish, haddock, whiting, sea-trout and gurnard are recorded for the gannet). Cottam & Uhler (1937) state that the more sluggish surface-feeding and shallow-water fishes not utilised by man greatly outnumber the valuable species and are more easily captured, and in consequence they compose the bulk of the diet of fish-eating birds. In 1918 the American Federal Food Administration found that the eastern brown pelican (*Pelecanus o. occidentalis*), to the surprise of its accusers, was innocent of consuming large quantities of food-fish, and that it lived principally on the menhaden, an oily fish never used for human consumption. Shags (see p. 118) feed mainly on fish of no commercial value (Lumsden and Haddow, 1946, who examined the stomach contents of 81 shags in the Firth of Clyde). Flat fish form about 40 per cent. of the diet of European cormorants (Steven, 1933). Other fish commonly taken include pollack, wrasse, haddock, codling, whiting, garfish, sand-eels, herring, mackerel, small conger-eels, plaice, mullet and sticklebacks. They are coarse feeders, especially the cormorant which has frequently been known to attack crabs, and to eat carrion—a kitten eleven inches long was found in the stomach of a British-taken cormorant. Both cormorant and shag, when diving, may sink under from the surface with scarcely a ripple, but the usual habit is to make a semi-circular leap out of and back into the water, so gaining impetus for swimming below. When travelling fast under water, the bird keeps its wings closed; and the body is propelled with simultaneous strokes of both feet. The wings are only used when the bird is beating about on the bottom of the sea hunting for flounders and other fish concealed there. It has been suggested that a silvery "flash" of light, reflected from the back of the cormorant's head, as observed in a cormorant in an aquarium, attracts fish towards the bird, but there seems to be no proof of this as a fact of such biological importance.

The food and fishing methods of the gannets have been well described by Gurney (1913), who concludes that the deeper the fish are swimming the higher the altitude from which the gannet's plunge is made. He records that the Belfast fishermen are thereby guided as to the depths at which to set their nets. There is generally a mistaken notion that the gannet dives in order to gain impetus and strength to *spear* its prey; and the story is handed down of how trawler hands tie a fish on to a piece of floating wood so as to deceive the gannet, which is killed by the impact of its dive upon the board, or else —more popular report still—its bill is embedded in the wood. These tales are largely without foundation in fact; one trawlerman told us that every time he tried this experiment of tying a fish to a board and trailing it astern when gannets were present, the fish was devoured by other birds which alighted beside the floating wood. The gannet does not spear the fish: the dive is for the purpose of gaining depth and velocity under water in order to attack a fish or shoal *from beneath*, and the fish is seized in the open bill as the bird rises to the surface. It is usually swallowed under water, unless it is large; gannets are sometimes attacked and pursued in the air by skuas, and boobies are chased by man-o'-war birds; and it is probably from fear of these and of fellow-competitors (Kay, 1948) that the gannet and booby swallow as much of their fish-food as possible under water. Having done so, however they are by no means free from the air attacks of the skuas (great, arctic and pomarine skuas are recorded as attacking the gannet), and man-o'-war birds, which will often pursue them until they are forced to disgorge. Some skuas, particularly the great skua, will tenaciously follow a gannet which has been feeding, and several reliable observers have reported that the skua has grabbed the tail of the gannet in its determination to force the gannet to throw up.

It is true that gannets and brown pelicans dive from various heights, according to the depths at which fish-prey are swimming (for this purpose their binocular vision must be functionally important) but records of their reaching great depths in their dives are not sub-stantiated. Pelicans make shallow dives, and often do not submerge completely. Gannets are said to be able to dive to thirty fathoms (180 feet) on the evidence that they have been caught in nets set for fish at these depths. Anyone who has seen gannets diving when a herring-net or a trawl is being brought to the surface at sea will realise that it is during the somewhat slow process of hauling, when the net is floating near or at the surface, filled with fish, that the gannet is attracted by the sight of this food, into which it dives and so becomes entangled, and after a vain struggle may be drowned before the net is brought on board. A net may take many hours to be completely hauled, depending on its length and the amount of fish taken. It is extremely unlikely that the gannet dives and swims to a greater depth than fifty feet. The cormorant and shag, which fish in shallow water, remain longer under the water (cormorant, 20/71 seconds; shag, up to 170 seconds, with an average of 53 seconds: *Handbook of British Birds*, IV, 1940). The gannet rarely remains under the surface longer than ten seconds and often much less; in this time it could not possibly reach a depth of 180 feet. Dewar (1939) finds that diving birds spend half the underwater time in going down and up, and the other half in fishing below. The rate of descent of coot and duck was 1 and 1½ feet per second. Gannets, plunging from a height, would descend a little faster. No, the dive is short and shallow, and if it is unsuccessful the gannet rises into the air immediately to gain height for a fresh dive. The gannet and brown pelican, naturally very buoyant owing to the subcutaneous cellular tissue of the neck and upper breast, which is automatically filled with air before diving, do not usually dive from a floating position.* They float much higher above the water in swimming than do the cormorants. They are fast swimmers on the surface, and also underneath, when the wings may be used to prolong the dive and beat along the sea-floor (Kay). Before touching the water in their power-dives the brown pelican partly, but not quite, folds its wings; slow motion films have proved that the wings of the gannet are stretched back, unfolded, behind the body. It is generally believed that the wings are not used under water until the impetus of the dive is expended and the diver has seized, or failed to secure, its prey. The wings are then half opened as the bird comes to the surface, and typical flight motions of the wings may take place almost before a gannet has breached the surface. It resumes the search for fish, usually flying about thirty feet above the water, but when shoals are at the surface it flies very much lower, moving slowly and frequently diving slantwise.

All species of the pelican tribe, after gorging themselves with fish at a rich feeding-ground, may form quite large parties flying close together in irregular lines and chevrons on the return to the breeding or roosting grounds. Gannets and boobies, which have a thick plumage

*But may do so if a shoal is at the surface, when, with head under water to look for the fish, a gannet will dive, guillemot fashion, wings half open.

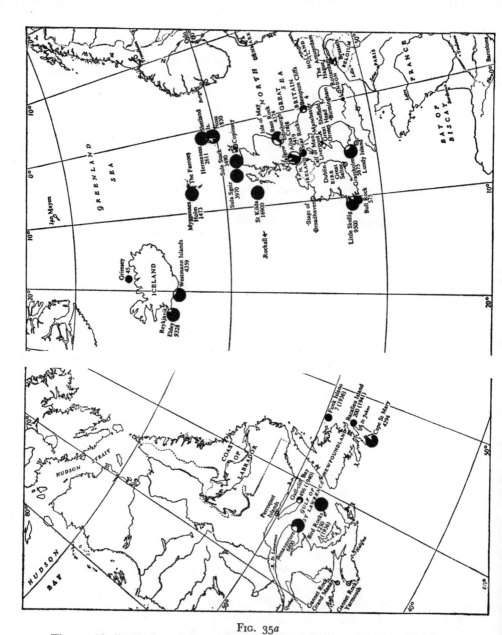

FIG. 35a

The world distribution and numbers of breeding North Atlantic gannets; the results of the world gannet census in 1939. All the known colonies are marked and the number of occupied nests (which is approximately the same as the number of *pairs*) at each colony is shown. Circles with dotted centres show the sites of extinct colonies; at Great Saltee about six birds were about but no nest was found.

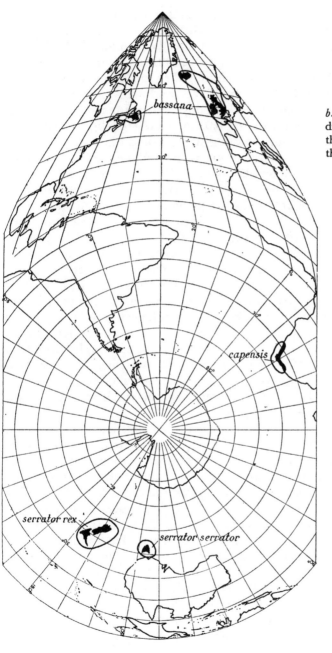

b: World breeding distribution of the three species of the gannet super-species.

impervious to water, roost or sleep at sea except in the breeding season, but cormorants, shags and frigate-birds spend as much time as possible on land or in the air, as already mentioned. Their loose feathers are easily penetrated by water, and therefore they do not enter it except when fishing; and after fishing they spend much time extending their wings and drying them in the wind and sunlight. They rest and roost on sand, shingle, rocks, buoys and sea-marks, posts, trees, even on electric power cables. Bartholomew (1943b) records 2,300 double-crested cormorants roosting at one time on a power line in San Francisco Bay—a considerable strain on the cable. He found that non-breeding cormorants contested for the best perching sites on piles in California, but that the success of a fight depended not on absolute "peck-right," as in the domestic fowl, but upon external conditions such as the direction and speed of the wind, which governed the approach of a bird wishing to land, and a bird might have to crash its way through to a successful landing upon the overcrowded perches. These contests were purely psychological and often ended in what he terms "incomplete display," although the birds were non-breeders.

The gannet and the pelican are extremely tenacious of their breeding sites; many of the gannetries have been known to be occupied for hundreds of years and doubtless some have been occupied for a thousand or more. The colony on Lundy was known to be occupied from 1274 to 1909; that on the Bass Rock has been known since 1447, on Ailsa Craig since 1526, on St. Kilda since 1696, on Sula Sgeir since 1549, on the Westmann Islands since about 1687, on the Bird Rocks in the Gulf of St. Lawrence since 1534.

Where the colony is a large one, the gannet, like the guillemot, returns correspondingly earlier in the spring. A few may settle on the breeding cliff at the beginning of December, although it is usually January before the best nesting sites (i.e., the oldest established ones) are occupied: at least two months before the egg is laid. One of the reasons for this early return has already been suggested: it is important for successful breeding to claim desirable housing sites within the densely packed colony. There is some evidence that the nest-sites on the periphery, the region most exposed to outside influences such as predatory animals and weather, are the last to be taken up—by the younger inexperienced adult gannets, which are last to arrive, as in the case of the tubenose and other sea-birds.

All the pelicans breed in colonies, some less gregariously than others, like shags which, though found in colonies, sometimes build in

Plate XIX. Man-o'-War
Birds

(*Allan D. Cruickshank from the
National Audubon Society*)

Plate XXa. Dark phase of Arctic Skua incubating, Shetland

b. Light phase of Arctic Skua incubating, Shetland

caves or dark holes alone, or at some distance from the nearest neighbour. Gannets never, but cormorants and shags occasionally, shift their colonies although usually remaining for several years in one place; when they move they may not travel far from the previous site, to which a few years later they may return. On the European mainland cormorants frequently build in trees or cliffs near or over fresh water, which they fish, but sometimes they build on the ground surrounded by fresh or salt water. Some cormorant colonies may number as much as 3,000 pairs, with other species, such as herons and spoonbills, nesting among them (Holland); but there are no cormorant colonies in the British Isles with a thousand nests.

The display of the cormorants is more one-sided than that of other sea-birds. Lewis (1929) considered that it was the male double-breasted cormorant who initiated the breeding cycle, by taking up position at the nesting site and displaying and croaking when the female appeared. Selous (1927) thought that the female shag solicited the male; and Portielje (1927) and Haverschmidt (1933) showed that it was the female European cormorant that did so. As reversed coition occurs, it is still open to doubt which sex of the European cormorant displays most, and there may not be any hard and fast rule. In display the tail is held up over the head at a sharp angle; the head is then frequently shot forward with the bill open to exhibit the yellow mouth with what has been described as a "feather-duster" effect. The head may rest almost on the back, and the throat or gular pouch distended and vibrated. The whole performance is quite violent and seems to fascinate the watching bird, drawing it towards the performer until coition takes place. Some promiscuity in the cormorant, and polyandry in the shag, has been recorded, associated with this female display.

Display in the gannet is mutual, while in the man-o'-war bird it is the male who displays, ballooning his purple throat-sac as he builds and guards the nest, while the large plain female brings him material. And it is he who will perform the major part of incubation and brooding. To a lesser extent Brandt's cormorant, *Phalacrocorax penicillatus*, expands a gular pouch, which is a brilliant caerulean blue, in display (L. Williams, 1942).

The voice of the pelican family is not exactly musical; it consists of harsh guttural notes, although the sexual note, uttered in coition and fondling, may be a pleasant crooning one. The young have a plaintive "uk-uk-uk" note which is the forerunner of the adult "oak-oak" of double-crested and European cormorants, shag and gannet).

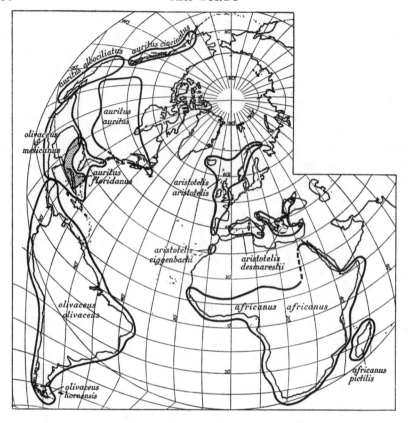

FIG. 36
Breeding distribution of four cormorants: Double-crested cormorant
Phalacrocorax auritus; Mexican cormorant, *P. olivaceus;* Shag, *P. aristo-
telis;* Red-cormorant, *Haliëtor africanus*

The nest, built by both sexes, is usually of marine materials;
seaweed, flotsam, etc. Cormorants collect heather and sticks from
cliffs near the nesting site. Gannets fly together to grassy slopes whence
they tear off and convey vegetation to the gannetry (Ailsa Craig,
Grassholm). Boobies and man-o'-war birds, building in trees, steal
twigs from neighbours' nests, and gannets rob each other in like manner.

Little is known about the pairing of the gannet; probably formation of the love-bond is a slow process, beginning with the meeting
of inexperienced young adults late in the summer at the gannetry;

such gatherings of gannets in immature plumage occur in August and September, Having familiarised itself with the territory and even built a nest and paired with a bird of the opposite sex late in the summer, the young adult may spend one or more summers in this adolescent fashion before successful breeding begins. But once the bond is formed, probably it persists for life—at any rate the fully mature birds appear to be paired on arrival early in spring. It becomes a habit to meet at the nest, with all its associations of stimulating contact and ceremonial—and eventually of consummation. More research by the marking of individual gannets is however needed to confirm the invariableness of this life-partnership of this long-lived sea-bird.

Having settled upon the nest in the early part of the season, at least from late February onwards, one or other of the pair of mature gannets will not leave it until the following July or August, when the young bird is sufficiently well grown to be able to defend itself from enemies. This alternate watch, by male and female is very necessary; the human observer who enters and disturbs a gannetry will notice how the first birds to return to their nests take the opportunity of the absence of immediate neighbours to steal as much nesting material as possible. The dry grass, seaweed and flotsam is grabbed from the unoccupied nest by the extended bill of the sitting bird and added to the robber's pedestal.

There are other dangers to which the nesting-site is exposed when an adult is forced to leave the nest by the human intruder. In many colonies there are predators, chiefly great and lesser black-backed and herring-gulls, ready to pounce upon an egg or chick left undefended. These gulls act as scavengers to the colony, and are in constant attendance at many gannetries, and at cormorant rookeries. When disturbed by human visitors gannets freely, and cormorants sometimes, disgorge the undigested fish in their gullet before flying away. Young birds do the same, although they may be unable to fly; but if old enough they will shuffle out of the nest with cries of distress. This disgorging is probably an automatic reaction due to fear, but it has the useful result of lightening the bird for flight. The gulls eagerly snatch up the ejected fish, which they appear to prefer as food to the egg or very young gannet. The gull which takes an egg from the nest of a gannet which has taken flight to escape a human trespasser may open it and eat it in the nest, or may carry it away. Only the youngest gannets, in their naked black stage, are devoured, and they may be gulped down whole by the gull. These, then, are excellent reasons why the adults should maintain a watch throughout the critical months of nest-building and incubation and the period of the chick's helplessness.

Displaying paired gannets stand face to face, the wings half open and the tail depressed; the head and the wings are waved, the bills clashing, rattling and colliding like castanets. This astonishing mutual display may continue for minutes, with short pauses. It is varied by one of the pair curtseying, but as there is already little room for two birds on the narrow pedestal nest, the performer sometimes loses balance in an undignified manner. The curtsey is best seen when the performer is alone at the nest—and the individual, without or with egg or chick, frequently indulges in this peculiar, graceful, and dignified ceremony. The head is thrust underneath the body or one wing with a serpentine movement, and next thrown high in the air and shaken to and fro, usually to the accompaniment of strident *urrah* cries. This performance is usually repeated in a sequence of three curtseys. Another activity is the picking up of a piece of nesting material, which is held in the bill, shaken, and sometimes tossed into the air and caught again as if it were a fish. Probably most of these motions (except the billing) are derived from actions used in diving for, catching, tossing up and turning, fish. Gannets do not feed each other at the nest, but they have been observed to pass seaweed from one to another during mutual billing.

When about to take off from the gannetry the individual usually adopts a special posture, not unlike that of the male pelican when changing duty at the nest. It may be associated with the filling of the subcutaneous cells with air. The neck is stretched out until the beak points upwards at right angles to the ground, and the bird marches towards the edge of the colony, the wings slightly open, the whole attitude suggesting fear of attack from the bills of neighbouring birds; to the human observer this fear seems perfectly justifiable—if the marching bird passes within striking distance of a sitting gannet it is at once attacked. When the site of the gannetry is on level or fairly level ground, and there is no easy take-off from the cliff-edge, the posturing gannet turns round and round on the nest before suddenly launching itself into the air. But this leap may not be successful; the bird may crash into the ranks of its neighbours, and will then receive a severe drubbing from their beaks as it blunders down towards the sea.

The coition of all pelicans takes place on the nest. The male gannet grips the golden head of the female in his bill; as a result it is

Plate XXIa. Light phase Arctic Skua in flight

(Eric Hosking)

b. New-hatched chicks of Arctic Skua showing egg-tooth

(C. A. Gibson-Hill)

C. A. Gibson-Hill

Plate XXIIa. Courtship and threat display of Great Skua

b. Stooping to a frontal attack on the camera-man. A Great Skua or Bonxie at Noss, Shetland

James Fisher

usually possible to recognise the sex of breeding pairs during the summer by the pecked condition of the back of the neck of the female. The gannet only lays one egg, although two have been recorded. The majority of gannet eggs are laid in April and May. A second egg is laid if the first is taken or lost soon after being laid. There is no brood spot, the egg being incubated under the webbed feet; one foot is carefully placed over the egg and the other is rested over the first, the whole being covered by the bird as it sinks on to the nest. The gannet egg hatches after six weeks, those of cormorant and shag in less than four. The nestling is entirely dark blue, without down, blind and almost helpless. It is kept warm for the first seven days or so in the same way as the egg is incubated: that is, by the feet cupped over it, with the adult body feathers as an outer "quilt." But this special brooding ceases after 10-14 days. The early stages of feeding show a remarkable tenderness and care of the small chick by the large and somewhat clumsy adult. The wobbly head and neck of the new-born chick is scooped up in the wide-open adult bill, which is pressed sideways over the nest and apparently steadied in this position, while the semi-liquid partly-digested fish is mouthed down by the half-hidden chick.

The nestling is not able to open its eyes until it is at least a week old, when the first down begins to appear; this is white on the gannet and boobies, and black on the cormorants. Voice comes to the chick at the same time, and it is able to hold up its head more steadily. When hungry, the chick now makes a soft throaty call, and reaches up to bill the adult invitingly. Growing still stronger, it is able to reach further into the distended gullet of the adult, until when it is between fifteen and twenty-five days old, the young bird's head actually disappears into the distended upper throat of the adult. Compare this method of feeding (with stored and largely undigested fish) from the elastic gullet of the gannet, booby and pelican, with that of feeding in the petrels, already described, in which the adult has a non-elastic throat, and the semi-digested food is pumped up from the proventriculus and carefully controlled and doled out through the constricted throat aperture.

The gannet chick, now covered in a thick white down, preens constantly at this stage, especially after meals; and clouds of down float over a large gannetry from June to September. Meanwhile the supply of fish has become larger in quantity and size, until at thirty to forty days old the young gannet is swallowing quite substantial

P

fish, even well-grown mackerel, gurnard and garfish (the spike-nosed eel-like garfish is doubled over and presented to the chick middle first.) The heads of such fish are always partly digested, as they lie head downwards in the stomach of the adult—this makes them soft enough for the chick to swallow, although the tails remain still quite fresh and hard. How the turning round of the ejected fish is accomplished, during the act of transference from the gullet of the adult to the gape of the nestling, so that the hard spiny fins and tail enter the stomach of the young bird with their needle-like points trailing backwards, does not seem to have been studied. But we have watched captive young gannets swallow large fish tail first occasionally.

Gannets feed their chicks usually in the early part of the day, on the return of one of the parents which has been at sea all night. While in camp for a week in June 1934 at Grassholm we noticed that at night each nest contained one adult only, with the egg or chick. There was no activity of any kind during the midnight hours when the whole colony was silent and asleep (as in booby, pelican, cormorant and man-o'-war colonies). Early in the morning parties of gannets began to fly in from the sea; many seemed to have arrived earlier and were discovered to be floating on the water near the island at dawn. Some feeding takes place at odd hours throughout the day, but the young gannet is not fed at all frequently, probably not more than two or three times during twenty-four hours.

At six weeks of age the nestling gannet has begun to grow feathers, the speckled or so called "pepper-and-salt" plumage of its first winter. Soon it appears larger than the adult, on account of the amount of fluffy white down still adhering about the feathers. Its head is now too large to enter far into the gullet of the adult when it is being fed, and the whole process of feeding at this stage looks remarkably awkward, almost violent, giving the appearance of the young bird stabbing the open mouth of the adult, and of the adult trying to swallow the beak of its child. It does not seem surprising therefore that the adults give up this uncomfortable feeding process gradually; and about the eleventh week, or a few days later, the parents cease altogether to feed their chick. In its turn the chick appears to show no further interest in the adults, although some of these (it is not proved that these are the parents, however) may continue to visit the colony long after the last chicks have become independent. At this stage the young gannet is excessively fat, as the wild-fowlers of the last century well knew. This was the season when the men of St. Kilda, as recorded

Plate XXIVa. Herring-
Gull at nest
(Llew. E. Morgan)

b. British Lesser Black-
backed Gull
(Eric Hosking)

Plate XXIII. Laughing Gulls
(Allan D. Cruickshank from the National Audubon Society)

in chapter 3, p. 93, collected many thousands of gannets and preserved their carcases for the winter.

The fledgling gannet remains on the cliffs for a week or ten days,
during which it loses the rest of its visible down. It may not remain
in the nest, but often wanders to the edge of the cliffs where it exercises
its wings, frequently in the company of other fledgelings. Any adults
present appear to ignore the grown fledgeling, and to be much occupied
in their own posturings in a recrudescence of the ceremonies of spring
—nest-building and emotional interchange. For the young bird this
is a period of fasting which will reduce its weight from over 9 to under
8 pounds and enable it to launch itself on a long flapping downward
flight to the sea. Thus, quite unassisted by its parents, which may or
may not be present on the cliffs at the time (but which, if so, have
completely lost interest in their child), the fledgeling takes to the sea.
Floundering downwards (since it is yet incapable of sustained flight),
the young gannet, in the absence of any headwind, ends up by striking
the water clumsily and with some force. It may even fail to reach the
sea in the first attempt and may bounce against the rocks, but, being
fat and well covered with feathers, as well as possessing a shock-absorber
of air-filled cellular tissue about the neck and breast, it is not usually
seriously damaged, and continues to scramble downwards until it
reaches the water. It cannot fly, and it has not been observed to dive
from the floating position. It remains floating on the surface, swimming as fast as possible away from the land. Drifting on the strong
tides which beset the islands and headlands where gannets breed, the
young bird makes all haste to get out in the open sea. Kay (1949)
gives an account of the haste of the fledgeling to get away from the
Noss colony, swimming at a half to three-quarters of a mile an hour,
unable to fly or dive, but flapping its wings often. It is quite alone
and makes no effort to associate with its fellows which are launched at
the same time. The adults continue to ignore it; all reliable evidence
proves this in spite of published stories about young gannets following
their parents (or other adults) at sea in autumn. If anything, adults,
meeting them by accident at sea, may attack (Perry, 1948). The evidence that casual adults may respond to the food-begging actions of
young at sea (Perry, 1950) is, in our opinion, unsatisfactory. Boobies
and tropic-birds are likewise independent and solitary at this age.

Up to the end of the first week of its existence the life of the young
cormorant or shag is similar to that of the young gannet. But cormorant
and shag lay from two to six eggs, and these hatch in about 24 days,

in the order in which they were laid. The young birds are therefore of different sizes while in the nest, and it is usual for the first hatched, by claiming the largest share of the food supply, to remain the largest and strongest throughout the fledging period. In times of food shortage the youngest may perish of hunger. H. F. Lewis (1929) found that the young double-crested cormorants were given pebbles incidentally with their fish food from the parental gullet; and they accumulated large numbers in this way—75 small pebbles weighing 46 grams in one bird about three weeks old—because they could not get rid of them until they had sufficient strength to regurgitate.

The stench of a gannetry, cormorant or pelican colony is due to the voidings of these birds, which subsist on large fish; but the young bird, except during the first few days of its life when its excrement is minute, is soon able to eject its waste matter to fall outside the nest-cavity. This, and the pedestal shape of the nest, ensure a comparatively dry and clean bed in stinking surroundings.* Lewis, testing the sense of taste and smell in the double-crested cormorant, found that fish, treated with strong liquids such as quassia and asafoetida, and also stinking bad fish, were freely eaten.

Lewis considers that cormorants are intelligent and can become fond of their human owner. Man-o'-war birds are easily tamed. Gurney remarks on the affectionate disposition of the gannet, both in captivity and towards its mate. A friend tells us that a gannet became so tame in captivity that it used to delight in rubbing its neck against her legs, and liked to be taken in her arms, when it would press its head against her neck. Shaking and rubbing movements of the head are characteristic of the emotional ceremonies at the nesting-ground.

Haverschmidt suggests that European cormorants may raise more than one brood in the season. Eggs may be found from February to August in southern Britain and the Channel Islands, and all the year round in the tropics. Young cormorants and shags certainly mature rapidly and are able to fly well at six weeks old when, although some-what neglected by their parents, they do not appear altogether deserted. Turner (1914) records how the adults accompanied their young back to the nest 18 days after they had been fledged; these young cormorants were born in a tree-nest, and were observed play-fully pulling off leaves, dropping them outside the nest and then watching them flutter out of sight, as if idly curious.

*The booby, *Sula dactylatra*, nesting on arid tropical cliffs, makes no nest, but squirts its faeces in a circle clear of the centre. The hot sun immediately dries the waste matter.

The ability to fly well would seem to be important for the survival of juveniles of a species with non-waterproof plumage, at least in stormy northern latitudes where a heavy surf might make a landing from the sea hazardous. (But in the calm equatorial waters of the Galápagos Islands there is a flightless species of cormorant; its life history otherwise resembles that of other cormorants.) Thus young cormorants can escape equinoctial gales by flying to the shelter of the rocks, for they would drown if they could not. At what age the brown-black plumaged *Phalacrocorax* species breed is not known. It is rare, but not unknown, to see a gannet mated and with egg or chick while still carrying signs of immature plumage. It is not until the third summer and fourth winter (that is, when it is three years old) that the head and neck of the gannet are quite white, but the golden tinge is almost absent; the rest of the plumage is like that of the fully adult, but some of the wing feathers are still black (the secondaries are black with some white), and the outer tail feathers are white and the inner ones dark. The bird is in adult plumage when it is between four and five years old.

The vital statistics of sea-birds have ever been a puzzle to ornithologists. The northern gannet, laying one egg, and today subject to hardly any persecution by man, thrives and is increasing. The cormorants lay between two and five or more eggs, are very heavily persecuted and shot, chiefly by fishermen who resent their depredations, but yet numerically they remain scarcely changed from year to year. Out of many hundreds of cormorants ringed in the British Isles more than 50 per cent have been shot, caught in nets, or otherwise killed after five years; while their breeding colonies are frequently raided by fishermen who destroy the young birds. It is therefore obvious that in order to keep their number even stationary, the cormorant must be a fairly long-lived species. In captivity it will live about 10 or 12 years. David Stuart (1948) finds that the expectation of life on 1 March (following the year of its birth) of the young cormorant (born and ringed in a colony of 200-220 pairs at Mochrum, Wigtownshire, Scotland) is only 2.2 years; which he finds makes it impossible for the cormorant to maintain its numbers (on paper) as it has done in fact, at Mochrum, for at least 80 years. But it should be remembered that aluminium leg-rings wear and drop off the legs of sea-birds after a few years; the data accumulated by ringing can only be a guide to the vital statistics. Among some birds (e.g. Manx shearwater) which nest year after year in accessible sites, it is possible to obtain greater accuracy by frequently renewing the rings of individuals under study.

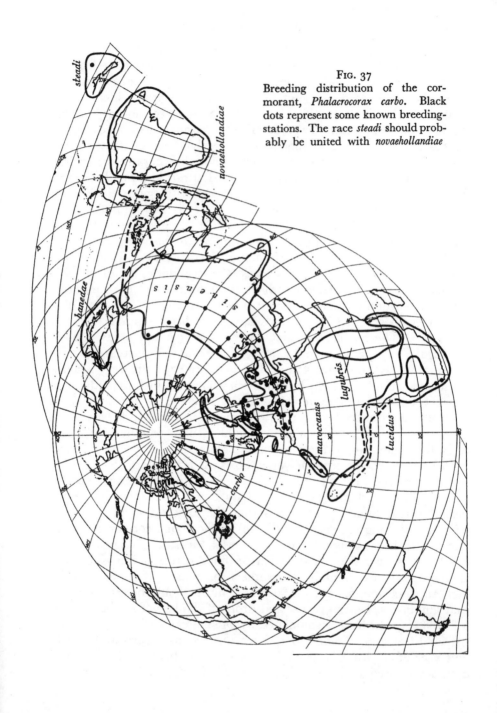

FIG. 37

Breeding distribution of the cormorant, *Phalacrocorax carbo*. Black dots represent some known breeding-stations. The race *steadi* should probably be united with *novaehollandiae*

Man of course is not the only enemy of the cormorant. Southwell
(1904) records that a hump-backed whale (*Megaptera novaeangliae*)
was "found dead after indulging too freely in cormorants," having
swallowed six and choked on the seventh. There is also a record of an
angler-fish which had attempted to swallow a cormorant; the strength
and buoyancy of the cormorant had raised both to the surface, where
they were captured, but the cormorant did not long survive its wounds.
Cormorants have also been taken by cod, angel-fish and pike (p .114).

Cormorants have been exploited by man for several centuries,
the Chinese breeding and training them to catch fish, on a commercial
scale, usually in daylight; the birds are free to work in packs together
in shallow water and are taught to return, each to its own perch on
its owner's boat. The Japanese control their trained cormorants with
reins attached to neck-rings, and work at night, using flares to attract
the fish. The collection of the guano of pelicans and cormorants forms
a major industry on islands off the west coast of South America. The
droppings of double-crested cormorants roosting on racks along the
shore of California are also collected to be used as fertiliser. Gannet-
guano is regularly collected on islands off Cape of Good Hope, South
Africa. An important account of guano is given by Hutchinson (1950).

The true pelicans are never found far from the land in the North
Atlantic, and therefore need not be considered in detail here. *Pelecanus
rufescens* is the only breeding pelican on the east side, where it frequents
estuaries, bays and lagoons, and nests in water-side trees.   This is
the grey or pink-backed pelican : it can drive fish downstream in a
river, corner and devour them in shallow water. On the west side
of the Atlantic is *P. occidentalis,* the brown pelican, a tree-nester
which will also nest on the ground. Pelicans lay two or three eggs,
and their breeding biology resembles that of cormorants: they are as
tame, gregarious, and quarrelsome as the gannets, and just as stupid
in failing to recognise and rescue a nestling if it falls out of the nest or
is attacked (it may even be devoured) by a neighbouring adult.
Both sexes incubate the egg and brood the naked chick. They have
been seen to open the wings as if to shelter the growing nestling from
the tropical sun, but the action appears to be instinctive. and the shadow
may not fall on the young at all. Those young pelicans hatched in
tree nests remain there until they are fledged, and are fed by their
parents; but in ground colonies the youngsters, growing impatient
for food, wander over the nesting area in bands, pursuing each adult
arriving with fish; a mêlée ensues, in which they fairly attack the

gullet of the loaded bird, which lays about with its long beak, hitting those it does not approve of, and apparently trying to "clear the carpet" for its legitimate family.

Food is not carried in the pouch: this is used only for catching the fish. After the gannet-like dive, which is spiralling like that of the tropic-bird, the brown pelican appears at the surface quickly (since it makes a shallow dive and usually in shallow water), facing the wind. Its first act on emergence is to drain the pouch of a gallon or so of water by tilting the bill; this done, the bill is flung up, releasing the fish, which is caught in the throat and swallowed—if it is not snatched skilfully in mid-air by a gull or tern hovering near.

The boobies are the tropical representatives of the gannets of temperate waters, and although some workers prefer to separate them generically, their life-histories are so similar that the field observer accepts them readily under the genus *Sula*. Feeding and breeding habits are identical in main features: incubation is by both sexes, the young are born blind and naked, are fed by regurgitation, acquire a first down of white colour, and remain in the nest for about three months, being finally deserted by the adults. Three distinct species (Fig. 38) breed in the tropical North Atlantic: the blue-faced booby *Sula dactylatra*, breeding on the bare rock or cliff and making little or no nest; the red-footed booby *Sula sula*, a tree-nester; and the brown booby *Sula leucogaster*, nesting indiscriminately between these extremes of habitat, usually on vegetation-covered ground, but also in the open. All boobies feed largely on flying-fish, caught by diving, gannet-fashion. Two eggs may be laid and hatched, but at North Atlantic sites only one chick survives: the later-hatched one is starved and trampled to death by the voracious appetite and activity of the first-born.* Murphy (1936, p. 853) describes how the chick of *S. dactylatra* gropes "far into the throat of the adult, where it remains for a long time, picking and jabbing and pumping, in what looks like a most uncomfortable manner, until all the available flying fish have been extracted. The inordinate length of time devoted to the feeding of the chick . . . may be still another reason why no food ever remains in the gullet to profit the second offspring." One adult guards egg or chick, but when the nestling is large enough to defend itself at a month or so, the old birds leave it by day and go out on their excursions into

*The Pacific representatives of the three boobies found in the North Atlantic, however, often rear more than one chick, which may be due to the abundance of fish food, especially in the Humboldt Current (Murphy).

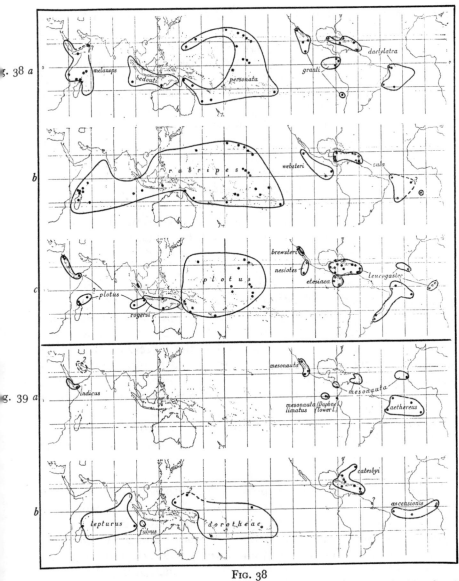

FIG. 38

Breeding distribution of the three Atlantic boobies: (a) *Sula dactylatra*, the blue-faced booby; (b) *S. sula*, red-footed booby; (c) *S. leucogaster*, brown booby. The last also breeds on an island SE of Formosa, and *S. dactylatra personata* also on the Kermadec Is.

FIG. 39

Breeding distribution of the two Atlantic tropic-birds: (a) *Phaëthon aethereus*, red-billed tropic-bird; (b) *P. lepturus*, white-tailed tropic-bird.

blue water (never fishing close to land) after flying-fish. In the heat of noon, as in northern gannetries, the downy young lie with their heads hanging over the edge of the nest as if dead; they are fast asleep. Heat is a trial surprisingly well borne by many tropical sea-birds. The small chick of *S. dactylatra* hatched on the naked rock may be seen climbing on to the webs of the brooding adult in order to avoid the fierce radiation. This species, sometimes called the great white booby, is the largest (and clumsiest on land) of the three, and roosts on open rocks when not breeding. The other two, however, roost much in trees: *S. leucogaster* will alight on the booms and wooden superstructure of ships and sleep soundly all night.

The female red-footed booby *S. sula*, builds a slovenly tree-nest of sticks brought to her by the male (who is smaller in size). The material is laboriously collected from the sea or snapped from the trees, for this booby will not willingly alight on the ground, from which it has difficulty in rising. The young ones show the same fear of the ground and cling tenaciously to the trees long after they are fully fledged. Deserted by the adults, they climb to the tree-tops, grow thin with much wing flapping and fasting, and at last take off, flying well— far better than the fledgelings of other *Sula* species, some of which can only flutter downwards to the sea. The red-footed booby is also more crepuscular than the others—it has the largest eye of all the boobies—sleeping much at noon and going out in search of the nocturnal squid early and late in the day. Some observers suggest that its frequent late return to the roosting ground, after the man-o'-war birds have gone to sleep, is due to fear of these pirates which lie in wait along the edge of the breeding-roosting tree-covered shore. The red-foot's habit of skirting the shore until directly opposite the nesting tree on its return from fishing enables the man-o'-war bird to intercept the food-laden booby the more certainly.

The astonishing man-o'-war bird, *Fregata magnificens*, obtains a good deal of its food by robbing boobies of theirs. In spite of its wonderful powers of flight it is very restricted in its range from its nesting-sites which, in the North Atlantic, are the West Indies and the Cape Verde Islands. The range is between fifty and seventy miles: the bird's presence in the Pacific was often a guide to "ditched" airmen during the war, as to the nearness of land. Like that of the cormorants, to which it is closely allied, its plumage becomes water-logged if it is forced to swim: its preen gland is small, the size of a pea, and probably insufficient to yield much oil for waterproofing the feathers. But the man-o'-war or frigate-bird never deliberately enters the water. It is the most buoyant flying machine among all birds, having the greatest wing area in relation to body-weight. Its long narrow pointed wings and great long tail are perfect instruments for the high-speed manoeuvres, as well as for the effortless soaring, of its incomparably graceful and elegant flight. The boobies, by comparison, seem to lunge clumsily into the sea after the flying-fish; but the arrow-fast frigate-birds easily overtake the flying-fish long before they drop into the water. The "half-beaks," fish which skim on the surface of the water are likewise seized by the dashing frigate-birds; and probably fifty per cent. of their food is taken direct in this way. Especially in rough weather does the frigate-bird earn an "honest living," plucking fish from the hollows and crests of storm-waves. It is during calms that boobies and other birds are most pursued by frigates which follow on the tail of the food-loaded booby or gull, and if the contents of the crop are not ejected, the tail itself or a leg of the victim may be seized and viciously wrenched. Frigate-birds will attend the cleaning of fish at sea and deftly snatch offal thrown from trawlers and smacks. They follow tropical rivers, frequenting slaughter-houses together with black vultures: the vultures snatch up the offal thrown on the ground and the man-o'-war birds that which is flung into the water.

Although sedentary in its range the man-o'-war bird has been watched crossing over the Panama isthmus and the breadth of Cuba. It will visit fresh water; and has been seen to dash down and buffet the surface as if desiring a shower-bath and possibly a drink.

As with the boobies, the breeding of the frigate-birds is not fixed to one season of the year in its tropical range. The male first occupies a tree-site and sits there, inflating the bright crimson globe of his throat-sac as an intimidation to other males or as an invitation to the larger, duller female, or both. She brings the nesting material and, as soon as the flimsiest platform is built, mating takes place. The male continues in occupation of the site: it is absolutely necessary for him to do so if he would retain a nest, since the slovenly platform would disappear, bit by bit, in a few minutes, if he left it. Nest-hungry females are always ready to steal twigs and sticks; although there is abundant material under the trees, the man-o'-war is unwilling to alight on the ground, from which it finds it difficult, with long narrow wings and tail, to rise. She therefore robs her neighbours, which are often red-footed boobies, taking sticks from unguarded nests or from boobies returning with material in their bills. The best frigate-nests are nevertheless very poor, but as the season advances they become solidified with excrement. The male takes a large part in incubation; his ballooning of the gular pouch ceases then. They are tame when unmolested at the nest, and are heavy sleepers at night. Buller (1905, p. 50) quotes the case of frigate-birds being so tamed by feeding that they were used to carry messages between two islands 100 kilometres apart; the birds became accustomed to being fed at perches placed for them outside human dwellings in a number of Samoan islands. They were easily handled at night when it was desired to affix or remove the message contained in a reed cylinder fastened to the wing; and since these birds never enter the water the cylinder would be safe from destruction by that element.

That curious appearance of harmony at the breeding ground between parasite and host often seen in other species exists between frigate-bird and booby nesting in the same tree colony. The booby may be relentlessly pursued over the sea, but enmity (except for stick-stealing) ends on the land. The frigate chicks may be seen in nests close to those containing booby youngsters, both species lying fast asleep at noon with downy heads drooping over the side dejectedly, the new quillshafts, surrounded by powerful young muscles, charged with blood to feed the developing wings.

Two more remarkably beautiful tropical wanderers of the Pelecaniform order breed in the warm North Atlantic : the red-billed (*Phaëthon aethereus*) and the white-tailed (*P. lepturus*) tropic-birds. Boatswainbird is a title earned from the shrill whistle, the long pointed tail resembling a marlin spike, and the habit of coming up to inspect a passing ship, of these white sea-birds—which cross and recross the ocean desert of the Sargasso Sea, with swift dove-like flight, at points farthest from the mainland in the whole North Atlantic. At Bermuda the colony of 2,000 pairs of *P. lepturus* was counted and studied by Gross (1912) and Plath (1914). The one chocolate-splashed egg is laid in a hole or burrow in the cliff. Features of the breeding biology resemble those of the petrels: the clumsy shuffling on land of these wonderful fliers, the hole-nesting, incubation by both sexes, the long fledging period, the desertion of the young. Pairing takes place at the nest. After twenty-eight days or more of incubation the feeble blind chick hatches. It opens its eyes in a few days, and grows rapidly on a diet of fish and squids. The adults make two foraging journeys each day: at dawn, returning in the morning; and some hours before sunset, returning before dusk; probably these times are selected because the squids are not found on the surface of the sea at noon. The chick is fed by regurgitation; it is well feathered by the fortieth day and leaves about the sixty-second day after a short fast, the adults having quite deserted it. Like the shearwater it cannot fly, but only flutter down to the water, where it swims alone into the open sea.

The red-billed tropic bird has not been so intensively studied, but undoubtedly has a similar life history. It is a small species. Murphy says it is "well named after Phaëthon, the son of Apollo, who hurtled from the far sky into the sea. I remember the July day when I first saw one dive from the height of the masthead into the quiet transparent water. For several seconds it remained below and, after reappearing, shook a shower of pearls from its feathers, rested at the surface with wings spread and raised, and tail plumes cocked up, and finally leaped into the air as lightly as a tern."

CHAPTER 10

THE SKUAS

THE GULL-LIKE SKUAS are perhaps the most primitive and certainly the most specialised of the families of the Laro-Limicolae, a large order containing the rest of the sea-birds described in this book. Skuas are essentially predators and parasites: at sea they neither dive for food nor seek it by swimming; nor, on the land, do they seek much of their food by searching and probing on foot, as gulls do. Although they swim well, and walk with a waddling gait, they prefer to swoop and grab their food while in flight, piratically. All four species of the family (Stercorariidae) are North Atlantic, indeed, arctic, birds; it seems likely that the suborder Lari, to which both skuas and gulls belong, originated in the north. The largest of the skuas, the bonxie or great skua, *Catharacta skua*, is one of the few birds with a bipolar distribution. As explained (p. 143), we think it likely that this interesting species, or superspecies, originally came from the north but colonised the south; and that the presence of great skuas breeding in the North Atlantic may be a fairly recent development (geologically speaking), a return, so to speak, to the north of the descendants of the ancient stock. These are now, at least subspecifically, distinct from their antarctic and sub-antarctic relations. The great skua's rather narrow distribution in the north is described on p. 144.

Although gull-like in appearance and habits, skuas are far more oceanic than gulls, travelling considerable distances on migration and remaining at sea throughout the winter, never or rarely roosting on land at that season. The bulky brown form of the bonxie, with its triangular white wing patch, is unmistakable; with its short tail it looks almost clumsy on the wing compared with the graceful long-tailed smaller species—the pomarine, the arctic and the long-tailed.

These three smaller skuas resemble each other considerably in form, habits and distribution; and much remains to be found out about their fundamental ecology, in which no doubt lies the biological secret of the separate existence of the three. Much of our knowledge of their at-sea distribution is obscured by the difficulty of identification at a distance: immature birds are almost, and sometimes quite, indistinguishable to the observer; they lack the long central tail feathers by which the adults may be specifically identified. Only the heavy thick-bodied immature great skua cannot be mistaken for any other bird, being too dark for an immature gull, and too short in the tail for another skua. The adult arctic skua can be recognised by the two long straight feathers which project from the centre of the wedge-shaped tail; these are distinct from the much broader and twisted features of the tail of the somewhat larger and heavier pomarine skua. The graceful long-tailed skua may be recognised by its buoyant swallow-like flight, and the very long and streamer-like central tail feathers. Both arctic and pomarine skuas have dark and light phases (p. 52); in the arctic skua the dark form is more numerous in the southern part of its breeding range. The dark form is scarcer in the pomarine.

At the Fair Isle Bird Observatory, Williamson (1951) found that the phases of the arctic skua could be divided into dark, intermediate and pale (white-bellied) types: D, I, and P. In eight nests under observation the following matings were recorded in 1951: D x I, P x I, P x D, I x I, P x I, D x I, D x I, D x I. Two adults, ringed as non-breeders in 1950, were again present but not breeding in 1951, arguing a non-breeding period of at least three years in this species.

The Fair Isle arctic skuas obtain most of their food by forcing the abundant kittiwakes to disgorge the sillocks and other small fish which are the staple kittiwake food in summer. All skuas pursue other birds at sea in an attempt, not always successful, to make them deliver their fish catches. This food, often partly digested in the victim's crop, is secured by the skua with a sudden swoop before it reaches the water. The great skua in normal flight appears sluggish and slow, as it forges along with laboured movement of the broad wings, but when attacking another bird it displays great aerial power, although in a deceptively leisurely manner, following the twists and turns of its quarry with ease. It has been seen to grab a gannet by the wing-tip or the tail and force its victim to disgorge, and even to retain hold until the gannet has crashed into the sea. It will even pursue a fulmar; on 16 June 1935, when about ten miles E.S.E. of the Westmann Islands, Iceland, we saw a great skua persistently harry fulmars following our ship; this does not seem, however, to be a habit, and probably the skua in this instance was exceptionally hungry. During ten days at midsummer 1948, from a trawler working the Rockall Bank, we saw great skuas frequently, but they did not harry any birds (and there were thousands of fulmars present), being apparently content to search for food far in the wake of the trawler, evidently taking the roughest offal of the fish guttings which had been thrown out plentifully and floated astern, after the bold fulmars in their hundreds close to the ship had seized the livers and tender parts.

Gulls and terns are the principal victims of the piracy of the skuas, which seldom select a gull or tern that is incapable, through a long fast, of throwing up a contribution; in all probability the skua recognises the appearance of a food-laden gull or tern (if the fish it is carrying is not visible) by its more leisurely, less hunting flight. Skuas also prey on smaller birds, both over the sea and the land; and if these are unable to escape by taking cover or diving they are relentlessly followed, tired out, killed and devoured. A pomarine skua has been seen to pursue to the death a phalarope at sea (Bent, 1921): and to force a fulmar to drop a fish, just south of the Newfoundland banks, 14 April 1921 (Fisher, 1952).

Some skuas may breed far inland, as in northern Europe and Siberia; and the food then consists much of small mammals (lemmings especially), small birds, eggs, freshwater fish, insects, worms, etc. The great skua is probably the most marine and gull-like in its feeding habits, living mainly on fish, pirated or legitimately taken, and killing large and small birds, adult or young, along the seaboard of its nesting area; and it is a gull-like scavenger of stranded carcases of seal, whale, fish and other carrion.

The breeding habits of the great and arctic skuas have been, and are being, studied, but little is known about the lives of the pomarine and long-tailed skuas. To their most southern nesting haunts the great and arctic skuas return during April. The eggs are laid a month later. Some of the display and posturing is similar to that of the *Larus* gulls, including the food-begging actions and mating ceremonies. In courtship the male raises his wings and flutters them as he approaches the female. He holds his head upwards and backwards and puffs out the neck hackles, displaying with sharp excited calls in his effort to gain her attention. She responds with a wheezing or hissing note, sometimes standing upright and at other times bowing to the ground as if to invite coition. The male continues for some time a kind of strutting dance in a half-circle round his partner; and wing play goes on steadily. The wings, when raised above the back, seem, indeed, to indicate heightened emotion at all times in the life of the skua while on land. Both sexes indulge in an attractive aerial display: sometimes soaring together in circles; or one bird will make a spectacular dive, or will perform an amazing twisting tumbling evolution in mid-air, symbolic of the piratic chases at sea. The swift downward dive is turned upon the human intruder as he crosses the breeding territory, and he will be persistently dive-bombed until he leaves the area, and perhaps struck on the head. The great skua also makes a frontal attack, by a low approach over the ground, upon man, ponies, sheep, dogs and other large animals, which is rather terrifying to face. This skua will strike with determination, and often with successful results, at sheep, even clinging to the wool and beating its wings about the head of the intruding animal. The arctic and long-tailed skuas are adept at injury-feigning in order to draw away from the nest the unwanted visitor; the adult staggers over the ground with wings trailing as if they were broken, but rather spoils the effect—at least for the human observer—by rising into the air occasionally before resuming the display. Williamson (1929) considers that this is probably derived from primitive food-begging and courtship actions.

Great and arctic skuas nest in colonies, often of large size (500-750 pairs of great skua on Foula, Shetland, 1951). They are more sociable than the pomarine and long-tailed skuas which scatter their nests more widely on the tundra. The skua prepares a hollow for its nest, but adds very little material as a lining. The usual clutch is two, occasionally one, exceptionally three, eggs. These are protectively coloured: brown or grey, splotched with irregular dark brown spots. In all respects the incubation resembles that of the gulls: it is by both sexes, and of the same duration, 26-29 days. The new-born skua is covered with a dark unmottled but protectively coloured down. It is more precocious than the gull chick, develops rapidly and leaves the nest early, being at first jealously attended by the adults. Skuas may attack and kill chicks belonging to neighbours, but there does not seem to be any record of that cannibalism within the family circle found in the gulls. At one nest on Fair Isle the parents continued to give the injury-feigning or lure display for five days after the death of their single chick (or, as Williamson (1951) puts it, "the normal parental response to intrusion persisted for some 5 days after all biological need for it had ceased to exist.") This chick was eleven days old, and the disturbing distractive behaviour of the adults is

Q

probably strongest at that age (Williamson, 1949); but it gradually weakens, until, at the end of the fledging-period, the adults have lost all interest in defending their young in any manner at all. Williamson found that the arctic skua was fledged in 27-33 days, the period varying probably with the abundance or otherwise of the fish-food pirated from the kittiwakes.

The adults do not accompany the young skuas at sea (Perry, 1948), which gradually learn to feed for themselves, hawking over the sea after kittiwakes, gulls and terns; they will chase small birds industriously, if seldom successfully at first. The flocks of young skuas at British breeding grounds thin out by mid-August as one by one individuals take to the open sea. The adults have gone ahead, likewise singly or in very small parties. For the most part skuas are solitary at sea; but where gulls and terns concentrate to feed on shoals of fish, a number of skuas will gather with intent to plunder the fishers.

The immature birds do not hurry north in the spring. We have seen numbers off the south coast of Portugal at midsummer. They may not reach the breeding ground until they are in their third summer. They will then take part in those social activities seen in individual non-breeding sea-birds of other species, previously described, including communal bathing in fresh water (a favourite habit of skuas), and incomplete courtship displays; and so they familiarise themselves with the future nesting region.

The departure of the adults may be hastened in August by the early autumnal moult which takes place at sea. In spring there is another moult, into the richer coloured summer body plumage in which the adults arrive at the breeding grounds. The wing-coverts, quills and tail are apparently moulted only once a year, gradually during the winter, so that the skua is never much incapacitated in his piratical profession by this annual process.

CHAPTER II

THE GULLS

G ULLS ARE STRONG aggressive well-built birds with long wings capable of sustained and powerful flight. They have webbed feet, but are good walkers on land. In the air they move with ease and grace, and glide without effort for long distances. The majority have white bodies with grey or black mantles or wings. Some have a dark hood during the breeding season, but this is moulted in the autumn. The young gulls are more difficult to identify in the field, the juvenile and first year plumages of the larger species being a drab mottled brown.

The full beauty of flight of the gulls may be watched from the deck of a ship, when it will be seen that gulls are expert at taking advantage of the wind-eddies caused by the passage of the vessel; again and again they skim and circle about the ship, using the wind deflected against the hull to lift them, with scarcely any movement of their outspread wings. Over land they frequently soar, wheeling upon a thermal pocket of air and spiralling to a great height with no more than an occasional beat of the wings and twist of the tail. On the water they swim buoyantly as they scavenge for food. They are however poor divers and rarely submerge completely.

Although some gulls migrate over considerable distances, they are seldom long out of sight of land; the kittiwake, which ranges over the whole of the North Atlantic, being the exception. At the other extreme, most of the dark-headed gulls spend much of their lives inland, often breeding far from the sea; and during the winter months feeding in or near large towns, and roosting on the open water of lakes and reservoirs at night. These smaller *Larus* gulls live much on terrestrial insects, worms and small invertebrates during the summer, when breeding inland; and nearly all the gulls, excepting the pelagic kittiwakes, and the ivory-, Ross's and Sabine's gulls of the Arctic, regularly visit the land for food in autumn and winter, when seeds and grain may be procured at harvest time; and they follow the plough. Gulls in fact are omnivorous, freely taking vegetable matter where the normal diet of fish and flesh—alive or as carrion—is in short supply. The ivory-gull lives on the droppings of seal, walrus and polar bear all the year round, supplemented with crustaceans, molluscs and insects when these are available (particularly at nesting times). The larger gulls in summer devour the eggs and chicks and even adults of other sea-birds, and often the chicks of their own species. Most gulls work the mud, sand or saturated turf, trampling with both feet until worms or sand-eels appear. The great blackback drops eggs of birds (the pink-footed goose included) from a height to break them, but cannot distinguish between hard and soft ground. Herring-gulls drop small shell-fish (clams, cockles, mussels, and whelk-shells containing hermit-crabs) from a height of not more than about 25 ft., (possibly because of fear of a rival getting to the crushed delicacy first) on rock and sand indifferently, apparently unable to appreciate the greater effectiveness of the rock compared with the sand for crushing the shell. Common gulls do the same. It does not appear to be an instinctive habit, but rather one acquired by a few individuals only; but it is copied by others watching the expert at work. Rooks drop mussels and walnuts in the same manner. It is recorded that a highway bridge in New Jersey, U.S.A., was littered with the remains of clams dropped by herring-gulls, which in this instance seemed to have discovered that the road there formed a more suitable surface for the purpose than the nearby shore.

Gulls like to wash their food, if it is of any size, in water. Herring-gulls may be observed rinsing their fish food in tidal pools. Great black-backed gulls will wash the sea-birds (puffin, shearwater, various auks) and small mammals which they have killed, in the sea, or on the edge of a freshwater pond or stream at their breeding grounds; and they leave behind in these places quite an accumulation of clean-picked skins and vertebrae.

The beautiful laughing gull (*Larus atricilla*), with the dark glittering eye encircled with a fiery ring, is an adept at stealing eggs from the nests of terns; it also has a trick of alighting on the head of the brown pelican, and snatching food from its pouch. In turn it is much pursued by skuas and man-o'-war birds.

Goethe (1937) has given us one of the best accounts of the breeding of a *Larus* gull in his study of the herring-gull breeding among sand-dunes. His descriptions of courtship, display and nesting may be

Allan D. Cruickshank from National Audubon Society

Plate XXV. Ring-billed Gulls

Plate XXVIa. Iceland Gull, immature, winter. Lerwick, Shetland

J. D. Rattar

b. Iceland Gull, summer plumage

J. D. Rattar

accepted as typical for the genus. Another classical account is that of the black-headed gull by Kirkman (1937). Both accounts, which appeared simultaneously, have done much to increase our knowledge of gull behaviour. Paludan (1951) and Tinbergen (1953) have followed with other intensive studies.

These two gulls make an interesting comparison. As a rule the black-headed gull arrives quite suddenly and in a large flock at its breeding ground, much as the puffin does, but almost a month earlier, in the first fortnight of March; although some scouts pay visits in February. But it does not settle down immediately. Its visits are somewhat spasmodic, and always during those early weeks it withdraws to roost away from the breeding ground. When the adults settle at the nesting sites in March and April, they appear to be paired like gannets, rooks, and other social nesters. We know very little as to the actual pairing up, which is said to take place before arrival. Kirkman insisted that the birds "have arrived paired at the breeding place," but Tinbergen (1952) provided proof that the male and female arrive separately at the breeding ground and there discover each other or a new mate on or near the familiar nesting site. There appears to be no firm evidence that any gull remains with its mate throughout the winter; or that they pair regularly before they leave for the breeding ground in early spring, in February and March. In short, we only know that the birds are faithful to the colony and nest-site. This applies also to the migratory lesser black-backed gull, which arrives in a body at the nesting ground in March (with a few scouts earlier), and it would appear to apply to all the gulls (as well as to the terns) which perform mass movements from wintering to breeding grounds.

Faithfulness to the old nesting site, however, is very strong. Kirkman suggests that the big nest in the centre of a group of smaller nests in a black-headed gull colony may be the parents' home, and the other nests round about are those of the children. Extensive ringing alone can prove this attractive explanation of the grouping of nests, and might also explain the interiorly family (or neutral) attitude of the owners, who adopt an exteriorly aggressive attitude to all others outside the family group. But other factors operate, and Kirkman himself notes that the size of the nest is largely determined by the number of times a bird is prevented from sitting on its eggs; if its mate refuses to leave the eggs the frustrated bird finds an outlet (displacement activity) for broodiness by collecting and depositing material in the nest.

In order to begin breeding there must be a suitable environment against which the mutual stimulation of the sexes will become effective. Probably in most if not all gulls it is the male which sets up this environment by occupying the breeding site first and displaying towards later arrivals. Almost as soon as the shortest winter day is past lone males of the herring-gull (which in the British Isles is largely a sedentary species) settle on cliff-sites on fine days (Lockley, 1947) and give the moaning call at sight of another gull passing near. Each male parades on or near a suitable platform in the rocks cliffs or dunes. He challenges a neighbouring male by drawing his head in stiffly. He picks up small pebbles or plucks the stems of plants much as a farmyard cock will peck and pluck at the ground when approaching a rival. Usually the challenged male begins to pluck also as if warning the intruder that he has come far enough. The warning often suffices; energy has been released without wasteful fighting and each male retires to his own plot of territory. Even if a scrap develops no real wounds are inflicted. The unmated continues to show hostility to all comers (unless he is a very mature male experienced in sex and mate recognition) but gradually changes his mood if a female persists in visiting him. Once male and female have accepted each other the herring-gull pair recognise each other up to a distance of 30 yards apart; in view of this fact it is remarkable that the herring-gull is quite unable to distinguish between its own eggs and those (differing in pattern much more than male and female gull do in appearance) of another gull if given a choice test (Tinbergen, 1951).

The mutual display of gulls has already been described (p. 170). It is generally considered however that the food-begging ceremony is performed more often by the female. In a typical instance the head is jerked up and down in front of the male's bill which may be actually struck or tapped thus imitating exactly the behaviour of the young bird. But much of courtship "feeding" is a mock affair, and often no food is transferred, probably because the male's stomach is empty, although the bills may be locked for a moment. Sometimes, in a crowded colony, a female may be "fed" by a second male; at all times the female appears anxious to beg food, even in winter. This must be derived from behaviour as a chick and a juvenile; for juveniles will beg food of any adult in winter, though rarely or never with success. This supplicating of the adults by immatures far from the breeding ground has given rise to the belief that the young bird remains attached to its parents long after the nesting season.

But this is not the case, as we shall demonstrate later. Billing and mock- or real feeding often precedes coition, which is conducted with much wing-flapping on the part of the male, as he maintains position, utter- ing a special loud deep note. Occasionally homosexual behaviour has been recorded (Noble & Wurm, 1943; Goethe, 1937).

In mild western districts, where, as at Skokholm, pairing may begin even before the new year, mated herring-gulls may temporarily desert the breeding ground, and fly together to the feeding ground. But as spring approaches they are reluctant to leave the nest-site entirely, and once nest-building begins one or other of the pair remains at or near the focal point of the season's activities, especially in large colonies, where stimulation and competition is greater. This stimulation, as we have seen, may come from other species nesting close by. On many islands and some cliffs two or three species of gull may nest together, and occasionally there is interbreeding (as between herring- gulls and lesser blackbacks). But if there is stimulation between related species, there is no very visible interspecific competition. On Skok- holm and Skomer, for instance, great blackbacks and herring-gulls share the same plateau with much larger numbers of lesser black- backs, but each species selects a slightly different ecological niche within the gullery. Thus the first two species are semi-resident, and lay their eggs at the end of April or the beginning of May, always selecting an outcrop of rock or a large stone against which the nest is constructed; the great blackback dominating the higher outcrops, the herring-gulls making use of rock- and loose-stone sites (which are available in plenty) on the lower terraces of the outcrops not occupied by the larger gull. The lesser blackbacks, arriving later (in February and March), and laying their eggs from 10 May onwards, use the ground between the outcrops, ground unencumbered except with low vegetation of wind-blown bracken, heather, *Molinia*, etc. On Skokholm there is probably enough room for all three; changes occur in the numbers of each species, but the total gull population tends to be more or less stable, and is kept from any great increase by the regular collection of eggs throughout May and June by lighthouse-keepers and others.

The figures in the table (p. 232) are interesting as showing population trends. The great blackback is known to be an increasing species in the British Isles; at Skokholm the increase must come from outside sources, since here this gull has been prevented from rearing more than a very few young, by regular egg-collecting. Herring-gulls are able

Census of Gulls at Skokholm (pairs breeding)

	1929	1939	1949
HERRING-GULL	250	300	572
LESSER BLACKBACK	700	805	350
GREAT BLACKBACK	34	55	72
Total pairs	984	1160	994

(taken from *Letters from Skokholm* (Lockley 1947) and 1949 Skokholm Report)

to rear proportionately more young per pair at Skokholm because many nest on inaccessible parts of the cliffs. The lesser blackbacks, nesting principally on the plateau of the island, suffer most from egg-collecting. It is probable that the gulls established their large main colonies during the years 1890 to 1920 when the island lay more or less abandoned and unfarmed (it was a prosperous farm one hundred years ago), and before the lighthouse was placed in commission. 805 pairs in 1939 was a peak figure, and there has been a rapid decline since, groups and little colonies disappearing from inland sites, while more herring-gulls appear to have come inland to breed. But many factors must be taken into account in trying to arrive at the true reasons for the alterations which occur in sea-bird populations, especially in studying the dynamics of the gregarious and migratory lesser black-back, which is known to shift its breeding-grounds occasionally.

At Hirsholmene in the Kattegat, Salomonsen (1947) found that there was a similar, and even more, competitive sequence in the place-ment of nests in three gull species nesting on the island. The black-headed gulls formed the nucleus of the colony by laying eggs first—from 25 April onwards. A few common gulls, laying on 1 May, placed their nests in a ring around the closed territory of the black-heads. The smaller numbers of herring-gulls were also forced to breed on this perimeter. The arrival of the Sandwich terns, which lay on 6 May, caused an upheaval due to the aggressiveness of the terns, which forced their way into the centre of the black-headed gulls, destroying eggs and driving the gulls away. Salomonsen suggests that the attachment of the Sandwich terns and the common gulls to the black-head colony may be due to the aggressive behaviour of the black-heads in successfully driving away crow, hawk, fox, stoat, etc.: also that the nesting drive of the terns is released by the sight of the breeding colony of black-headed gulls. Other species of terns and gulls are known to associate in breeding colonies; thus Sabine's gull

(*Xema sabini*), nesting in swampy tundra along the arctic shore, is often found close to, or among breeding arctic terns. However, there are so many other factors to be considered, such as the relative abundance of each species from year to year (this appears to be unstable; in some years the terns do not reappear in the old haunt), and the dominance of the species most suited to the environment. Palmer (1941) even suggests that the presence of gulls is detrimental and eventually drives

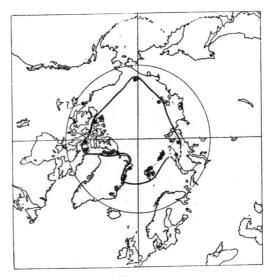

FIG. 40
Breeding distribution of the ivory-gull, *Pagophila eburnea*

the terns away. The herring-gulls at Hirsholmene were not in a typical environment. A numerous herring-gull colony, in a typical sloping cliff site or Baltic sand-dune, may dominate the breeding area to the virtual exclusion of all other gulls, as at Lambay Island cliffs, Ireland, where in 1939 we estimated 10,000 pairs present, with only 40 pairs of lesser black-backs and 20 of great black-backs. Such dominance can of course only occur in colonies at or near the centre of the geographical distribution in summer; thus on the edge of its distribution, in the Faeroe Islands, the herring-gull is a rare, shy and unaggressive species (Lockley, 1938).

In the arctic the ivory-gull, *Pagophila eburnea*, is known as the ice-partridge or snow-bird, living as it does constantly in the vicinity of snow or ice, where its pure cream-white plumage matches its surroundings. It constructs a well-insulated nest of moss about 18 to 24 inches across and raised 6 to 9 inches above the ground; but on cliffs a less elaborate structure may be built of more variable materials. The nests may be begun on snow- or ice-covered ledges. Two eggs are usually laid. The new-born chick is covered with a white down, which later becomes pearl grey; both colours are adaptively protective, the first matching

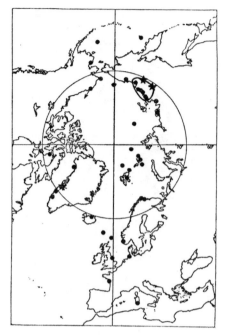

FIG. 41

Distribution of the rosy, or Ross's gull, *Rhodostethia rosea*. Black line embraces breeding distribution; known breeding-places marked by stars. (Greenland once only.) Dots represent some sight and specimen records.

the late spring snow and the latter the grey summer tundra. Clarke (1898) states that mortality may be heavy among the young ivory-gulls, many having been found dead in the nest, "their crania indented" from some avian attack (not improbably the ivory adults themselves? But see note on terns attacking gulls, p. 232).

The ivory-gull is about the size of the common gull, but much more bold and aggressive. It must be one of the hardiest gulls in the world, since its southern boundaries of breeding distribution are more northerly than those of any other bird (extreme north Greenland, east and north Spitsbergen, Franz Josef Land, probably Lonely and Bennett Islands, and in the Canadian arctic archipelago on Prince Patrick, Melville, north Baffin, and Ellesmere Islands; see Fig. 40). Under the circumstances it is not surprising that its habits have not been more than spasmodically studied. Even in winter the ivory-gull only reaches regions where other arctic birds summer—round the mainland shores of the Polar Basin.

The beautiful Ross's or rosy gull, *Rhodostethia rosea*, with pale grey mantle and rose-flushed white head and breast, and neat necklace of black is one of the most mysterious birds of the world. For long the breeding-quarters of this species were unknown; as the *Handbook* says, "very few ornithologists have seen this gull alive." It is therefore worth giving the details of its strange distribution.

The rosy gull was first discovered for science in June 1823 at Alagnak on the east side of Melville Peninsula in the central Canadian Arctic by W. E. Parry's second expedition in search of a north-west passage. It was named (almost inadvertently) *Larus roseus* by William Mac-Gillivray in 1824 on one of the two specimens brought back by the expedition, and *Larus Rossii* by J. Richardson in 1832 (Swainson and Richardson, 1832). Richardson named it after James Clark Ross, who was one of Parry's lieutenants and who found it. MacGillivray gave it the English name of Ross's rosy gull, Richardson the cuneate-tailed gull. Moreover J. C. Ross, once more with that prince of polar explorers, Parry, was the first to find it in its real autumn and winter home, the sea-ice of the Polar Basin; he saw it north of Spitsbergen on the astonishing attempt to reach the Pole across the pack in July 1827.

Fifty years later Ross's gull was still only a legend in most parts of the world and less than a dozen specimens existed. Nobody had seen a flock, nobody (even at that time in Greenland) had seen or heard of a nest. It is possible to imagine the interest, then, when the American explorers in G. W. DeLong's *Jeannette* (imprisoned in the ice on 6 September 1879 and slowly drifting from the neighbourhood of Wrangel Island to that of the northernmost New Siberian Islands) met largish numbers of these very rare gulls over the east Siberian pack-ice. R. L. Newcomb, the naturalist, shot eight of them in October 1879. When the ill-fated ship foundered on 12-13 June 1881 not far from Henrietta Island, the expedition salved its collections and journeyed in the ship's boats across the ice and 'leads' via Bennett Island through the main New Siberian Islands across the Laptev Sea to the Siberian mainland at the Lena Delta. DeLong and many others died on the way; and all suffered terribly: but Newcomb kept three of his precious skins of Ross's gulls under his shirt during the long journey.

Between 3 and 8 August 1894, almost exactly between the Lena Delta and the Pole, Nansen shot eight rosy gulls from the *Fram*, more than ten months frozen in the pack. After Nansen had left the *Fram*, and when he was (without at the time knowing it) about thirty miles north-east of Hvidtenland, the north-eastern group of the Franz Josef Archipelago, he and his companion Johansen began to see single adult rosy gulls on 11 July 1895, and continued to do so until they passed beyond this particular group on 8 August; sometimes the birds were in small flocks. They saw no more after that, as they travelled west and south through Franz Josef Land; indeed F. G. Jackson who by chance (!) encountered them, and gave them hospitality for the winter of 1896-97 in his camp in the south of the archipelago (at Cape Flora on Northbrook Island), only saw one in the whole of his three years stay—an adult on 5 July 1897.

After Nansen had parted from the *Fram* its crew saw rosy gulls in the pack several times between 18 July and 11 August 1895. The furthest north record was at 84°41 N. So by the end of the century, then, it was clear that the species inhabited the pack north of Spitsbergen and Franz Josef Land. Further contemporary evidence of this came tragically to light in 1930, when the last diaries of S. A. Andrée (who attempted the Pole by balloon)were discovered with his body on White Island, off the east of North-East Land, between it and Franz Josef Land. The log of the last struggles of Andrée and his two companions over the pack from their wrecked balloon two hundred miles to the northward contains at least fifteen and probably seventeen records of rosy gulls, seen between 25 July and 30 August 1897, from 190 to 120 miles north of White Island.

The secret of the breeding place was uncovered in the summer of 1905, when S. A. Buturlin collected thirty-eight skins and thirty-six eggs of *Rhodostethia rosea* in the delta of the Kolyma River, which flows into the Polar Basin in eastern Siberia, east of the delta of the Lena River. He established that the mysterious rosy gull nested, *not* on the tundra, but in low marshy places, among alder-scrub, in the subalpine and wooded zones of the lower reaches of the rivers Alazeya, Indigirka and Kolyma, sometimes nearly a hundred miles south of the tree-line, and that it probably also nested westwards from this district to Swjatoi Nos, the promontory of Siberia opposite the New Siberian Islands. Buturlin's description (1906) of the rosy gulls nesting in the boggy moorland of this lonely country is a most vivid document, and well depicts the unexpected habitat of this extraordinary bird, which it shares with Hornemann's redpoll and the snow-bunting, the white-tailed eagle, the willow-grouse, the vega herring-gull and the arctic tern, the pectoral sandpiper, curlew-sandpiper, dunlin, grey and red-necked phalaropes, snipe, Asiatic golden plover, grey plover, ruff, the long-tailed duck, the white-front, the thick-billed bean-goose, and Bewick's swan, amongst others.

Perhaps this huge area of the Siberian wastes is the sole reservoir of the rosy gull, which appears so promptly each September in the Eurasiatic arctic islands and on the Alaskan coast? If new breeding-grounds are still to be found, they are surely in other alder-scrub delta-floods of Siberian rivers, or perhaps (the possibility seems rather remote)

Plate XXVIIa. Immature Glaucous Gull

b. Immature Bonaparte's Gull

Plate XXVIIIa.   Little Gull, winter

F. P. J. Kooymans

b. Chicks of Yellow-legged Herring-Gull, *Larus argentatus atlantis*, Berlengas Island, Portugal

R. M. Lockley

in similar habitats in the Canadian north. The rosy gull breeds almost in a habitat suitable for Bonaparte's gull, yet does exactly the opposite in winter—goes *north* into what to a human is the most horrible area of the world, excepting the upland gale-swept below-zero ice of the antarctic continent.

John Murdoch (1885) found that Point Barrow, Alaska, was a main concentration point for rosy gulls between 28 September and 22 October 1881; he took "more . . . than there were before in all the museums of the world put together" and the birds were all moving north-east. He saw no more until the following 21 September, when they were again abundant. The neighbourhood of Barrow has remained an important flyway for rosy gulls; birds have been noted there in Septembers and Octobers ever since, always flying east. Charles D. Brower, who lived at Barrow until his death there in 1945, told A. M. Bailey (1948) that "a few are occasionally seen in the spring and they are irregular in the fall. However, thousands appear on gray days in September and October, always on a northwest wind. . . . They are excellent eating and often provide a welcome addition to our arctic fare. They come by thousands in the fall, and then suddenly disappear as quickly as they arrived, to be seen no more until the following year."

Sabine's gull, *Xema sabini*, is as strikingly beautiful as the rosy gull, having a rich dark grey hood edged with a fine black line, forked tail, black primaries, pale grey mantle, and white triangle on the wings. In flight both gulls are, like the other arctic gull, the ivory-, graceful and tern-like. Sabine's was first discovered on the northern shores of Baffin's Bay, on what are now known as the Sabine Islands in Melville Bay, north-west Greenland, by E. Sabine on John Ross's first expedition in 1818. (No ornithologist has visited these islands since.) The next example known to science was shot in Belfast Bay on 18 September 1822. Since then Sabine's gull has been found to be a rare (though not rare in the way the rosy gull is rare) bird, breeding fairly widely in the High Arctic, and wintering somewhat mysteriously on the Pacific coasts of North *and South* America, and on the North Atlantic coasts. By 'somewhat mysteriously' we mean that the main wintering-place of the Atlantic population is not properly known, though it may well be largely in the Gulf of Gascony (in the Bay of Biscay). The main wintering-place of the Pacific population appears to be off the coast of Peru! Whether the Bay of Biscay really is a wintering-place remains to be proved; if it is, the birds seem to start their return passage early, before Christmas (as many petrels do), and nobody knows

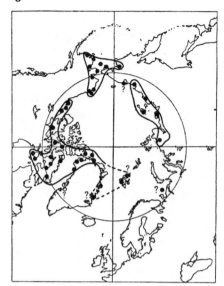

FIG 42

a (Left) Breeding distribution of Sabine's gull, *Xema sabini.* In east Greenland and Spitsbergen it is sporadic

b (Below) Breeding distribution of the kittiwake, *Rissa tridactyla;* black line encloses usual breeding range and black dots represent some known stations. Asterisks mark the three known breeding-stations of *R. brevirostris,* the red-legged kittiwake.

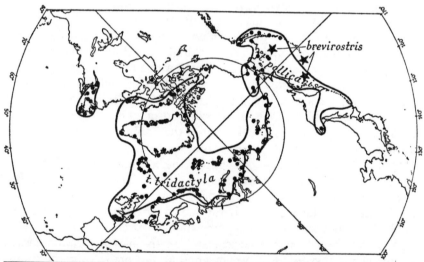

*In the nineteen-forties the following breeding-places were occupied (though not all in every year):

Scillies (Menavaur and Gorregan), Mainland Cornwall (Carn-les-Boel, Tolpedn, Morvah, St. Agnes), Lundy, South Devon (Berry Head, Hopes Nose, Scabbacombe), Cumberland (St. Bee's Head), Northumberland (Farnes, Dunstanburgh, North Shields), Durham (Marsden), Yorkshire (Flamborough, Speeton, Filey, Bridlington). In 1946 a pair laid eggs on a seaweed nest-drum on flat sand among a group of Sandwich terns on Scolt Head, Norfolk.

where this passage takes place. Perhaps it is far at sea. Sabine's gull, like most high arctic breeders, nests late, and the few seen on spring passage have been mostly near their breeding-grounds in May and June. (In California the Pacific spring passage has not been observed before 7 April, and most birds have passed in late April and May—Grinnell and Miller, 1944). A. C. Bent (1921) gives no egg-date earlier than 28 May, and most in late June and early July. What happens to Sabine's gull between November and May?

The romance of the discovery and the distribution of the rosy and Sabine's gulls has led us a little astray in this chapter on the life histories of the gulls; but owing to the inaccessibility of their homes in the arctic we know more about the first than the latter aspect of their lives. We must now go on to discuss another species, also arctic, but much better known.

The kittiwake, *Rissa tridactyla*, is the most oceanic of all the gulls, if we except the ivory- and rosy gulls which range widely over the pack of the Arctic Ocean. But the kittiwake is a bird of the full Atlantic, and indeed operates over a wider area of the North Atlantic than any other sea-bird which breeds in it; for it goes a full ten degrees south of the normal range of the fulmar. It breeds almost as far north as the land goes; it is a pan-arctic breeder with penetrations into the temperate zone. In the Old World it breeds on very many arctic islands north of the Siberian coast, including most of the New Siberian Islands, Svernaya Zemlya, Novaya Zemlya and Waigatz, though not apparently Kolguev. As far as we can detect, it nests nowhere on the actual *mainland* between the eastern Chukchi Peninsula of Siberian Asia and the Murman coast. From the Murman coast along the Norwegian coast it nests on many steep cliffs islands south (until recently) as far as Rundø, on the corner of Norway between Ålesund and Stat. It is a common breeder in Franz Josef Land, breeding on Rudolf Island, the northernmost, and on many others; in Spitsbergen it nests in thousands on many coastal cliffs, and it is extremely abundant on Jan Mayen and round Iceland. However, its only known colonies in East Greenland north of Angmagssalik are in Rafle Island at the entrance to Scoresby Sound and high in the north, Mallemukfjællet in Kronprins Christians Land. It is vastly abundant in the Faeroes and in the northern and western isles of Britain, and common on many cliffs of Ireland, and some of Wales and the Isle of Man. In England it breeds in a limited number of stations—so few that they can be enumerated.* *(footnote on facing page)*

In the Channel Islands it was not known to nest until 1938, when Roderick Dobson found a small colony on Sark. The first colony in France was established on Tas de Pois in Brittany in about 1914, and there are now colonies in that province also at Toulinguet, Douarnenez, Préhel and Rouzic.

The kittiwake has a purely arctic distribution in the Atlantic New World, apart from an isolated outpost breeding group in Newfoundland and the Gulf of St. Lawrence whose colonies are on the same rocks as the gannet colonies of the New World, and a few others. There is a separated subspecies in the North Pacific (see fig. 42, above).

From its habit of building its nest upon a very narrow ledge or foothold of rock on the side of a steep cliff, the kittiwake has little room to perform the more spacious ceremonies of the larger gulls, but much of the display is related to those expressions of the emotions in gulls already described. The kittiwake's note is shriller, yet softer and more pleasing to the human ear. It is, of course, traditionally rendered as "kitt-i-wake," and on the whole this must suffice, since it is extremely difficult to give satisfactory phonetic renderings of the cries of birds, at least on paper. Fortunately they have been captured for us extensively today by sound-recording specialists.

Kittiwakes arrive at the breeding cliffs in pairs in late February and March (or April and May in arctic latitudes). They frequent the older nesting niches which become plastered with fresh droppings before the new nests are built. Often the last year's nest has been swept away by the heavy winter seas. But on the old site the paired birds stand close together, breasts inwards and touching the cliff face and each other. Frequently they break out into their mewing cries, which seem to have a contagious quality, and may spread rapidly through a colony until there is almost an uproar. Then suddenly all is silent for a short space, and the wash of the sea on the rocks below is loud by contrast. Small and dove-like, the kittiwake is attractive to watch as each pair is roused to affectionate exchanges; these consist of delightful movements, a graceful bowing, dipping, lifting, and waving of the head to the accompaniment of the excited mewing notes. The mouth is opened quite wide to show the orange-red interior, and the bill is used in fondling motions. At a later stage the male will place one foot upon the back or neck of the female, pawing her gently until she submits; he then climbs into position upon her back, but may rest there for a few moments before actual coition. During this time the female turns her head up towards his

Allan D. Cruickshank from National Audubon Society

Plate XXIXa. Laughing Gulls

b. Black-headed Gulls at nest

Eric Hosking

Plate XXXa (above). Gulls are above all scavengers. Here is **a** crowd of young and old birds (chiefly Herring-Gulls and Lesser Black-backs) rushing to take offal at the fish wharf, Milford Haven *(R. M. Lockley).* *b (below left)* Sabine's Gull, winter (Holland) *(F. P. J. Kooymans).* *c (below right)* Black-headed Gull in winter plumage, Thames Estuary *(R. M. Lockley)*

solicitously. She also adopts the typical begging-for-food position, described for the other gulls.

Gulls build nests from materials near at hand: of seaweed, grass, maritime plants, heather, lichen, etc. Bonaparte's gull (*Larus philadelphia*), and occasionally the black-headed gull, nest in trees. The great black-backed gull will decorate its nest with the remains of the carcases of its victims: shearwaters, puffins and auks. The black-headed gull uses rushes, sedges and small sticks; but individuals may make little or no nest, laying their eggs in a scrape in the ground. Kittiwakes form collecting parties, like gannets, and tear grass and herbage from the sides of cliffs; they cement the nest together in its precarious situation by much treading with the feet, and they have been observed to carry mud-like material in their bills. Both sexes assist in nest construction; the male of the black-headed gull takes the initiative, doing much of the construction with material supplied by the female, but in some species the amount of nest building by each sex has not been fully ascertained owing to the difficulty of identifying the sexes in the field.

The eggs of gulls are usually three in a clutch, and vary considerably in the shade of the brown, olive or greenish-blue ground colour, but all are spotted or blotched with darker brown or black. Although this colouring is protective and renders them inconspicuous at a distance, this advantage is somewhat lost by the conspicuous appearance of the head (white or dark brown) and white breast of the sitting adult; and also by the fact that when a large breeding colony of gulls is disturbed by man or other large mammal, the occupants rise in a screaming mass overhead, advertising the position and extent of the colony. This action does, however, divert attention from individual nests which are then partly protected by the drab camouflage colour of the eggs or chicks. However, as we have seen, unless disturbed by human beings or other formidable enemies, one or other of the pair remains at the nest, once the eggs are laid; and incubation may or may not begin with the laying of the first egg. There is an interval, among the larger gulls, of at least one day between the laying of each egg. Incubation is by both sexes, but apparently the female takes the greater share. As will be seen in the following table, the period varies between twenty and twenty-eight days.

There is often severe loss of eggs and chicks occasioned through egg-collecting (for food) by humans, and raiding by dogs, foxes, otters, stoats, etc. Individual gulls, members of the colony, indulge

R

Incubation Periods of Gulls and Skuas

	MAX. WING-LENGTH	CLUTCH	INCUBATION
SABINE'S, *Xema sabini*	280 m.m.	3	23-26 days
BLACK-HEADED, *Larus ridibundus*	315	3	20-24
LONG-TAILED SKUA, *Stercorarius longicaudus*	320	2	23
KITTIWAKE, *Rissa tridactyla*	325	2	21-24
ARCTIC SKUA, *Stercorarius parasiticus*	328	2	24-28
COMMON, *Larus canus*	371	3	22-25
GREAT SKUA, *Catharacta skua*	415	2	28-30
LESSER BLACK-BACK, *Larus fuscus*	435	3	26-27
HERRING-, *Larus argentatus*	450	3	25-27
GLAUCOUS, *Larus hyperboreus*	490	3	27-28
GREAT BLACK-BACK, *Larus marinus*	510	3	27

in cannibalism, by seizing and carrying off, or devouring at the nest, eggs and chicks left temporarily exposed by the absence of the owners or by the intrusion of visitors. In gannetries, great and lesser black-back and herring-gulls pounce on unguarded gannet eggs and small chicks; in gull colonies the same gulls seize and devour the eggs and chicks of their own as well as other species. When the eggs are lost from any of these causes the female will lay a second clutch after 11-12 days, provided the first clutch has not been long incubated. In colonies where regular egg-collecting takes place for human food (e.g. in black-headed, herring- and lesser black-backed gull colonies in the British Isles) fresh eggs are collected up to the beginning of July. If the eggs are taken as soon as laid the female gull is capable of protracted laying (Paludan, 1951), and egg-collectors assert that she will lay up to fifteen if each egg is collected during the twenty-four hours after laying; but that the nest-site may be changed during this long laying period. Many thousands of gulls' eggs, particularly those of the black-headed species, are collected and sent to large consumer centres, notably London, where they are more often than not sold as seasonal delicacies, and until recently were passed off as "plover eggs."

So long as one egg of the original clutch remains the female gull is content to continue incubation. Experiments have shown that a gull will brood almost any object which is only approximately the same size and shape as its own egg although some individuals are more discerning than others (see Kirkman 1937, pp. 82-99). Large gulleries in fact have been convenient grounds for several kinds of experiments. Kirkman moved the eggs from a black-headed gull's

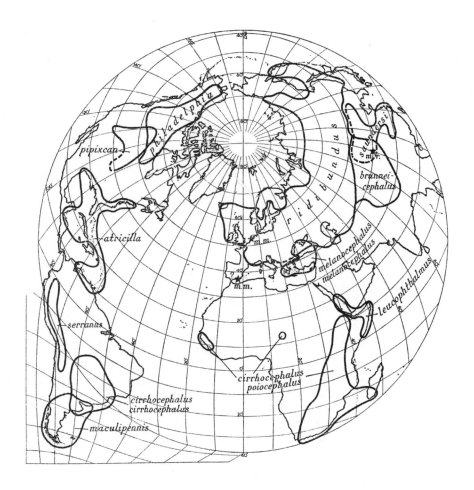

FIG. 43

Breeding distribution of some dark-headed gulls: *Larus pipixcan*, Franklin's gull; Bonaparte's gull, *L. philadelphia*; Mediterranean black-headed gull, *L. melanocephalus* (*m.m.* = *melanocephalus melanocephalus*; *m.r.* = *melanocephalus relictus*); Brown-headed gull, *L. brunneicephalus*; Saunders's gull, *L. saundersi*; White-eyed gull, *L. leucophthalmus*; Grey-headed gull, *L. cirrhocephalus*; Brown-hooded gull, *L. maculipennis*; Andean gull, *L. serranus*; Laughing gull, *L. atricilla*.

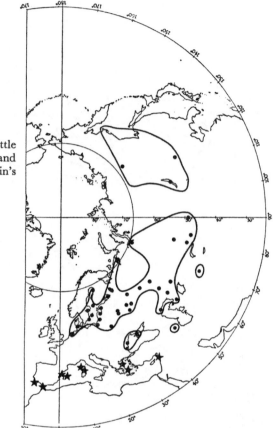

FIG. 44
Breeding distribution of the little
gull, *Larus minutus* (black line and
dots), and of *L. audouinii*, Audouin's
gull (stars)

nest over distances of, 3, 4, 6 and 10 feet away. One bird sat on the
eggs after each removal, and its mate sat on the empty nest. Some
gulls were found by Kirkman to roll their own and other eggs back
into the nest from a distance of 9-12 inches from the centre of the nest;
this was a useful function when a gull's own eggs were retrieved, but
became useless when the gull collected all the eggs placed within
rolling reach (a distance varying between twelve and eighteen inches).
The perception or intelligence of the birds in these experiments varied
considerably. Paludan found that gulls rejected foreign eggs placed
in an empty nest up to nine days before the laying of their own eggs.
But from nine days before that event they accepted foreign eggs and

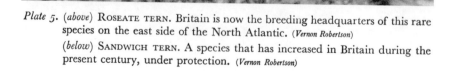

Plate 5. (*above*) ROSEATE TERN. Britain is now the breeding headquarters of this rare species on the east side of the North Atlantic. (*Vernon Robertson*)

(*below*) SANDWICH TERN. A species that has increased in Britain during the present century, under protection. (*Vernon Robertson*)

incubated them, and in some instances did not lay any eggs of their own. A skua will not recognise its own egg if this is placed outside the nest, but will devour it.

Gulls are born with their eyes open, and are covered with a thick down. They are able to walk almost immediately. When danger threatens the *Larus* chick will leave the nest when it is only two days old and, at the alarm cry of the adults, will try to hide in some nearby crevice, or crouch under a tuft of herbage. At the age of five to six days and upwards it runs freely, and often in its haste to escape an enemy it will walk right over the edge of a cliff. This is a frequent cause of mortality when human beings walk about in gulleries. If the chicks drop from a great height they may be killed, but falling from lesser heights they may bounce unhurt from the rocks and boulders below; if these are sufficiently shelving and tiered, they may be able gradually to climb back to the nesting site, by hooking themselves along with beak, legs and their unfeathered wings, encouraged by the calls of their parents —always provided they are not intercepted by some predator. In normal undisturbed conditions, however, the young *Larus* gull remains on or near the nest for a month to six weeks.

The diet of the large *Larus* adults changes to one of small crabs, shrimps and fish when the young are first hatched. These are fed by both parents; at first the female has begged the male for food with which she has fed both herself and the chicks. The male brings in a crop loaded with food, and on the begging of his mate he regurgitates this in front of her. Frequently both adults and chicks will then proceed to devour the salivated mass, the adults picking up and holding the food in the bill so that the chicks can feed more easily. As the chicks grow larger and stronger they themselves beg for food insistently, stretching up to tap the bill or peck the face of the parent newly arrived with a full crop. They show a definite reaction to bright objects by pecking. N. Tinbergen has proved that the red spot on the bill of the adult is a signal (releaser) to the young that food is ready. The occurrence of red on the bills of gulls and terns thus has a special significance; but other fish-eating species such as cormorants and gannets have no brightly coloured bill spot, although the young bird invites feeding by a similar tapping or pecking action. Young kittiwakes, like young gannets, grope into the parental gullet for the regurgitated fish.

The manners of the young *Larus* gulls become more and more unruly, and they soon learn to snatch at the food before it has been fully ejected and they quarrel among themselves for the best bits. The first hatched chick, being usually twenty-four hours or so older than the second, may sustain throughout the fledging period a physical dominance due to its ability to secure the lion's share. Where food is plentiful, however, the three chicks may eventually level up in growth and become indistinguishable from each other, but more often than not, one, and sometimes two, of the younger ones, disappear during the fledging period (this occurs in other species, e.g. the black guillemot). They have been underfed as a result of the greed of the first chick, and have become progressively weaker and less able to resist the bullying of the first-born. They die, or are eaten by their own kind, even by their parents who later may feed the partly digested carcase to the survivors.

It is remarkable that in a large colony of gulls the number of chicks successfully fledged is probably, on the average, much less than one young bird to each pair of breeding adults. Where losses have not been suffered as a result of depredations by man and other animals earlier in the breeding season, and young chicks have hatched in fair numbers, great losses may occur as a result of adults preying upon the chicks of their neighbours. Probably the amount of cannibalism in any colony will depend on the abundance of normal fish-food. Kirkman found that young black-headed gull chicks which wander from home are sometimes adopted by chickless adults, but more often are killed by adults with chicks of their own. There is strong evidence that once a very young chick wanders from the nest it may not survive; even when it returns home it may be killed and eaten by its own parents. An example of this type of unreasoning cannibalism may occur when a nestling wanders away among burrows or nests of a species which is normally preyed upon by its parents. Moreau (1923) saw a herring-gull go to its own chick, which had strolled away among puffin burrows, and kill it with great ferocity. We have seen herring-gulls and lesser-black-backs attack chicks of their own species which were wandering among the nests of neighbours, and great black-backs killing and devouring new-born and up to half-grown chicks of the two smaller species. Such chicks are ruthlessly grabbed and battered to death. If small, a chick is swallowed whole, if well grown it is beaten until the bones are broken and the body is more or less shapeless; then it is gulped down in one mass, though often with difficulty. As a rule, after a heavy meal of this sort, the gull will rest for a while, looking very uncomfortable, and at first with the neck much swollen. The bulky mass passes slowly into the crop. An hour or so later it may be thrown up in front of the brother or sister of the murdered chick, which, however, cannot tackle such a gargantuan feast. The adult then usually re-devours the horrid mess. It may be that the cannibal throws up the meal less with a desire to feed its young, than to relieve its crop; but if so, having relieved its crop, it is immediately hungry again and, after a further battering, the pulpy remains of the chick are swallowed once more.

This cannibalism is prevalent among the great and lesser black-backed and herring-gulls, less so in the case of the black-headed gulls and the skuas, and apparently never occurs among kittiwakes.

Glaucous gulls encourage their young in the art of egg-sucking as soon as they are able to wander and explore, or even in the nest. The adult breaks a hole in the egg (generally of some arctic-nesting duck) and the chick leisurely helps itself. Later the fledged deserted gulls gather on the flat tracts along the tundra shore and feed on crow-berries (*Empetrum nigrum*), eating great quantities in default of other food.

The picture of the sociable *Larus* gulls during the summer is hardly a pleasing one; they are shown, by human standards, to be disgusting and cannibalistic. The greatest mortality during the year must occur during the breeding season. That the powerful dominant gull lays two or three eggs each year in order to maintain its numbers, while some weaker species which the gulls prey upon, such as certain auks and petrels, lay only one egg, is the more comprehensible if we regard cannibalism as an effective controlling factor in the population of larger gulleries.

By comparison with the *Larus* gulls the kittiwake is as inoffensive in character as it is charming in appearance. It is true that at the nesting site it is noisy and a little quarrelsome, but this behaviour seems childlike and playful by contrast with the savage habits of the larger gulls. Probably the kittiwake has less opportunity to interfere with its neighbours, since each nest is usually isolated from the next, that is to say it is seldom connected by a bridge of rock over which it is possible for trespassers to walk. Contact between neighbouring nests can only be made by flying, and there is very little serious inter-ference by wandering or unattached birds. The kittiwake never preys upon the eggs of its own kind or of that of any other bird; it lives almost exclusively on small fish, crustaceans, plankton and molluscs taken upon or near the surface of the sea. But it often loses a large proportion of its eggs and chicks to predators. Keighley & Lockley (1947), observing ten nests from 4 July to 14 August in Pembrokeshire, found that only two chicks eventually flew, the remaining fourteen eggs or chicks having been taken, one by one, by *Larus* gulls.

In northern waters where its feeding grounds are close at hand, the kittiwake will occasionally nest on the ledges of buildings overlooking the sea. It frequently builds well inside caves, and, in the Arctic, on precipices some distance inland. A most unusual site is recorded by Salomonsen (1941c) on Tyrholm in the bird sanctuary of Hirsholmene in the Kattegat. In a colony of 2,902 pairs of black-headed gulls, 437 pairs of Sandwich terns, 6 of black guillemot and 3 of common gull, were 11 pairs of kittiwakes, which had placed their nests on the ground, among boulders or in lyme-grass clumps, an interesting abnormality. It was found that the chicks in these kittiwake nests made no attempt to run from them on the approach of human intruders, as *Larus* chicks do. The adults also remained at the nest, showing the typical cliff-nesting fearlessness. There is also a dune record for Britain (p. 238).

The fledging-periods of most gulls are difficult to assess accurately since *Larus* chicks may wander from the nest for considerable distances before they become independent of the adults; and the adults themselves become less territorially minded at this stage, moving the "defended" area around the growing bird as the young bird itself moves, and gradually losing interest in the chick and its safekeeping. The age at which the young gull is able to fly for the first time may be reasonably considered its fledging period. But of this period surprisingly little appears to be known with certainty. The following figures therefore are estimates only:

Estimated fledging-periods of Gulls and Skuas
(mostly from *Handbook*)

BLACK-HEADED GULL	(O. Heinroth)	about	40 days
COMMON GULL	do.	,,	30
HERRING-GULL	do.	,,	42
BRITISH LESSER BLACK-BACK	(R. H. Brown)	,,	32
GREAT BLACK-BACK	(O. Heinroth)	,,	50
KITTIWAKE	(F. C. R. Jourdain)	,,	35
GREAT SKUA	(W. E. Glegg)	,,	42-49
ARCTIC SKUA	(W. E. Glegg)	,,	28-35
LONG-TAILED SKUA	(A. Pedersen)	,,	21

The great disparity between these figures cannot be due entirely to specific variations—there must be faulty estimating. This is indicated when we compare the above estimate for the kittiwake by Jourdain with two accurate records of the fledging period of this species: 44 and 45 days (Keighley and Lockley, 1947). There is plenty of room for more exact observation.

Literature dealing with the period between the time when the gull chicks are fledged and their dispersal to winter quarters is scanty. At Skokholm, Lockley (1947) found that the adult great black-backs, the lesser black-backs and the herring-gulls gradually left the island in August, September and October, and a small number of the fully fledged young gulls appeared to leave at the same time. But many of these juveniles were left behind, and there were periods when the island held about one hundred juveniles and few or no adults. In calm weather these juveniles managed to get a living by wandering about the island picking food from the surface of the land, including food obtained from the carcases of dead puffins, shearwaters and rabbits, and along the tide-line. But in stormy weather, which was frequent in autumn, many of the young gulls whose powers of flight seemed feeble, would remain in a loose flock in the centre of the island, mewing a great deal as if hungry, but unwilling to fly in search of food. It was found that many of these birds were thin and generally in very poor condition; and if the weather continued rough some of them died or grew so feeble that they could easily be run down and caught in the open.

Comparative figures from other gulleries reveal that an extremely small proportion of chicks is raised each season, due to egg-stealing, cannibalism, and other factors, including rough weather at fledging time. Paludan (1951) records only 20% chicks fledged in herring-gulls and 5% in lesser black-backs on an island near Bornholm in the Baltic. The possibility of disease attacking young gulls in crowded colonies should also be borne in mind; it may have been the cause of the enfeeblement of so many of the young gulls at Skokholm, where, in August 1947, three juvenile herring-gulls died after a few days of sickness. Examination of the corpses revealed that all three had blistered feet, a characteristic feature of an epizootic which has caused the death of many juvenile Manx shearwaters in the autumn on Skomer and Skokholm (Surrey-Dane, 1948).

It is doubtful if juvenile gulls remain attached to the adults for long in the autumn. They do, however, frequently follow adults, calling querulously for food, and an adult which happens to have its crop full of food may respond to the persistent begging of a juvenile, not necessarily its own child. The young gulls, like many other juvenile sea-birds, drift away from the breeding ground on their migration route, independent of the adults. The lesser black-backs travel farthest —as far south as the Iberian peninsula and North Africa. Many of these migrants remain in waters about the southern limit of their winter range until full adult plumage is acquired during their fourth year. They may be seen about the harbours of Portugal and the Bay of Biscay. Few return to their breeding grounds with incomplete adult plumage. But the juveniles of glaucous, great black-backs and herring-gulls do not travel far from their breeding coasts, although there is a general local southward trend; the majority remain within a few hundred miles of their birth-place. The adults are even more sedentary than the juveniles. During adolescence gulls of sedentary species will frequent harbours and estuaries the whole year round, but a few of the older ones, whose plumage is nearly mature, may visit in summer those breeding grounds which lie within easy flight of these feeding grounds.

The complete moult takes place in autumn, and a second moult, of the body feathers only, occurs early in the spring, when the streaky winter appearance of the adult head and neck is replaced by pure white, or, in the brown-headed species, by the typical dark hood. The smaller gulls, e.g. the black-headed, common and kittiwake species, acquire the mature plumage after their second winter, one or two years in advance of the large *Larus* gulls.

CHAPTER 12

TERNS AND SKIMMERS

THE FORTY-TWO SPECIES in the subfamily Larinae, or gulls, are fundamentally northerly in their present distribution, and probable evolutionary origin. The thirty-nine species in the other big subfamily of the Laridae, the Sterninae or terns, are fundamentally tropical, and there are more (thirty) species in the Pacific than in any other comparable region of the world. However, there are a good number in the Atlantic—twenty-three, or twenty-five if we include the Mediterranean with it, and it is certainly not possible to conclude from the relative number of species that the Pacific is the evolutionary home of terns; but it is likely that the adaptive radiation and evolution of the terns has mainly taken place in the tropics. No less than nineteen species breed on or near the shores of the smallest of the warm oceans, the Indian Ocean. Seventeen species breed round the borders of the North Atlantic. The breeding-distribution of only two species, the arctic tern *Sterna paradisaea* and the common tern *S. hirundo*, crosses the Arctic Circle—that of the latter only in one small region. However, four species breed in the cool climate of the cold waters of the Antarctic Ocean. Many terns are birds of rivers or inland marshes— nine species breed inland in Eurasia, six in North America, five in the Indian region, and several inland in Africa, Australia and South America. Some, like the black-bellied tern *Sterna melanogaster* of India, Burma and Ceylon, or the common river-tern *S. aurantia*, which has a rather wider distribution in the same region, or the yellow-billed tern *S. superciliaris* of S. America, are exclusively, or almost exclusively inland species. Others, on the other hand, like the noddy and fairy terns (*Procelsterna*, *Anoüs* and *Gygis*) and the sooty tern *Sterna fuscata* have very wide and very oceanic distributions, and many other *Sterna* terns work into the pelagic and oceanic zones of the world's seas.

The majority of terns are white with, in spring, a black crown and a grey back; a minority are darker, especially the less marine species.

The terns, like the gulls, may be divided conveniently into these two categories: one containing the strictly marine species, nesting largely on sand, shingle or rock, and chiefly white, with grey back and black crown; and the other containing those species, some of them black or black-winged, and black-backed, which nest on salt- or fresh-water marshes. The latter in the North Atlantic region include the gull-billed tern *Gelochelidon nilotica*, Caspian tern *Hydroprogne caspia*, Forster's tern *Sterna forsteri*, black tern *Chlidonias nigra*, whiskered tern *C. hybrida*, and white-winged black tern *C. leucopterus*.

Terns are gull-like in their habits, but their longer wings and long, usually forked, tails, give them a distinctive appearance. Their flight is more buoyant and graceful. Because the wings appear to pass through a greater arc in their slow measured beating, the flight may not seem so effortless, and it is also less gliding than that of the gulls. The general impression is of a light hovering progress, and the synonym "sea-swallow," often applied to the tern, is only appropriate in as far as the long wings and tail of the tern resemble those of the swallow.

Terns were formerly killed for the millinery trade, but are now protected in English-speaking countries. As already described in chapter 3, p. 84 the little tern was taken in "incredible numbers" and almost exterminated along the eastern U.S. coast by collectors for this trade, in Audubon's time. From about 1800, for nearly a hundred years, the feathers of this tern and many other species of birds, including the roseate tern, were in demand, wings and whole skins being used to decorate women's hats.

All terns are considerable migrants, the arctic tern (see p. 142) greatest of all, breeding as far north as there is land in the Arctic, and migrating as far south as there is open water in the Antarctic; in both polar seas arctic terns may fish among pack-ice, and rest on ice-floes head to wind, especially in their antarctic winter quarters (Falla, 1937). Thus, although they are called arctic terns, these birds enjoy more hours of daylight (eight summer months in the year) than the tropical species, by wintering in the southern summer. The majority of terns arrive at their breeding ground later than the gulls. The vanguard appear in March in the British Isles, with main arrivals in April and May; but they may be a month or six weeks later in the High Arctic. Like gulls, they roost at first away from the actual nesting site, only settling down to sleep in the breeding ground a few days before the eggs are laid. As the sexes are superficially alike it has not yet been established whether the single birds which are sometimes seen

Plate 6a. Little tern on eggs—a sand-and-shingle-bank nester. *(John Markham)*
b. Black tern on eggs—a marsh-land nester. *(Eric Hosking)*

to arrive first are males; but sometimes it is a pair that is first seen, or a flock.

In general, terns are extremely capricious, nervous, and sociable; these characteristics are shown in erratic movements, and in sudden changing of a breeding site. A colony may be apparently fully occupied, and often nests built up to the middle of May; then the majority of the flock may suddenly leave the site and settle on a new one, perhaps several miles away. In that case the few which have started to breed may forsake their nests and eggs in order to join the main colony, rather than continue in isolation. They are most successful as breeders only when able to nest in large numbers close together. Like other species of sea-birds terns seem to require this stimulation of numbers. It is for this reason, it is suggested, that they will settle down in an already advanced breeding colony of gulls or related species, causing considerable disturbance and even driving away the original gull colonists by their aggressive behaviour (see p. 232). But A. O. Gross (1951) states that herring-gulls drive out terns (Massachusetts); and Palmer (1941) observes that "when a gull species nests in great numbers close to a tern colony, the terns usually go elsewhere eventually." Sandwich terns were found by Salomonsen to dominate black-headed gulls, and royal terns are known to boss black skimmers. Among marsh-terns, the black tern is bold and domineering inland in North America (Bent). Other terns live socially in harmony: as sooty and bridled terns; and common, arctic and roseate terns. This harmony is generally due to differing ecological requirements. Austin (1929) points out a possible ecological relationship in a mixed ternery: the roseate tern has comparatively long legs, adapted for walking about and nesting in fairly long grass; the common tern with shorter legs prefers barer ground to walk upon; the arctic tern with very short legs hardly walks at all and nests as a rule on vegetationless ground. (In the Faeroes, however, the arctic tern, with no competition from other species, nests freely in low annual vegetation and grass.) Social stimulation and its significance in the reproductive cycle of sea-birds has been discussed in chapter 7.

Salomonsen (1943) found that large colonies of common terns start laying and hatching earlier than smaller ones; but he found that "the difference is only slight"—which might reasonably be expected of terns, with their habit of arriving late, simultaneously, and ready to breed.

The breeding habits of terns have been intensively studied by

Watson (1908), Tinbergen (1931), G. & A. Marples (1934), Palmer (1941), and others. The Marples observed that "a tendency for the birds to fly in pairs while on migration rather points to a permanent union;" and these indications of permanent matings are recorded by other observers, including Palmer. Terns may however often be seen travelling singly, and the migrating flock does not appear to consist of paired birds; it may be that these records of two, four, six, etc, terns in flight are only coincidental signs of normal sociability, out of the breeding season.

The fish and crustacean food of terns is secured either by diving, or by snatching without actually wetting the plumage as the bird skims over the water. Terns can swim, but do not do so very much— or very well; and if confined in a glass-sided water tank without a resting place will drown. When hunting for food the tern quarters the surface, its head down and beak vertical, like the fishing gannet. In diving it drops like a stone, wings closing as it descends; but it makes much less splash than the gannet, being smaller, and also usually diving from a lesser height. Terns are skilful fishers, pausing in mid-air and hovering until sure of a successful strike. Some species submerge partly or completely (royal, Sandwich, common, roseate, arctic, Caspian, and little terns); other species (black, whiskered, white-winged black, gull-billed, sooty, bridled and noddy terns, and black skimmer) do not dive, or dive but rarely. Noddy terns catch minnows as these jump clear of the surface of the sea. Skimmers, feeding at night, are even more specialised; they plough the surface with the long lower mandible, and by so doing they attract small fish to the moving phosphorescent water. The skimmer then turns back and, flying over the disturbed area, snatches and scoops up the shrimps and small fish which are attracted to the glistening track. Some terns, including the skimmer, occasionally wade in shallow water in search of food.

The captured fish or shrimps, etc., may be swallowed immediately, as the diving tern rises, and, with a shivering motion of the wings, shakes the drops of water from its plumage; or larger fish may be held in the bill for the lengthy display ceremony described below, or may be carried to mate or chicks. In the majority of cases the fish is carried hanging down on the left side of the bill, although there appears to be no ready explanation of this custom. Fish-carrying is sometimes disadvantageous, as when skuas are about, which force terns to drop their catches.

The marsh-terns feed mainly on aquatic insects, such as beetles, flies, dragon-flies, spiders, etc., as well as tadpoles and small fish. They will hawk for insects over the land, like swallows. The sea-terns catch insects, beetles, etc., on the wing, especially in cold windy weather when marine food is difficult to obtain. Forster's tern, a bird of the northern marshes of the New World, arrives on the newly unfrozen grounds in time to feed on the numerous dead fish, insects and amphibia released on the melting of the winter ice.

The visitor to the sea-ternery in the early summer will immediately note the typical "fish-flight." One bird, which may be the male or the female, flies circling about the colony with a fish in its beak, calling loudly with the characteristic grating tern cry which is not unlike the sound produced by a wooden stick drawn rapidly over serrated metal. The other bird usually flies in front of its partner carrying the fish. The foremost bird flies with its neck stretched out; the bird with the fish has its head bent down. The pair may settle and the fish may be exchanged, the bird receiving the fish immediately flying up and performing the same actions, preceded by its partner leading the way with outstretched neck or one flier may be joined by another and suddenly both will rise steeply into the sky, and presently make a long glide to earth.

A tern carrying fish almost invariably screams with excitement, and it seems as if the fish in the bill is an essential part of the emotional display used by terns. Tinbergen considers that the male may carry the fish in flight over the ternery when he is seeking a mate. Many variations in the "fish-flight" occur. Sometimes strange birds pursue the bird with the fish, and make ineffectual attempts to snatch it. Other chases occur without fish. There is also a curious gliding flight and a circling high over the colony, with darting downward rushes at great speed. The abnormally slow, lazy, deliberate beating of the wings ("butterfly flight"), recorded of other sea-birds (e.g. the auks), is not uncommon, and appears to have a social as well as a sexual significance: Palmer (1941) considers that it results from an attempt to carry out normal display in the air; it is often concluded by a delaying of the folding of the wings on alighting near another tern.

The pre-courtship of terns at the nest-site follows the pattern of the gulls and many other birds. The overall sexual bond has attracted the female towards a male in possession of a scrape in the ground; but in order to keep this territory and win a mate he must peck at and assert his dominance over all comers. Palmer considers that the unmated tern can only discover the sex of another tern by testing its reactions: if it submits to pecking it is female; if it fights it is a male. The female, desiring to occupy a scrape, soon submits. After this "ground recognition test," the two birds are mated for the season, and recognise each other at some distance. But the dominance of the male is kept up throughout the nesting season (Palmer). If an intruder is a male the owner of the scrape must drive the visitor away, or risk losing the territory. Even the arrival of the partner at the nest immediately sets up this ceremony, or a modified form of it. The bird at home is excited by the appearance of another from out of the sky—excited and at first probably suspicious, in spite of visual or vocal recognition—and so some form of greeting ceremony is performed before all is quiet between the pair. These formalities are instinctive, usually beginning with threat display which is then changed to the opposite—invitatory or sexual movements, which serve as outlets for the thwarted fighting instinct. These nest-visit ceremonies happen, of course, in many other organisms; in some birds, such as the herons, they are quite elaborate and prolonged before the arriving bird is able to relieve the bird in possession.

Males, presumably unattached, sometimes visit occupied nests and, encountering opposition, fight quite fiercely; and eggs may be broken or rolled out of a nest as a result. In courtship the male noddy invites the female, by nodding his head (hence perhaps the name), to take the fish from his bill. This is characteristic of the sea-terns. The female may accept and then return it to her mate; or, more rarely, eat it. The pair may walk side by side in what the Marples call "the parade." This is not unlike the action of the farmyard cock soliciting the hen, and it has the same stimulatory function of promoting hormonic activity and so releasing sexual desire. The cock pivots round the hen, who pivots to face the performer. But the aggressive pecking is over: as sexual excitement increases the head and tail are raised at a sharp angle, the head being lowered again in a bowing movement, displaying the hackles of the handsome nuptial cap. Coition is initiated by the female crouching with her head down. The cock may stand on the hen's back for some time, perhaps to be interrupted by a neighbouring bird who has likewise been stimulated by these attitudes.

Nests are made rapidly and simply, by scraping in the sand or shingle, or by adopting a depression in the rocks. In the sand the bird falls forward on its breast and scratches backwards with its feet,

C. A. Gibson-Hill

Plate XXXIa. Common Gulls, summer plumage

b. Eggs of Gull-billed Tern

F. P. J. Kooymans

Plate XXXII. Royal Terns in flight over nesting colony, Cape Romaine, South Carolina, U.S.A.

(Roger T. Peterson)

pirouetting in a perfect circle. If there is no nesting material handy, within a few yards, a nest may not be lined at all. The Marples made interesting experiments in which they proved that the lining of the nest (with a variety of material) depends entirely upon what is available in the immediate environment. Birds which were incubating eggs in shallow scrapes in the sand, with no nest lining whatsoever, at once built a substantial rampart around the eggs when material (scraps of jetsam) was placed within a few feet of the scrape. They also proved that terns have a very precise sense of geographical position. When the Marples buried the nest so that the site could not be distinguished from a wide environment of smoothed-over sand, the owner of the nest alighted above the hidden eggs, quickly dug down, discovered the eggs, and brooded them after scratching them clear of sand. Nor were terns deceived by extraneous alterations to the environment of the nest, even when the nest was again buried in sand. Other experiments showed that when a nest was moved fifteen feet away from high tide, the owner found it, in its new position, after only a little hesitation. Terns would also follow their nests for a considerable distance if they were moved a few feet at a time. When the eggs of terns were painted in various bright colours (terns accepted eggs painted bright yellow, but were somewhat put off when the eggs were painted bright red or blue), or their shape altered by the addition of plasticine, the owner would peck at the eggs as if to test their genuineness, after which it would settle to brood as if nothing had happened. In these experiments the terns showed themselves more perceptive and tolerant than gulls. This perception is perhaps understandable in a species nesting so close to the edge of the sea: high tides may flood the nesting area at times, or at least change the superficial environment, by depositing seaweed and jetsam, or by altering the contours of pebbles and sand; and so an ability to deal with these hazards is important for the tern's survival. The ability to defend the nest against shifting sand on windy days is probably instinctive. When storms blow the brooding bird will constantly scratch accumulating sand away from the nest, or will protect the young chick by nursing it carefully, so long as the sand is on the move.

Incubation is by both sexes, but the female is believed to take the larger share. With most species, incubation begins with the first egg. There are generally three, sometimes two, and less often four eggs laid at intervals of about forty-eight hours. Nests have been recorded with up to ten eggs, but the Marples have shown that where nests

s

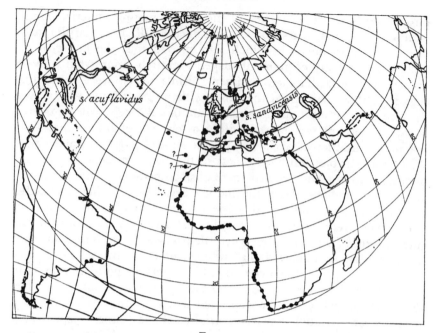

FIG. 45
Distribution of the Sandwich (Cabot's) tern, *Thalasseus sandvicensis*. Black
lines embrace breeding range; black dots are some sight or specimen
records.

are placed (artificially) too close together, a dominant female on one
nest will rob a neighbouring nest by rolling the eggs from it into her
own; but she is unable successfully to hatch more than the normal
clutch against her brooding patch. Coition, which takes place on the
nest, continues after egg-laying, but it slows down, and the male
may rest for longer periods on the back of the female and finally step
down without actual consummation. He appears to be an anxious
and fussy husband, displaying vigorously as he brings fish to feed his
sitting mate; but she also feeds him when he takes his turn on the
nest. As in other sea-birds mutual display continues, in lessening
degree, during the incubation and fledging periods.

The eggs are much like those of the gulls, with ground-colour
varying from pale grey to a dark brown, streaked and spotted with
still darker greys and browns. Blue eggs, with or without markings,
occur, but the erythristic type is not common. The incubation period

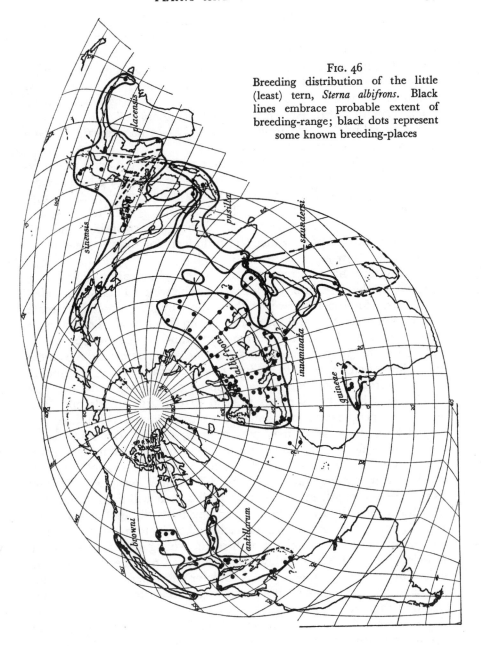

Fig. 46
Breeding distribution of the little (least) tern, *Sterna albifrons*. Black lines embrace probable extent of breeding-range; black dots represent some known breeding-places

seems to vary considerably, with a minimum of 21 days. The new-born chick is covered with a long soft down with fine hair-like tips, and is protectively coloured: the background of the down is some shade of buff, marked and streaked with patterns of black and brown. Terns will lay a second clutch if the first one is lost, or abandoned by a shift of the whole colony, and a third if a second is freshly taken. Black terns in North America lay three clutches (of 3, 1, 1) if con-tinuously robbed. Little terns in South California are said to raise two broods in a season.

The Marples record that the greatest anxiety of the adult at hatch-ing time is to remove the egg-shell as soon as the young bird is free, and to carry the shell off and drop it at a distance; they argue that the female does this instinctively, but by so doing she "removes, one after the other, the evidence of the birth of her offspring, and this was presumably to protect them from danger, for the presence of the shells would draw attention to the nests."

Young terns have a peculiar shrill chittering, squealing or whistling note, which they use until they are well on the wing. They are brooded in the nest for the first two or three days by the female, the male feeding both his mate and his chicks during this period. Both parents feed the chicks subsequently, bringing in sand-eels—among the princi-pal food of the Atlantic sea-terns. When one parent is feeding the chicks the other often appears to mount guard, driving away neighbours which approach too near. When handing over a fish to its mate or chick, the adult always places it head first in the other's bill. It is never dropped, except occasionally, on the ground. If it does fall to the ground the adult may pick it up again, but the chick seems incapable of doing this, and many fish will be found lying about on the ground in a ternery, with the young terns, oblivious of this food at their feet, calling hungrily to be fed. Young terns will swallow fish of greater length than their own bodies, and will gulp uncomfort-ably for a long time with the tail hanging from the mouth while the head is being digested in the stomach. The old tern thrusts the fish only sufficiently far into the mouth of the young tern for the throat muscles to grip it. On hot days the adult may provide shade for the chicks by partly opening its wings, but for short periods. Chicks not provided with shade have been known to die from heat upon sand (Austin, 1932b).

In some cold stormy summers there is great mortality among young terns, due to lack of food and to the dangers from drifting sand

Plate XXXIIIa. Little Tern, Holland

b. Black Tern, autumn plumage

Plate XXXIVa. Common Terns mating

b. Caspian Tern, Hat Island, Lake Michigan, U.S.A.

and wind which may blow the chicks about or bury them when they are in a weak condition. Sudden violent thunderstorms with torrential rain may kill many. In America snakes and owls prey upon chicks, and elsewhere foxes and rats are predators.

Under normal conditions, however, the chicks grow rapidly, and begin to fly when they are about a month old. When they are undisturbed by trespassing man and mammals, the chicks remain close to the nesting site. But if disturbed they are apt to gather into dense flocks which wander or are driven about the ternery, causing great anxiety to the crowd of adults flying above them. It is a matter of wonder to the observer that the chicks ever sort themselves out and are claimed again by their parents. It may well be that, as with the penguin and the guillemot, the lost tern chick is able successfully to beg food from other adults than its parents, but this has not been actually proved. Most observers agree that there is voice recognition between the adults and their own young at an early stage in the rearing period.

Incubation and Fledging Periods of Terns

	Incubation	Fledging
BLACK TERN, *Chlidonias nigra*	14-17 days	21-28 days
GULL-BILLED, *Gelochelidon nilotica* ..	22-23	28-35
CASPIAN, *Hydroprogne caspia*	20-22	28-35
SANDWICH, *Thalasseus sandvicensis* ..	21-24	35
ROSEATE, *Sterna dougallii*	23-25	28
COMMON, *Sterna hirundo*	22-26	28
ARCTIC, *Sterna paradisaea*	21-22	21-28
LITTLE, *Sterna albifrons*	19-22	28
SOOTY, *Sterna fuscata*	26	30-35

(From the *Handbook of British Birds,* with corrections)

The marsh-terns have not been so thoroughly studied. As far as we know their breeding habits do not differ very substantially from those of the sea-terns. The small marsh-terns (e.g. the black, white-winged black and the whiskered terns) frequently build their nests on floating heaps of water-weeds, but more often among rough herbage in marshy ground. Apparently the incubation periods in the smaller marsh-terns are shorter than in the sea-terns.

In Britain the black tern has had an unfortunate history, for since the year 1885 it has been probably quite extinct as a breeding species, except for an interlude in 1941-42. It is an example of the effect man can have on a species by altering its habitat. Formerly it nested mainly, if not solely, in the fenlands draining to the Wash, in the Norfolk and Suffolk broads, and in Romney Marsh in Kent. From all of these places (fig 48, p. 265) it appears to have been driven by drainage and reclamation.

Its reappearance as a breeding-species in Britain was discovered by R. Cooke (1946) at Pett Level near Winchelsea in Sussex, on an area of a thousand acres that was submerged as part of the invasion defences. On 10 June 1941 he found eight occupied nests on an island formed by a collection of stranded débris. In 1942 five pairs returned to the island, and young were safely hatched; but in 1943 only seven individuals arrived, were much disturbed by black-headed gulls, and did not nest, and in 1944 the area was once more drained. Since then no black tern has laid in Britain, though it would seem that the broads and coastal marshes of Norfolk and Suffolk, now most thoroughly administered as sanctuaries and for the preservation of marshland habitats, are ready once more to provide the species with a home.

The sooty, noddy and bridled terns are more oceanic in their habits, breeding on remote islands and reefs, and fishing far out at sea. According to G. H. Wilkins (1923) sooties may feed as far as 200 miles from their breeding place. Their pelagic habit has caused differences in the routine of the breeding season; thus the incubation period is shared in much longer shifts, according to Watson (1908): each noddy tern sits for twenty-four hours, changing over at night; and the incubating bird is fed by its mate. The clutch is normally only one egg.

The black skimmer (*Rynchops nigra*) is a black-backed red-footed tern with specialised crepuscular feeding habits already described. Rather clumsy and stupid at their breeding grounds, skimmers may be persecuted by the nimble and powerful royal terns in search of desirable nesting territory. The royal terns scratch for themselves a home in the heart of the black skimmer colony, covering the skimmers' eggs with sand or vigorously kicking them aside while the helpless owners look on. Young skimmers are able to half-bury themselves in sand by wriggling and scratching a hollow with a few vigorous leg-movements. They show a "marked instinct of recognising parents' raucous cries" (Bent, 1921). The peculiar long lower mandible is not fully developed until the chick is able to fly.

The nervousness of terns and their high excitability, higher than that of the sociable gulls which are also subject to mass "alarms and silences" (e.g. black-headed, lesser black-backed and kittiwake gulls), is expressed in what the Marples call "dreads" and "panics." These are distinct from the ordinary alarm when the sitting bird leaves the nest, flies into the air for a short time, calling loudly, and then returns quickly to the nest. "Dreads" and "panics" are characterised in all the sociable terns at their nesting grounds by a sudden rise in the normal clamour of the breeding group. It is succeeded by the whole colony rising and sweeping away in a compact flock in complete silence, only to return in a short time and resume their normal behaviour. The movement appears to be so regimented that the observer could believe that a command had been simultaneously obeyed. Although dreads and panics apparently occur as a result of the visit of a human being to the ternery, they have frequently been witnessed from a long-established hide; therefore they cannot be considered solely due to human agency—often they appear to be caused by no external disturbance whatsoever.

Tinbergen attributes the dread to a temporary re-assertion of the flocking instinct, as against the dominant reproductive instinct. Sometimes a flock will rise and hover over the body of a dead or wounded companion; and perhaps afterwards attack it for awhile. Sometimes only part of the ternery is affected by a dread. Sometimes it is a flock of one species only that rises from a large ternery, thus revealing the position of that specific colony. It appears that there may be one individual which constantly starts and leads a dread. The panic is a variation of the dread, according to the Marples, who give this name to the sudden dashing about in the air of a group of terns which afterwards zig-zag rapidly to earth or water in complete silence, immediately flying back to the colony as noisily as usual. Of the sea-terns only the little tern appears to take no part in a dread; this may be due to its less colonial nesting habit.

The apparently co-ordinated mass flights of terns are never directed to the expulsion of a common enemy, such as man or another creature trespassing in the territory of a ternery. But like the skuas and some of the larger gulls, the individual tern will attack any trespasser passing its nest. The ensuing fight with another bird may embroil several other neighbours. Also like the gull, but with much greater accuracy, the individual tern will defaecate upon the visitor, fouling his clothes or person; and some species are extremely bold, freely striking the intruder on the head (arctic and common terns). The noddy attacks human beings quite savagely; this and other species will knock a

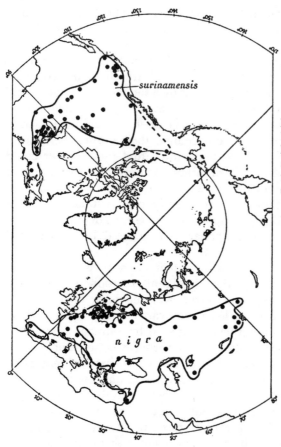

FIG. 47
Breeding distribution of the
black tern, *Chlidonias nigra*.
Black lines embrace prob-
able extent of breeding-
range; black dots represent
some known breeding places

hat off, and draw blood with the sharp pointed bill. Sometimes
two or more join forces, hurling themselves repeatedly at an enemy,
screaming and striking. Yet this behaviour is not always successful:
skunks ignore it and kill terns freely. Short-eared owls will pounce
on and carry off both adult and young terns. But dogs, rabbits, rats,
sheep, lambs and other birds are effectively driven away.

Gulls especially seem to draw the anger of terns and are successfully
driven away from tern eggs and chicks. The common tern has been
known to kill young ring-billed gulls, driving them to the water and
stabbing their heads—the old gulls offering no resistance. Herons,
which if permitted would no doubt do a great deal of damage by
devouring chicks, are violently attacked and driven away.

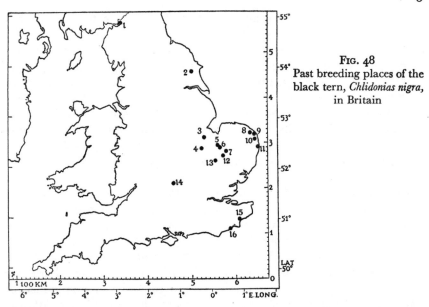

FIG. 48
Past breeding places of the black tern, *Chlidonias nigra*, in Britain

1 Solway Flow, ? 1855. 2 Streams near Driffield, 'not for some years' by 1844. 3 Crowland Wash, 1832. 4 Whittlesey Mere, 1843, ? 1844. 5 Poppylotts, Southery, early XIX century. 6 Fentwell, 1853 (flood). 7 Brandon, ? early XIX C. 8 Sutton 1858. 9 Horsey-Winterton, 1816, 1818, extinct before 1838. 10 Upton, 1818. 11 Oulton Broad, ? 1875. 12 Mildenhall, ? early XIX C. 13 Bottisham, 1824. 14 Ot Moor, ? *c.* 1857. 15 Romney Marsh *c.* 1787, 1824, *c.* 1884. 16 Pett Level, 1941, 1942, failed 1943

The relations between the fledged chick and its parents seem not to have been studied adequately. According to Palmer (1941) the chick remains attached to its parents and is fed by them at the start of the southward migration, which begins in August. The Marples remark that the "young ones which have been hatched early, set off with their parents for their winter quarters as soon as they can fly properly." According to the Marples the first autumn migration begins at the end of June in the British Isles, only a month after late-arriving adults (birds born in the previous year?) appear in the colony— birds which may or may not have time to breed. In a successful summer terneries may be quite deserted by the beginning of August in temperate latitudes. In the far north arctic terns do not arrive until mid-June, and they leave before the end of August.

Ringing has shown that some young terns will return to nests in the colonies where they were born, but others move to more distant terneries. Palmer (1941b) states that the common tern takes usually three years to reach breeding age. We have mentioned the complete removal of some terneries to a new site in an apparently whimsical fashion. It has been suggested that persecution by man is less important as a factor influencing the change of breeding ground than shortage of food supply, and that colonies suddenly reappear and breed in abandoned, or take up, sites, when the fishing happens to be good in that district. But these statements are very difficult to substantiate.

The annual moult takes place from July to December; it is of necessity gradual, since it is during the moult that terns perform their great migrations to the south. They do not, however, necessarily move south immediately after the breeding season. Ringing has proved that many individuals wander in the opposite direction. Juvenile Sandwich terns may fly for distances up to 350 miles northwards from their breeding quarters. This is the time of year when terns are widespread along the North Atlantic seaboard, appearing on shores far from breeding grounds, especially where there is an abundance of small fish. The arctic tern ranges the whole width of the North Atlantic during July, August and September (Rankin & Duffey, 1948). Its wanderings (see Fig. 23, p. 142) are astounding: it makes a round trip during the year of some 22,000 miles, or, during actual migration, about 150 miles per day in a straight line—if we make the generous allowance of 20 weeks for the period of both migrations. The main northward migration is believed to be speedy and relatively brief, consistent with the mass arrivals at breeding grounds. The autumn migration, as we have indicated, is leisurely and drawn out.

Early in the spring there is a second complete moult, when the adult tern acquires its full breeding plumage. In their first summer (a year old) young sea-terns generally lack the full black hood, but may breed in this plumage (skins of breeding birds in this plumage are in the British Museum), although probably the majority do not, but instead wander northwards more slowly than mature birds, and, as the Marples point out, arrive at the breeding ground too late to do more than familiarise themselves with the site. Lockley (1942, p. 214) found non-breeding common terns roosting on the Desertas, Madeira, in mid-July; this would be near the southern limit of their breeding range in the Atlantic. The marsh-terns migrate within a shorter range of latitude, seldom flying farther south than the tropics in winter.

CHAPTER 13

THE AUKS

IN THE COURSE of evolution many sea-birds, and groups of sea-birds, have independently become adapted to under-water pursuit. Three groups in particular, the penguins, diving-petrels and auks use their wings as the primary organs of propulsion under the surface. Different as the auks are in appearance from the gulls and waders, the structure of their palate and other anatomical considerations show conclusively that they are closely related to them: this is supported by palaeontological evidence, though the order Laro-Limicolae split into ancestors of the three present families Charadriidae (waders), Laridae (skuas, gulls, terns and skimmers) and Alcidae (auks) as early as the Eocene. The auk that most closely parallels the penguins, the quite flightless razorbill *Alca impennis*, the great auk, became extinct on 4 June 1844 (see p. 65). Twenty-one species of the family Alcidae survive; some people assign them to thirteen genera, though systematists more interested in points of similarity than points of difference, more interested in fundamental rather than easily-modifiable characters, could probably cut them down to a more realistic nine or ten; and might reasonably also take the number of species down to eighteen or nineteen by reducing some to sub-species.

There seems to be no doubt that the main evolution and adaptive radiation of the auks has taken place in or not far from the Bering Sea. Sixteen of the twenty-one surviving species breed in the northern part of the North Pacific, twelve in the Arctic Ocean, and only five in the northern part of the North Atlantic. These five are *Alca torda*, the razorbill; *Uria lomvia*, Brünnich's guillemot; *Uria aalge*, the guillemot; *Cepphus grylle*, the tystie or black guillemot; and *Fratercula arctica*, the puffin. All these breed also in the Arctic Ocean, and two of them (the guillemots) also in the North Pacific; moreover the tystie and puffin have replacement-species (which in the case of the tystie is considered here to be of only subspecies level) in the North Pacific. The razorbill alone has no Pacific representative; and its extinct relative the great auk (which though placed now in *Pinguinus* should be restored to *Alca*) had only a North Atlantic distribution. Besides the five mentioned, the little auk, *Plautus alle*, breeds only on the Atlantic side of the arctic, and operates in winter only from the edge of the Atlantic pack-ice to a varying distance in the open Atlantic Ocean and North Sea. It fills an ecological niche in the North Atlantic, similar to that occupied by the five auklets* in the North Pacific.

So we have six living auks to consider in our study of North Atlantic birds. The somewhat sombre history of the extinct one has already been enlarged upon in our discussion (p. 64) of the impact of man upon the sea-birds. The great auk was a large bird of penguin-like habits and appearance, standing about two feet high. Newton (1861) gives the following notes from descriptions by Icelanders who had seen the great auk alive: "They swam with their heads much lifted up, but their necks drawn in; they never tried to flap along the water, but dived as soon as alarmed. On the rocks they sat more upright than either the guillemots or razorbills, and their station was further removed from the sea. They were easily frightened by noise, but not by what they saw. . . . They have never been known to defend their eggs, but would bite fiercely if they had the chance when caught. They walk or run with little short steps, and go straight like a man." We would also quote Martin (1698) again: "It comes without regard to any wind, appears the first of May, and goes away about the middle of June" at St. Kilda. As already pointed out (p. 70), this may have been quite accurate, since it is just possible that the great auk could have completed the terrestrial period in seven weeks, allowing about 40 days for incubation, and nine days for the chick on the land (compare these periods in the razorbill, described below).

The great auk bred in colonies. It was easily driven into a cul-de-sac. As a result slaughter in a wholesale manner took place at its remote breeding grounds, fishermen and seal-hunters seeking the bird and salting numbers of them down for consumption at sea later. The great auk laid one egg, coloured and marked like that of the razor-bill, and brooded it between the legs, having only one brood-spot (Faber, 1826). Little else is known about its breeding habits, which

Ptychoramphus aleuticus, Cassin's auklet; *Aethia psittacula*, the paroquet a. ; *A. cristatella*, the crested a. ; *A. pusilla*, the least a.; *A. pygmaea*, the whiskered a. We follow R. W. Storer (1945) in regarding the 'rhinoceros auklet,' *Cerorhinca monocerata*, as a puffin.

Plate XXXVIa. Black Skimmer and chick, Oak Island Beach, Long Island, U.S.A.

b. Gull-billed Tern family

probably corresponded closely with that of the other member of the genus *Alca*, the razorbill.

Auks fly in a straight line with a somewhat bee-like whirring of the wings. The rapid beating of the wings gives the impression of speed and power, but this is illusory, and auks may be seen to make little progress against a strong wind, and are easily outdistanced by the gulls, whose wings beat in a leisurely fashion. The short narrow wings of the auks make the take-off from the level surface of the land or the sea difficult in calm weather. Their whole structure is better adapted for flying under the water; the wings, being then half-open with the primaries more or less closed, form in this position powerful paddles or oars, and the bird moves rapidly through the water. The feet are used in steering movements, turning both in air and water; but not as a means of propulsion under water, except when the bird is moving slowly or "marking time" in its search for fish, or when first diving down from, or coming up to, the surface.

The lives of many sea-birds are spent in three distinct ecological zones or habitats, which are shared harmoniously or competitively with other species: the feeding and wintering area of the open sea, the collecting or loitering ground (Johnson, 1941) near the breeding site, and the breeding or nesting site itself. The auks, feeding much on the same foods, share the first of these areas between themselves without coming into serious conflict. There are differences in feeding habits and in food taken, as we shall presently show; all auks are divers and live by capturing their food principally within twenty fathoms of the surface of the sea. Razorbills, guillemots, little auks and puffins frequently gather in huge dense rafts on the sea below the breeding grounds; this is the second functional area, the loitering or assembly place. The third area, the breeding ground, however, is split up between the species, each occupying its special part, or ecological niche, of the available nesting sites. Competition for territory here is principally between individuals of the same species, less often between individuals of related species.

The guillemots are the most social of the auks, forming densely packed "loomeries" of thousands of individuals standing or squatting less than a body's length apart; and, in spite of the vocal uproar and gesticulatory movements, territorial pugnacity (seen in other social species, such as the gannet and the gull) seems to be submerged in the general necessity for mutal tolerance. If guillemots were really pugnacious, each pair demanding the same amount of nesting room (one body's

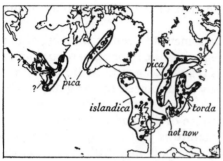

FIG. 49

Breeding distribution of the razorbill, *Alca torda*. Black lines embrace probable extent of breeding-range; black dots represent some breeding-places; there are many others in Britain and Eire

length, plus striking range of the bill) as the gannet, they would not be able to breed successfully in their familiar dense colonies on narrow ledges. They manage to do so often tolerating less than one body's width between sitting birds, although unmated birds do not usually stand together with their wings or "shoulders" actually touching. The first massing of the guillemots on certain favourite cliffs and the tops of isolated stacks takes place in England, Wales and Ireland in December, and, in Scotland and farther north, in January. In South Wales there is a belief among fishermen that the "eligugs" (guillemots) return "in time for Christmas." These early visits are few and irregular; they take place at dawn and last only for three or four hours. They may take place on two or three succeeding days, and almost always during fairly calm weather. In order to be successful the individual must early locate, claim and retain breeding territory—where a species is so congested in dense colonies that not a square foot of the coveted ground is unoccupied at the height of the breeding season. Nevertheless at many breeding sites, certain ledges (which may have been used by breeding guillemots in other years) which appear perfectly suited to the successful breeding of guillemots, may not be used at all, the colony continuing to crowd just as densely upon the occupied ledges; in this species slum conditions are a preferred habit rather than an absolute necessity. But crowded conditions may provide social stimulation which leads to more successful breeding (Darling, 1938). We have described how guillemots find this stimulation as well in contact with other sea-birds (p. 173): as when razorbills share the same ledges and where guillemots nest in the narrow "neutral" zones between the pedestal-nests of gannets (e.g. Grassholm, Alderney).

The razorbill, less colonial than the guillemot, returns later in spring. In large colonies it may come to land at the end of January in its southernmost breeding grounds, but main arrivals occur towards the end of February, and the paired birds do not settle finally upon the rocks until the beginning of April, or even, in the far north, a month later. Razorbills, too, migrate farther south than guillemots, which may be seen throughout the winter in home waters.

Puffins winter in deeper water farther at sea and are later in returning to the breeding ground, being seldom seen within sight of land, except casually, until the early part of March. At large colonies on the southern coasts of England, Wales and Ireland puffins settle on the water under their breeding cliffs with great regularity during the last week of March (in the north of Scotland and the Faeroes in mid-April). Yet although they are the last of the three common auks of Britain to arrive at their breeding grounds, puffins are the first of the auks to lay, and eggs may be found in the last fortnight of April, long before the main colony has settled permanently on land. This is some four weeks before egg-laying in the guillemot and the razorbill; and as we shall see in describing its breeding biology this early laying is probably connected with the much longer incubation and fledging periods of the puffin. Little auks return to the arctic land before it is free of winter and perform their courtship on ice in May and early June.

The three species of guillemots (the common, Brünnich's and the black) have been placed by many systematists in one genus; but the black guillemot, by its choice of habitat, more closely resembles the razorbill and the little auk; and it differs much from the other guillemots and the razorbills in having two eggs, a more markedly different winter plumage, and a different pelvic design. It lays its eggs (normally two) in a crevice under stones or boulders; in this well-protected site the young are comparatively safe, and do not leave the nest until they are fully grown and able to look after themselves. In this they resemble, not the razorbill, but the puffin. The majority of razorbills lay their eggs in more exposed situations where they are more subject to the depredations of gulls; only a minority nesting under stones or out of sight in holes.

We thus have an interesting ecological division of the rocky cliffs: the common and Brünnich's guillemots occupying the most exposed platforms and shelves, and the cliff-top, and rarely laying the egg under the protection of the talus; the razorbill, sometimes laying its egg upon ledges exposed to sun and wind, but usually nesting in more sheltered situations in the shadows of fissures and under boulders, and even well inside rabbit or puffin holes in the cliff; the black guillemot and the little auk with their eggs entirely shielded by the rock cover; and the puffin nesting in the safety and darkness of its burrow. It is even more interesting to find that of these living auks the common and the Brünnich's guillemots (like the extinct great auk) have a single large brood-spot between the thighs. The razorbill, the little auk and the puffin normally lay only one egg, yet, like the black guillemot (which lays two eggs), they carry two brood-spots. On the razorbill and the puffin the brood-spots are remarkably small and narrow, situated on each side of the body close to the wing and thigh. They are so reduced that only a comparatively small portion of the egg can be accommodated against the bare skin, the rest being covered by one wing which, being insulated by feathers, cannot, of course, provide the same amount of heat as the brood-spot.

The double brood-spot may be a relic of an earlier period in the evolution of these birds when two eggs were normally incubated. It might be argued that incubation of two large eggs within the narrow confines of an underground burrow, at least in the case of the puffin, would be inconvenient and therefore disadvantageous to the species. However, in the little auk this cannot apply; there is normally plenty of room in the little cavern under the rocks. The egg of the puffin is white, like that of most hole-nesters, but when held up to the light it exhibits a washed-out lilac or brown pattern, suggesting a protective colouring at an earlier stage of evolution, when presumably the species was an open-site breeder. It may well be that the puffin has become a hole-nester from an open-site breeder and that the razorbill is in a preliminary stage of evolution from the period when it brooded two protectively-coloured eggs in the open. Two eggs are sometimes, though rarely, brooded by both razorbill and puffin, but there is no record of their successful hatching. Further conjecture on this subject, however, does not seem called for in the present state of our knowledge. It must suffice here to point out that the razorbill incubates its egg under "one falling wing" not because the egg is so large (as has been suggested by one writer—an invalid reason: the guillemot is scarcely as large as the razorbill but it has a larger egg which it incubates between the thighs) but because of the situation of its brood-spots.

We have seen that territory-finding and claiming in the auks begins early in some species, later in others. The sexual bond brings the auk pair to the familiar nesting site in the spring. It has been stated that auks, on their arrival on the water below the cliffs, are already

Plate XXXVIIa. Razorbill chick, Wales (10 days old)

b. Common Guillemot chick, Wales (10 days old)

Plate XXXVIIIa. Black Guillemot, July (North Rona) *(Robert Atkinson)*

b. Little Auks, winter (Channel Islands) *(R. M. Lockley)*

paired, but there is little clear evidence of this. We do not know how early or where mate-recognition takes place, or how far the paired birds keep together after the breeding-season. It is only when a pair is completely isolated from the main colony, especially in the case of the more solitary black guillemot, that we can be sure that the mated pair associate regularly on the water near their home. There is strong circumstantial evidence that, in the larger colonies of common and black guillemots, razorbills and puffins, there is intermingling and some promiscuity between individuals on the water under the breeding-cliffs. Winn (1950) found the male black guillemot directed his attention to several females at first, but later concentrated on his mate. Similar behaviour may sometimes be seen in the puffin: the male has been seen guarding a female (presumed—from the smaller size of the head) from the attentions of other males, by swimming between her and other males, which he attacked "when the intruder was two or three body-lengths away from the female, and it seemed that as far as the male was concerned this area was part of the female and could be violated as if the intruder was actually touching her. The female was never seen to initiate attacks" (Conder, 1949). Male puffins have been watched by us pursuing one female after another, and the same male has been seen to "guard" a female for a short time before swimming after another female which finally allowed coition; it is not proved therefore that each pair seen together on the water in a large raft are necessarily mated and sharing the same burrow on land. However there is also definite mate-recognition on the water (Lockley, 1934), since occasionally a pair will rise in the air together out of the raft and fly to a single burrow in the cliffs. At the terrestrial nesting site mated puffins are faithful to each other, as we shall prove later in this chapter. We may compare this pre-egg-laying promiscuity with that of the cormorant, where it is the female which seeks occasional extra-marital coition; and with that of the Buller's mollymawk, where males adulterously attack and forcibly copulate with the females of mated pairs.

Although we have not been able to prove that mature auks, on arrival off the coast of the breeding cliffs, are already paired, it must be the case that a large proportion of the experienced breeders return to the same crevice or burrow or niche in the rocks where they nested a year ago, and there discover their mate, also of the previous year. A mated pair of auks can be watched flying close together, sometimes as far as the eye can follow them, from the moment they leave the edge

T

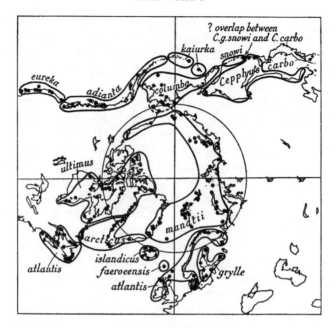

FIG. 50
Breeding distribution of the tystie or black guillemot, *Cepphus grylle* and its allies
and races. Apart from the black-winged guillemot, *Cepphus carbo,* the Pacific races
are considered to belong to *C. grylle,* though many American workers separate them
as the pigeon-guillemot, *C. columba.* Black lines embrace probable extent of
breeding range; black dots represent some known breeding-places.

of the cliffs; but often the pair separate soon after leaving the cliffs,
and one may alight on the sea while the other flies on.

When assembled in early spring on the water below the breeding
rocks and cliffs auks carry out mutual display, in the form of "water-
dances." Razorbills and guillemot pairs will swim around each other,
at the same time opening the mouth to display the coloured interior
and uttering guttural cries. The head is thrown back and upwards
with a jerky action, repeatedly. The other bird may show little interest
in this display, but usually keeps swimming so that it is face to face
with its partner: or both birds may display mutually, and a third or
fourth may join to form a circle of displaying birds. These water-
dances differ somewhat in each species. A party of razorbills or
of black guillemots will often form a line, sometimes two parallel
lines, swimming in this formation "line ahead" for short distances,

making almost a formal pattern on the water. But these lines last for a matter of seconds only and as excitement increases there is a convergence, which is broken up by the sudden submerging of the whole party, individuals frequently pursuing each other under water in an erratic and excited manner. They may afterwards disperse or come together in a fairly dense unit, and, after a pause of variable duration, resume the "line ahead" formation. Armstrong (1940) describes fully these water-dances of the black guillemot. Each bird appears very excited, frequently adopting an ecstatic posture with the tail cocked at right angles, the head from time to time thrown up parallel with the tail, the beak partly open to display the interior colouring of the mouth (chrome-yellow in the razorbill, vermilion in the black guillemot, flesh-yellow in the puffin and common guillemot). The puffin has no formal water-dance; but there is pursuit of the female by the male on the water, where coition takes place. In other auks mating takes place on the land; and there is more excitement on the crowded ledges of the guillemot loomery than on the water. Although common guillemots tend to join in the razorbill dances, their excitement on the water seems to find expression in mass dives or sudden skating over the surface, rather than in a stereotyped ceremony. Mass dives also occur when there is a convergence (of perhaps more than one species), with danger of collision. Such a concentration may be assisted by tide and wave action, forcing individuals so close that the boundaries of "individual distance" are violated; the observer notes the increasing alarm, expressed in the raising of heads and the rapid turning of the body this way and that, which ends in the simultaneous dive, and the escape and dispersal under water, relieving the pressure at the surface.

The huge painted bill of the puffin is used as an instrument of communication much more than are the bills of the other auks; for the puffin, by comparison with the noisy guillemots and the razorbill, is almost silent. The puffin's bill is thrust forward towards a neighbour, a mate, or a bird of the opposite sex at first in the threat position resembling the "forward display" of a fighting cock or a dog about to attack another. In this position (the bill slightly tilted groundwards) the brilliant colours, the eye-patches and the rictal rosette are most conspicuous. If the bird displayed at is male and stands his ground (or position in the water) he may be attacked and a short fight will ensue; if she is female, she may ignore the display, or move away. There is a tossing movement of the head, which is mutual, and is evidently an appeasing ceremony (possibly derived from actions when fishing under water), since it momentarily hides the conspicuous bill from a partner. The well-known bill-rubbing ceremony of the puffin is like the bill clashing of the gannet; it may have its origin in threat display. It is initiated as a rule by the male: approaching his partner in the threat attitude, he begins to quiver his head to and fro, thus signalising that his intention is not hostile (the bill remains stiff in hostile display). Elements of threat seem to remain in the violent pushing movements of the male as he shakes and presses his bill against one side of the female's, and she is sometimes pushed off her balance as a result. In a large assembly on land a bill-rubbing pair, or a pair fighting, at once attract neighbours, who crowd round, and, by joining in the ceremony, break it down; we have seen three puffins bill-rubbing together, with more trying to join in, or three or four in a fight—but always the action was broken off quickly, and the birds separated and moved their normal distance apart (Lockley, 1953). Puffins are intensely curious of all movements near them in the puffinry, and will toy with the snare or hook at the end of the fowler's rod as it slides over the ground towards them.

Bill-rubbing or pushing takes a milder form in the little auk (Foster *et al.*, 1951) and the razorbill (Paludan, 1947). Courting guillemots are so short of manoeuvring space on the crowded ledges that the pair may stand shoulder to shoulder in courtship, caressing each other in this position, bowing and groaning with heads sideways (Johnson, 1941). The holding of a fish in the bill of a guillemot early in the season Johnson considers to be part of the courtship ceremonial, and he records its retention for long periods—up to four hours. We may compare this with the fish flights of the terns (p. 255).

Armstrong (1940) considers that the brilliant red colour of the legs of the black guillemot may be functionally useful in the underwater chases which are "nuptial, connubial and recreational." As the tysties flutter along like large exotic water-butterflies just below the surface, they may be guided by the bright webs of the leaders. Certainly in this rotund species the feet are used as paddles more freely under the water than in other auks. But puffins, with vermilion-coloured legs and webs, are less given to this form of social behaviour than are the black-footed razorbills.

Black guillemots face each other, bowing and whistling until the female suddenly squats flat on the rock with her tail erect; the male mounts, paddling with the feet to maintain position while copulating. Razorbills and common guillemots mate, noisily groaning, at the

Plate 7. Razorbills sunning on the cliffs of Skokholm, Pembrokeshire

egg-laying site, and, like puffins copulating on the water, beat their wings to steady themselves as they rest far back on the back of the female. Little auks have a whining chatter, puffins a somewhat rare sighing double note, an inspiratory gasp, followed by an expiratory yawning note.

The puffin is the only Atlantic auk which is active in preparing a home. As it breeds under the ground it must and does dig efficiently, using its bill as a pickaxe and its webbed feet as shovels to fling the earth backwards—it will excavate a burrow even in soft sandstone, as at Skokholm. The other auks adopt ready-made sites. A razorbill may pluck and play with a piece of grass, but there is no attempt to use it for lining the bare spot in which the egg is laid. Some black guillemots will carry feathers, bones, shells, stalks and debris to the nesting crevice. Plucking, picking up, and toying with grass, seaweed, and feathers is a displacement activity. The puffin may transport these materials into its burrow and drop them in the nest at the far end. It may just as often drop them outside the burrow or in the passage, or even drop them before reaching the entrance. We have watched the puffin pluck furiously at a tuft of grass or herbage until it has accumulated an immense beak load, larger than its own head. This it has held in its bill for perhaps five or ten minutes, as if pleased and proud of its efforts. A puffin so burdened with material is an object of special curiosity to other puffins. They will approach, with their mincing steps, and even presume to snatch the material from the owner, who shows anxiety to avoid being robbed, and backs or runs away with it. A large feather is a much coveted object; its possession may be disputed in a tug-of-war, and it may pass from one to another of the assembled puffins before it is blown away or carried into a burrow. But in spite of this activity and play with nesting material little is finally deposited in the nest at the end of the burrow. Indeed the egg is often found with no nest lining around it.

The ringing of puffins by Lockley (1953) has shown that the male remains attached to the same female during the season (at least while on land), and takes a minor part in the incubation of the egg. As long as he is on land the male shares in all the activities, including that of spring-cleaning the burrow in April (or driving a new shaft where the old burrow has fallen in or become damaged during the winter). Puffins may excavate and clean out passages throughout the season; the tremendous burrowing capacity of a large colony may undermine the earthy slope of a whole cliff side, causing it to slide into the sea

FIG. 51

Breeding distribution of the puffin, *Fratercula
arctica,* and its Pacific counterpart the horned
puffin, *F. corniculata.* Black lines embrace
probable extent of breeding range; black dots
represent some known breeding-places

(North Rona, Darling,
1947), or render the site
so porous and flimsy
as to be untenable after
a few decades, as at
Grassholm (Lockley,
1938). The compara-
tive safety of the burrow
from predators enables
the puffin to leave the
egg or chick for long
periods with impunity.
It has been observed
that razorbills, nesting in
well-concealed crevices,
will also leave the egg
or chick alone, but for
a shorter period. The
habit is of further significance if we connect it
with the implications
of the double brood-
spot in these two birds:
if the puffin and the
razorbill formerly laid two eggs (as the double brood-spot suggests)
the present delay in beginning incubation of the single egg in these
species is explicable as the survival of a once useful habit (of com-
mencing incubation when the clutch was complete) which no longer
serves its original biological function. In this connection it is interesting to note that the black guillemot (with two brood-spots, near the
centre of the breast) itself may be following the same evolutionary
trend towards one egg. Frequently only one is laid, occasionally
three, but two is the normal clutch; but though two may be hatched
as a rule only one chick is reared (Armstrong, 1940). Mortality is
heavy: Winn found 73.8 per cent. loss of eggs and young in forty-six
nests. The brooding bird seems deliberately to incubate one egg only—
Winn found that "unwanted" eggs were pushed out of some nests,
even when he replaced them.

The common and Brünnich's guillemots, with the egg fully exposed
to attack from the air if it is uncovered, never voluntary leave the egg

(or the chick) alone; one or other of the pair (or of other adults of the colony?) remains with it. Thus it is protected from attack by gulls, skuas, etc.; but at the same time it is not safe from the risk of being stolen or pirated by neighbouring adult guillemots.

Puffins are essentially sociable birds. During the period when one or other of the pair is incubating it is out of sight of the main colony and is thus denied the stimulating visible presence of its fellows which the guillemot enjoys. As if to make up for this, at certain periods of the day, and especially on summer evenings, both male and female puffins abandon the egg for two or three hours at a stretch, and sit about and parade on the cliffs in a recreational assembly. The egg does not appear to suffer as a result of this temporary cooling. For the rest of the twenty-four hours it is probably much more steadily incubated than those in the restless colonies of the razorbill and guillemot. Observations on large colonies of these two species show that there is a constant interference in incubation by the shufflings and movements of the massed birds, the egg being frequently uncovered in the process.

The scene in the common guillemot colony is fascinating to watch. Gätke, in his book on Heligoland, describes the guillemots aptly as making an "endless obeisance" and the birds all talking volubly about nothing in particular. The larger colonies seem to bubble over with a non-stop excitement as a result of the perpetual bobbing and bowing and shaking of each head and of the mild squabbles of close neighbours and of the disturbances caused by each new arrival, who is greeted so boisterously. When alighting in a colony the guillemot announces its arrival with loud squawks, as if to warn those on the ledges to make room for it, and it is usually received with apparently aggressive cries. On the ledges progress is by means of a shuffling walk with the whole tarsus pressed on the ground at each pause, the body being held perpendicular. The razorbill walks in the same way. Sometimes, when flying down to the sea, the auk moves its wings at about half the usual speed, giving the appearance of slow motion or, as it has been called, "butterfly" flight; in the puffin this change in the usual mode of flight takes the form of a curious gliding with the wings held high and the wing-tips rapidly fluttering in a kind of "moth" flight.

The eggs of the guillemot, varying so much in colour, are large and pyriform; a design which minimises rolling but does not always save the egg from tumbling over the narrow ledge. Johnson (1941)

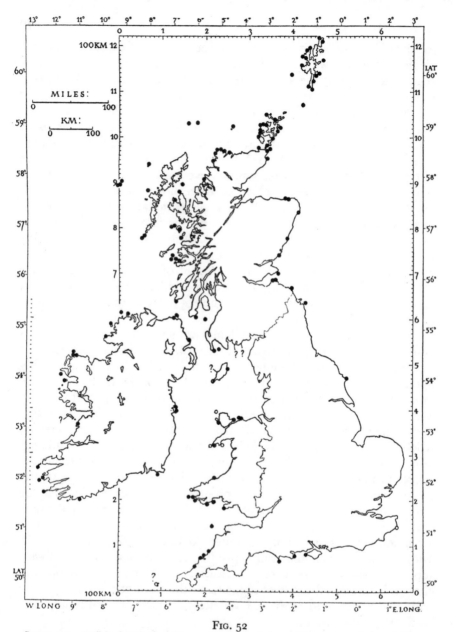

FIG. 52

Some present (black dots) and past (open dots) breeding places of the puffin *Fratercula arctica*, in the British Isles. There are unmarked breeding places on Eigg, N.E. Islay and Bishop Rock off Ramsey. No puffins were breeding at the station at the mouth of Loch Broom in 1952.

suggests that the chief functional value of their peculiar shape lies in a larger surface being in contact with the bird's belly during incubation. The great auk, with one brood spot, had a pyriform egg, too. Puffins and little auks, nesting in safer situations, have somewhat rounder (yet still pyriform) eggs (and two brood-spots). Both sexes incubate. There is evidence that in guillemot colonies of above a dozen pairs, eggs may sometimes be pirated and adopted by neighbours (Lockley, 1934). Johnson states that the common guillemot (or murre, as it is called in America, where his study was made) recognises its egg and moves it back into the old position if it rolls away or is experimentally transposed by the observer; in three instances the adults whose eggs had been moved "hovered" first on the vacant egg-site, then seeing the egg in a new postion, went to it and by degrees shuffled it between the breast and legs until the original site was regained. But one guillemot which had lost her egg was seen by Johnson to "steal" another from the mire accumulated in a depression on the ledge and "moved it about twelve feet to the location where last evening it covered (the lost egg)", further evidence of the determined pirating of eggs by bereaved adults.

Some eggs become so fouled with slime, which dries to a hard coat, that the original beautiful colour is lost, and many must be only recognisable by their position on the ledge.

Gulls patrol cliffs where guillemots breed, and become bold in the search for eggs and small chicks. We have watched a herring-gull alight on a ledge and try to force a sitting guillemot from its egg. After visiting a guillemot colony, many observers have watched gulls seize the eggs before the slower-flying guillemots, frightened away by the human intruders, returned. Small guillemot colonies may lose all their eggs as a result of a single visit by a human being. More rarely the sudden swoop of a gull will cause a panic in which the frightened guillemots leap from the ledges before disengaging their feet and breast from the egg, which is then accidentally carried out and dropped in mid-air. The guillemot will lay at least once again if the first egg is lost when fresh. Winn (1950) found that black guillemots replaced fresh eggs, which had been destroyed, in 15 days; but there was no re-laying after June.

Very little reliable data on the incubation and fledging-periods of auks was published until the work of Lockley (1934c) on the puffin, and Keighley and Lockley (1947, 1948) on the razorbill and common guillemot, and Winn on the black guillemot appeared. The results,

(averages), given in the table below, show that previous estimates
(*Handbook of British Birds*, Vol. 4) were wide of the mark.

			Incubation (days)	Fledging (days)	Total (days)
COMMON GUILLEMOT	..	..	?	15.8	
RAZORBILL	..	..	34.3	15.2	49.5
PUFFIN ..	..	..	41.7	49	90.7
BLACK GUILLEMOT	..	..	29.4	39.5	69

The disparity between the periods for the puffin and those for the
common guillemot and razorbill (and probably great auk) can now
be related to the amount of exposure of the breeding site. In the darkness and security of the burrow the puffin egg and chick is safe and
can develop slowly and fully. In the little auk and the black guillemot
colonies there is rather more danger from predatory creatures. (Winn
found that high tides, and young herring-gulls, caused mortality to
black guillemot eggs and chicks). The guillemot and razorbill are
constantly threatened by predatory birds. The most successful guillemots and razorbills therefore must be those which are hatched in
the shortest time and which spend the briefest period as chicks on the
ledges. When recording the fledging period of these two auks we noticed
a significant correlation; some of the strongest chicks were those which
flew to the sea within two weeks, and some of the less vigorous chicks
were those which remained for nearly three weeks on the ledges.
Where there are large colonies of breeding gulls near those of cliff-
breeding auks the young auks experience a heavy mortality. In
British colonies the herring-gulls are the greatest egg-thieves and the
great black-backed gulls the greatest persecutors of the nestling
guillemots and razorbills. During our observations of the fledging
periods of these auks, which were made at Skomer and Skokholm,
we ringed as many as possible of the chicks. Those which disappeared
before the fledging day were taken by black-backed gulls, whose
fresh castings we discovered to be full of the remains of young auks,
from which we were able to recover some of our rings.

Nestling auks are fed on fish or plankton, or both. The size of the
fish varies according to the age of the chick, as well as to its species.
As the chicks grow, which they do very rapidly in the case of the open-
site auks, larger fish are brought in. This is particularly true of the
guillemot and may be associated with the structure of the bill. When
the chick is about a week old, an adult guillemot will bring home a

single fish which is usually slightly longer than the bill and is held parallel to the bill, with the tail hanging from its tip. This fish may be almost as long as the chick itself; but this formidable meal will be swallowed by the chick, always head-first, and digestion begins with the head, although the tail of the fish may not visibly disappear from the mouth of the nestling for some time. Often after returning from the sea with a single large fish the adult will hold it for a long time, as during courtship, as it sits semi-upright upon the ledge. Why it should do this is not quite clear, but it may be that unless the chick importunes sufficiently the feeding reaction in the adult is not released. The adult may even fly away from the ledge, still carrying the fish, only to return later with it. If all the chicks near the alighting bird have been fed recently, there would, of course, be a wastage if the adult dropped the unwanted fish at random on the ledge. This does happen, though rarely, and if the chick is well grown, vigorous and hungry enough, it will pick up the fish then, or later. But usually the adult retains the fish until one or other of the chicks of the colony starts calling and pecking to be fed. Since both sexes in the adult are alike and the chicks themselves cannot be distinguished one from the other (unless they vary much in age), it has not been easy to prove that communal feeding exists; but hungry chicks will be seen making their way past satisfied chicks and brooding adults, to reach an adult holding fish. Also chicks have been seen to wander from one adult to another, and even to a third, and were brooded by each in turn (Lockley, 1934d). There seems no doubt that a chick will be adopted as easily as an egg may be pirated, even if the adoption of the chick is a matter of only a short period during the absence of the legitimate parent. There also seems little doubt but that there is voice recognition in this species; a chick which feels cold and temporarily has no adult to brood it will squeak until its wants are satisfied by the nearest willing adult. Yet these squeaks seem to cause more agitation to one particular adult than the rest (and this the observer presumes to be one of its parents), which may make its way towards the chick, calling, or call the chick to its side to be brooded or fed, or both. Promiscuous or communal feeding of young birds is not unique to the guillemot; it occurs regularly among other sociable species, notably the penguins, and has occurred spasmodically with passerine birds. Of mammals the female bat is said to feed the first young one which reaches her on her return to the crowded communal nursery-roosts (Casteret, 1947).

Little auks feed their chick on crustaceans and plankton, which they carry in cheek-pouches. Razorbills bring their young somewhat smaller fish than the guillemot as a rule, and puffins carry home still smaller fry and sand-eels. Razorbills usually hold the fish across the bill, and may carry any number from one to seven or eight in a beak-load. Puffins, with their enormous parrot bills, carry many more; we have counted 28 small fish dropped in one load from the bill of a frightened individual. This division of fish sizes between the three larger auks, varying according to the shape of the bill, is interesting, and suggests that the three species have their ecological share—a different food spectrum—in the harvest of the sea (see p. 122), just as they have their separate territorial niches on land; competition is thereby reduced and the species are able to live as neighbours harmoniously throughout the year.

We may complete the story of the young guillemots and razorbills born on the cliffs. The chicks have grown rapidly, but at a fortnight old are still only half the size and weight of the adults. Yet during these two weeks they have acquired their first coat of feathers at a remarkable speed. In the period that it takes the smallest of birds, such as the wren, to acquire its first plumage, the comparatively large young guillemot or razorbill has grown a thick cushion of feathers over the natal down. The flight feathers alone are incomplete; the rectrices or tail feathers have in fact not even sprouted. But the wings have the appearance of being complete (in relation to the small body) because, although the primaries are missing, the primary-coverts and greater coverts are well grown. And it is with the aid of these, and quite lacking quill feathers, that the young bird flutters down to the sea.

Earlier observers, some of whom obtained the evidence second-hand from fishermen and lighthouse-keepers, have asserted that the young auks are aided in their flight from the cliff to the sea by one or both parents, which were said to support the chick by holding one wing (just the thing to upset a flying bird completely); also that the parents sometimes pushed a reluctant chick over the edge. It is possible that an adult may accidentally jostle a chick which is hesitating on the edge of an overcrowded platform, but we do not believe that eviction is ever premeditated. Recent observations by Perry (1940), Kay (1947) and Keighley & Lockley (1948), have proved that the fledgeling takes off on its own account. What happens is at last quite clear: the young razorbill or guillemot begins to exercise its wings freely as soon as the coverts are sufficiently grown, and the body is well

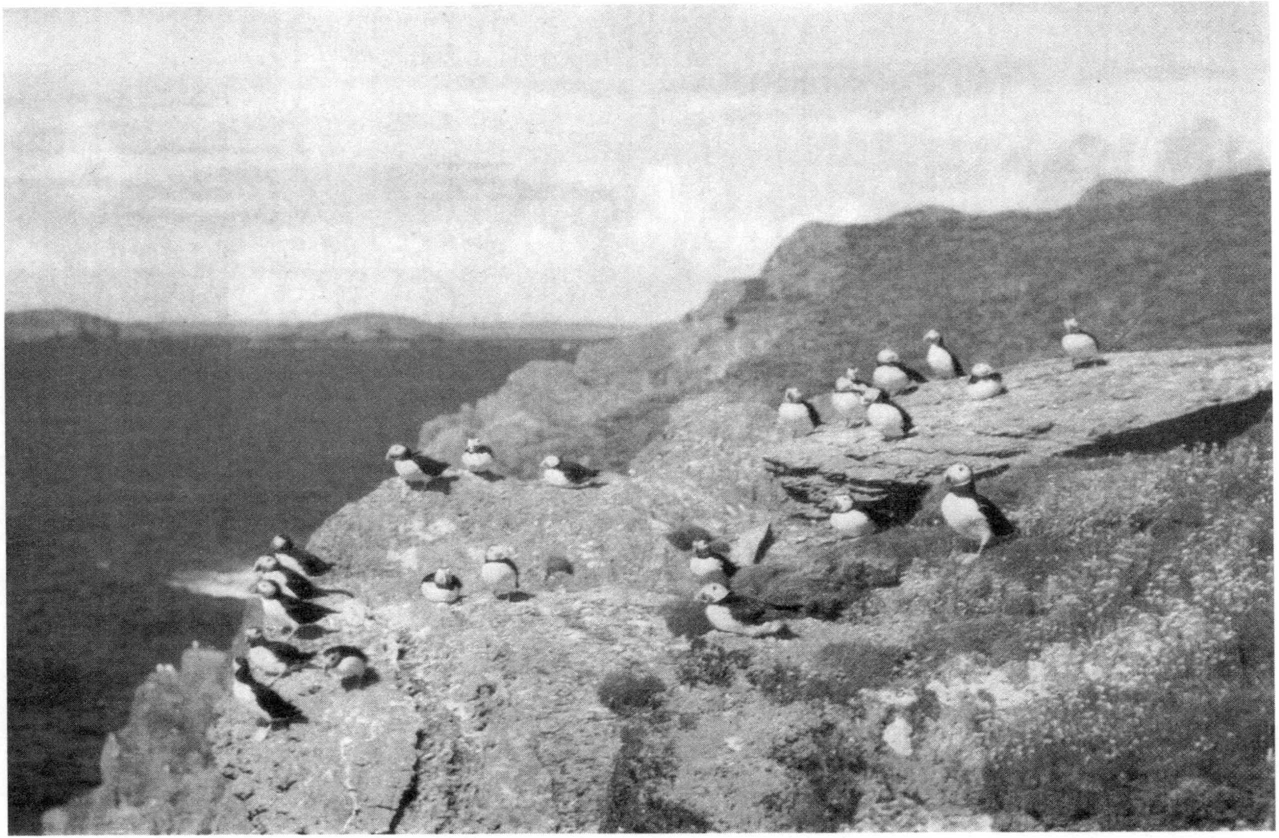

Robert Atkinson

Plate 8. Puffins sunning on a breeding-slope at the cliff-top of Skokholm, Pembrokeshire

covered in a soft loose coat of feathers above the thick down; this regular wing-exercising begins earlier in precocious individuals. The rapidly growing chick becomes restless and may wander some distance along a ledge or within the confines of the rocky guillemot plateau. It has yet to be discovered whether or not, at this period of about two weeks of age, the chick is fed less often; there is no evidence that this is so, but rather the contrary, since there always seems to be an abundance of fish being brought in by the adults which, as already suggested, are not necessarily, in the case of the guillemot, the parents of the chick which they are seen to feed. The young bird has now a louder and more insistent call, and appears more and more dissatisfied with its confinement on the cliffs. These calls seem to excite less those adults remaining on the ledges with them, than those on the sea below. It is generally presumed, but not scientifically proven, that it is the parents which call to the young bird from the sea. More patient observation is needed to clear up this point, which could only be done by colour-marking the adults and young. It is reasonable to suppose however, that as only one, or at most two, adults seem to answer the call of one fledgeling from the cliffs, there is definite voice-recognition at this distance. When at last the young chick makes the leap into the air and flutters down on a long plane to the water it is claimed by one, or by a pair, of adults. These eventually convoy the fledgeling away to sea.

The flight of the young chick from cliff to sea usually takes place at night or early in the morning, but has been observed during other hours of the day also. When it occurs in rough weather, with heavy seas breaking on the rocks and shallows below the cliffs, the young bird may have a difficult passage to get clear. But even when it strikes the rocks, it is seldom seriously hurt. It bounces off and continues to scramble and struggle towards the sea. It is sometimes engulfed by a heavy surf, but if so it immediately dives, swimming agilely forward, squeaking anxiously each time it reaches the surface for a moment, while a little farther offshore the adult continues to call encouragingly as it swims towards the chick.

The arrival of the chick upon the water excites the whole group of adults in the immediate vicinity. They may make short dives towards the young bird as it swims under water. They may surround it when it comes to the surface, and they may even make mock attacks, forcing it to submerge for a moment. (Contrast this excitement of the adult cliff-breeding auks over the fledgeling with the complete indifference

of the adult puffin or petrel towards its chick). The incident ends in
the youngster swimming close to the adult which most persistently
answers its calls, and it is led away to sea.   Usually only one adult
retains possession of the fledgeling in the open sea, but we do not
know whether this is the male or female, though it is generally presumed
to be the mother of the chick that takes on the duty. Nor do we know
the sex of the two adults which sometimes accompany a chick; this
is a matter for detailed observation by marking. For all we know
the loving adults may both be female, one the mother of the chick,
and the other a foster mother who, having lost her egg or chick earlier
in the season, has adopted the chick and, having fed it often, has
become attached to it by voice-recognition.

Convoying of the young bird at sea is recorded for the common
and Brünnich's guillemots, the black guillemot and the razorbill.
The chicks of the black guillemot and the little auk, both born in
crevices in the rocks, do not leave the nest until they are full grown
and in complete juvenile plumage. Before leaving there is much
exercising of the wings. The adults attend the departure from the rocks.
Winn (1950) found that in one case, at 8.30 p.m. on 12 August 1947,
a black guillemot parent enticed the 40-day-old chick from the nesting
crevice by dangling a live rock-eel before it. The chick was drawn to
the water and the open sea in this way.

The little auk often nests on cliffs far inland, and the young bird
has to face a longer flight to the sea. According to W. E. Ekblaw
(A. C. Bent, 1919) it is accompanied on its first flight by the adults,
which do not, however, assist it otherwise.   It flies quite well immediately, though its progress is naturally slower than that of the adult,
and occasionally a few fall by the way, and these may become the
prey of the prowling arctic foxes.

Very different is the story of the puffin at fledging time. For a
long time the imaginative accounts of early observers seemed to prove
that the adults tenaciously cared for the young throughout their
existence on land. Thus, writing of the Atlantic puffin, C. W. Townsend
(Bent, 1919) states that "when the young are 4 to 5 weeks old they are
able to leave their burrows and follow their mothers to the sea."
Of the horned puffin (*Fratercula corniculata*), L. McS. Turner writes that
"the old bird catches the young one by the wing and they flutter at a
long angle to the water. The old bird endeavours to keep under the
young one. I have seen them drop their young accidentally and cause
great consternation of the parent, which could not check her flight

immediately, but returned and showed great solicitude by turning the young one over and over in the water to see if it was injured. During severe storms the young are taken to the lee of some reef or islet until the waves become quiet."

Turner's account is the fabrication of a romantic imagination —the truth is much more astonishing. We now know that all *Fratercula* and *Lunda* species desert their young after a long fledging period. The young chick is well supplied with fish during the first month of its existence, the adults bringing in several beak-loads during the early and the late part of the day. The puffin chick, well covered with down when born, and quite active, has been continuously brooded for the first week only. We can only conjecture here how the young bird is fed in those burrows which are far down in the earth and which receive little or no light from the surface. At first it is probably fed by touch; but presumably the fish, which are partially phosphorescent, are discernible even in darkness, and as the chick becomes more nimble it is able to pick up fish from the ground. (It has not been proved that puffins have a sense of smell. The olfactory sense of sea-birds has been little explored, see Fisher, 1952, pp. 421-22. and notes on cormorants devouring strong-smelling fish, p. 212).

The newly-hatched puffin is fed first of all on very small fish and sand-eels. As it grows older, larger quantities of larger-sized fish are brought in, but, as already pointed out, these fish are never so large as those fed to guillemot chicks. The ability of the puffin to catch and hold up to thirty small fish in its beak at one time has often been remarked upon, and it is undoubtedly related to the peculiar structure of the bill, and the curious round tongue. The interior of the upper mandible has slight serrations which must assist in holding fish. There is no doubt that each fish, as it is captured, is immediately killed by the sharp pincers of the point of the bill. The popular conceptions that the puffin arranges its captures neatly with heads all to one side of its mouth, or alternatively, are of course, quite erroneous. They are held at random, although always across the bill.

About the fortieth day the young puffin is entirely deserted by its parents, which leave the land altogether and retire to the open sea to begin the moult of the body-feathers which takes place in the autumn. The deserted chick remains fasting in the burrow for about one week, during which the last of the down disappears and the first full juvenile plumage is completed, including all wing and tail feathers.

At last the young bird proceeds to the sea, alone and always at night, when the attacks from the predatory gulls and skuas are least likely.

In very dry summers, or in those burrows in dry sandy soil, the young puffin may be heavily attacked by red mite. Many may at this stage be so severely sucked by this ground-breeding parasite that they die through loss of blood. On the island of Burhou in the Channel Islands in June 1949, we found several hundreds of fledgeling puffins dying or dead, in or near their burrows, and covered with blood-sucking mites, identified by the British Museum as *Dermanyssus gallinae*, commonly known as the poultry mite. Ticks (*Ixodes uriae*) attack adult puffins in late spring and summer; often the white face of a puffin will be quite grey with the bloated bodies of these bloodsuckers, which are picked up in the grass and the burrows, and which drop off after a few days feeding, as soon as they are engorged.

At dawn on late July mornings the sea surrounding the islands where puffins breed numerously will be dotted with young puffins which have made their way to the water during the night. They have scrambled over the rocks or fluttered down from high cliffs. The strong tides will help to sweep them away to sea. The young bird paddles vigorously (for as yet it cannot fly), showing anxiety to get out into the open ocean. If attacked by a gull, it escapes by diving. The adults take no interest whatsoever in the fledged puffin when they encounter it in the water at this time of the year. Nor does the young bird betray, by calling or other sign, the slightest interest in the adult, except that it will usually swim away from, rather than towards, a raft of adults. It is worth noting that in those species described in this book which make a night passage to the sea at fledging time, there is this complete desertion of the young bird. These two events in the breeding biology of these species seemed to be linked with the factor of rearing in the darkness of a burrow; the adults, except in a few instances where a burrow happens to be short and well-lighted from the entrance, have never properly seen their chick, and are familiar with it only as a voice and a form in the twilight underground. They probably could not recognise it visually at sea in daylight, nor is it necessary for them to do so.

The young puffin, like so many other migratory birds, has to find its way alone to the wintering ground of its kind, to the gathering place of all juvenile puffins of its own subspecies which have left the islands and cliffs in early autumn. But little is known of this movement, or of how the juveniles meet with the adults, if they do, on the return

Plate XXXIX. Common Guillemots, Skokholm. On the guillemot ledges the adults out-number the chicks six to one, due to losses of eggs and young in such an exposed situation.

Plate XL. Brünnich's Guillemots, Green Island, Witless Bay, Newfoundland

(L. M. Tuck, Canadian Wildlife Service)

voyage in the next or some following spring. All we know at present is that two young puffins, ringed (by the Marquess of Bute) at St. Kilda in August 1939, reached Newfoundland in December of the same year; they probably crossed the Atlantic direct (Rankin & Duffey, 1948), since puffins have been observed occasionally in mid-North Atlantic in December.

Auks moult completely as soon as they leave the breeding ground, and are nearly flightless for a short period in early autumn. Puffins shed their facial adornments then, including the cerise eye-ring, leathery eye-patches, rictal rosette or "false lips," and part of the lower mandible. Guillemots and razorbills are much whiter in their winter plumage. The puffin is unique in that the quills are not moulted until the spring, when the new nuptial plumage is acquired.

Probably auks do not return to land in their second summer. They may be two or three or more years reaching breeding condition, during which they may visit the land as non-breeders, and stake out a claim to the future home. The proportion of non-breeders in any species of sea-bird laying only one egg each year is probably high, although no reliable figures are available. Lockley (1953) found many non-breeding puffins at Skomer and Skokholm in June and July, none of them less than two years old (the yearling puffin is distinguishable by its small triangular bill and other characteristics). Selous commented on the great number of common guillemots on the ledge after the last chicks had flown, and thought they could never have bred; their numbers were almost equal to the original breeding population. Perry saw the same thing, but misinterpreted it as a return to the cliffs of the old guillemots—but these of course were already at sea with chicks, and beginning the moult. Winn counted fifty non-breeders in July in a colony of fifty breeding pairs of black guillemots, and presumably the yearlings were absent; if we add the juveniles and fledgelings this gives a high figure, not far removed from parity of numbers with the adults. The number of non-breeding fulmars is very high (Fisher, 1952); at all but the largest British colonies it comprises at least half the birds present at the land-station at the peak of seasonal occupation, which is usually in early April. We ought not to be surprised at these figures. To counteract the heavy egg, chick and fledgeling mortality in a species laying only one egg expectation of life in the mature adult must be high. Long-lived animals do not usually begin breeding early in life; about one quarter of or one-fifth of their life-span is passed in immaturity.

U

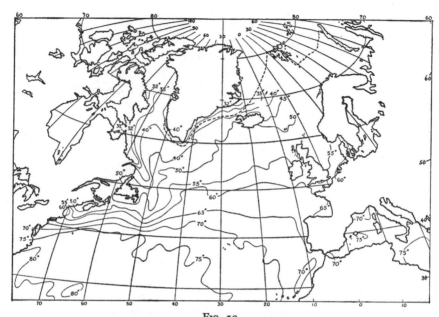

FIG. 53

Sketch map of the North Atlantic showing isotherms of surface water in July.
Broken line represents the approximate boundary of sea ice (degrees in Fahrenheit)

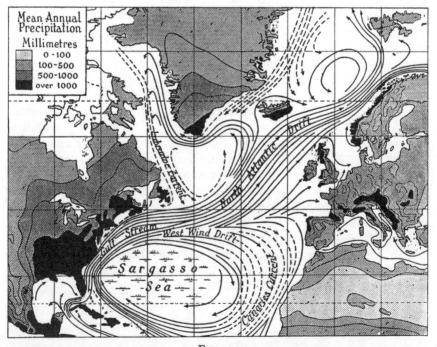

FIG . 54

Sketch chart of the North Atla ntic showing drift and precipitation

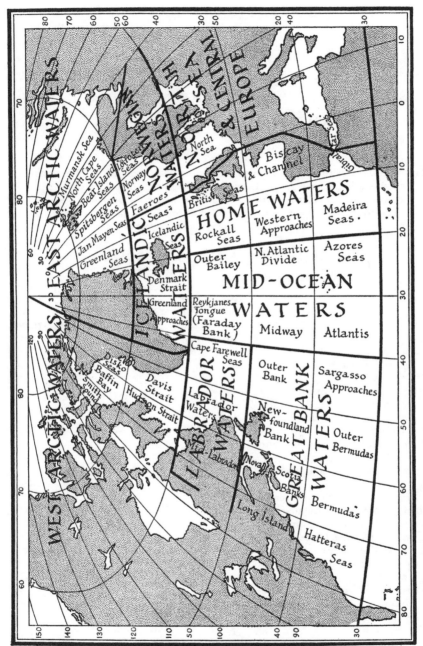

FIG. 55. Based on E. M. Nicholson's classification of the North Atlantic in ten-degree blocks. Higher groupings from *Fisher, 1952*.

LIST OF SEA-BIRDS OF THE NORTH ATLANTIC AND THEIR DISTRIBUTION

THE BOUNDARY between 'arctic' and 'temperate' has been taken, after long consideration, as the Arctic Circle, instead of some boundary more real geographically but less practical. For the same reason the boundary between 'temperate' and 'tropical' has been taken as the Tropic of Cancer. Species bracketed together tend to be ecological counterparts.

(i) PRIMARY SEA-BIRDS, BREEDING

	TROPICAL WEST ATLANTIC	TEMPERATE WEST ATLANTIC	ARCTIC	TEMPERATE EAST ATLANTIC	MEDITERRANEAN	TROPICAL EAST ATLANTIC
Fulmarus glacialis, fulmar	—	*just*	+	+	—	—
Puffinus diomedea, N. Atlantic shearwater	—	—	—	+	+	+
Puffinus puffinus, Manx shearwater	—	?	—	+	+	—
Puffinus assimilis, little shearwater	—	—	—	+	—	+
Puffinus l'herminieri, Audubon's shearwater	+	+	—	—	—	—
Pterodroma hasitata, capped petrel	+	—	—	—	—	—
Pterodroma cahow, cahow	—	+	—	—	—	—
Pterodroma mollis, soft-plumaged petrel	—	—	—	+	—	+
Bulweria bulwerii, Bulwer's petrel	—	—	—	+	—	+
Pelagodroma marina, frigate-petrel	—	—	—	+	—	+
Hydrobates pelagicus, storm-petrel	—	—	—	+	+	—
Oceanodroma castro, Madeiran fork-tailed petrel	—	—	—	+	—	+
Oceanodroma leucorhoa, Leach's petrel	—	+	—	+	—	—
Phaëthon aethereus, red-billed tropic bird	+	—	—	—	—	+
Phaëthon lepturus, white-tailed tropic-bird	+	+	—	—	—	+

	TROPICAL WEST ATLANTIC	TEMPERATE WEST ATLANTIC	ARCTIC	TEMPERATE EAST ATLANTIC	MEDITERRANEAN	TROPICAL EAST ATLANTIC
Pelecanus roseus, crested pelican	—	—	—	—	?	—
Pelecanus onocrotalus, white pelican	—	—	—	—	?	+
Pelecanus erythrorhynchos, American white pelican	—	+	—	—	—	—
Pelecanus occidentalis, brown pelican	+	+	—	—	—	—
Pelecanus rufescens, pink-backed pelican	—	—	—	—	—	+
Sula bassana, northern gannet ..	—	+	—	+	—	—
Sula dactylatra, blue-faced booby	+	—	—	—	—	—
Sula sula, red-footed booby ..	+	—	—	—	—	—
Sula leucogaster, brown booby ..	+	—	—	—	—	+
Phalacrocorax auritus, double-crested cormorant	+	+	—	—	—	—
Phalacrocorax olivaceus, bigua cormorant	+	*just*	—	—	—	—
Phalacrocorax aristotelis, shag ..	—	—	+	+	+	—
Phalacrocorax carbo, cormorant ..	—	+	+	+	+	+
Haliëtor africanus, reed-cormorant	—	—	—	—	—	+
Haliëtor pygmeus, pigmy cormorant	—	—	—	—	?	—
Anhinga rufa, African darter [1] ..	—	—	—	—	?	+
Anhinga anhinga, American darter	+	+	—	—	—	—
Fregata magnificens, man-o'-war-bird	+	—	—	—	—	+
Catharacta skua, great skua ..	—	—	—	+	—	—
Stercorarius pomarinus, pomarine skua	—	*just*	+	—	—	—
Stercorarius parasiticus, arctic skua	—	+	+	+	—	—
Stercorarius longicaudus, long-tailed skua	—	*just*	+	+	—	—
Pagophila eburnea, ivory-gull ..	—	—	+	—	—	—
Larus audouinii, Audouin's gull ..	—	—	—	?	+	—
Larus delawarensis, ring-billed gull	—	+	—	—	—	—
Larus canus, 'common' gull ..	—	—	+	+	—	—
Larus argentatus, herring-gull [2] ..	—	+	+	+	+	+
Larus fuscus, lesser black-back ..	—	—	+	+	—	—
Larus marinus, great black-back ..	—	+	+	+	—	—
Larus hyperboreus, glaucous gull ..	—	+	+	+	—	—
Larus atricilla, laughing gull ..	+	+	—	—	—	—
Larus cirrhocephalus, grey-headed gull	—	—	—	—	—	+
Larus ridibundus, black-headed gull	—	—	—	+	+	—

[1] regarded as conspecific with *anhinga* in index list.
[2] includes *L. glaucoides* (*leucopterus*), the 'Iceland' gull.

	TROPICAL WEST ATLANTIC	TEMPERATE WEST ATLANTIC	ARCTIC	TEMPERATE EAST ATLANTIC	MEDITERRANEAN	TROPICAL EAST ATLANTIC
Larus pipixcan, Franklin's gull ..	—	inland	—	—	—	—
Larus melanocephalus, Mediterranean black-headed gull ..	—	—	—	—	+	—
Larus genei, slender-billed gull ..	—	—	—	+	+	?
Larus philadelphia, Bonaparte's gull	—	inland	—	—	—	—
Larus minutus, little gull	—	—	—	+	—	—
Rhodostethia rosea, Ross's gull ..	—	—	+**	—	—	—
Rissa tridactyla, kittiwake ..	—	+	+	+	—	—
Xema sabini, Sabine's gull ..	—	just	+	—	—	—
Chlidonias hybrida, whiskered tern	—	—	—	+	+	+
Chlidonias leucoptera, white-winged black tern	—	—	—	casual	casual	—
Childonias nigra, black tern ..	—	+	—	+	+	—
Phaëtusa simplex, large-billed tern	+	—	—	—	—	—
Gelochelidon nilotica, gull-billed tern	+	+	—	+	+	?
Hydroprogne caspia, Caspian tern	—	+	—	+	+	?
Sterna hirundo, common tern ..	+	+	+	+	+	—
Sterna paradisaea, arctic tern ..	—	+	+	+	—	—
Sterna forsteri, Forster's tern ..	—	+	—	—	—	—
Sterna dougallii, roseate tern ..	+	+	—	+	+	—
Sterna anaetheta, bridled tern ..	+	+	—	—	—	?
Sterna fuscata, sooty tern	+	+	—	—	—	?
Sterna superciliaris, yellow-billed river-tern	+	—	—	—	—	—
Sterna albifrons, little tern ..	+	+	—	+	+	+
Thalasseus maximus, royal tern ..	+	+	—	?	—	?
Thalasseus bengalensis, lesser crested tern	—	—	—	—	+	—
Thalasseus eurygnatha, Cayenne tern	+	—	—	—	—	—
Thalasseus sandvicensis, Sandwich tern	+	+	—	+	+	—
Anoüs stolidus, noddy ..	+	+	—	—	—	+
Anoüs minutus, white-capped noddy	+	—	—	—	—	—
⌠*Rynchops nigra*, black skimmer ..	+	+	—	—	—	—
⌡*Rynchops flavirostris*, African skimmer	—	—	—	—	—	+
Plautus alle, little auk	—	—	+	—	—	—
Alca impennis, great auk ..	—	extinct	—	extinct	—	—
Alca torda, razorbill	—	+	+	+	—	—
Uria lomvia, Brünnich's guillemot	—	+	+	+	—	—

**only once on Atlantic side.

	TROPICAL WEST ATLANTIC	TEMPERATE WEST ATLANTIC	ARCTIC	TEMPERATE EAST ATLANTIC	MEDITERRANEAN	TROPICAL EAST ATLANTIC
Uria aalge, guillemot	—	+	+	+	—	—
Cepphus grylle, black guillemot	—	+	+	+	—	—
Fratercula arctica, puffin	—	+	+	+	—	—

(ii) SECONDARY SEA-BIRDS, BREEDING

	TROPICAL WEST ATLANTIC	TEMPERATE WEST ATLANTIC	ARCTIC	TEMPERATE EAST ATLANTIC	MEDITERRANEAN	TROPICAL EAST ATLANTIC
Gavia stellata, red-throated diver	—	+	+	+	—	—
Gavia arctica, black-throated diver	—	+	+	+	—	—
Gavia immer, great northern diver	—	+	+	+	—	—
Gavia adamsii, white-billed northern diver	—	—	+	—	—	—
{ *Podilymbus podiceps*, pied-billed grebe	+	+	—	—	—	—
{ *Podiceps ruficollis*, dabchick	—	—	—	+	+	+
Podiceps auritus, Slavonian grebe	—	+	+	+	—	—
Podiceps nigricollis, black-necked grebe	—	+	—	+	+	+
Podiceps cristatus, great crested grebe	—	—	—	+	+	+
Podiceps griseigena, red-necked grebe	—	+	+	+	—	—
Branta bernicla, brent-goose	—	—	+	—	—	—
Tadorna tadorna, shelduck	—	—	+	+	+	—
{ *Anas penelope*, wigeon	—	—	+	+	—	—
{ *Anas americana*, American wigeon	—	+	+	—	—	—
{ *Bucephala clangula*, goldeneye	—	—	+	+	?	—
{ *Bucephala islandica*, Barrow's goldeneye	—	+	+	+	—	—
Clangula hyemalis, long-tailed duck	—	+	+	+	—	—
Histrionicus histrionicus, harlequin-duck	—	+	+	+	—	—
Somateria mollissima, eider	—	+	+	+	—	—
Somateria spectabilis, king-eider	—	+	+	—	—	—
Somateria stelleri, Steller's elder	—	—	+*	—	—	—
Melanitta nigra, scoter	—	?	+	+	—	—
Melanitta fusca, velvet-scoter	—	?	+	+	—	—
Melanitta perspicillata, surf-scoter	—	+	—	—	—	—
Camptorhynchus labradorius, Labrador duck	—	*extinct*	—	—	—	—
Mergus albellus, smew	—	—	+	+	—	—
{ *Mergus cucullatus*, hooded merganser	—	+	—	—	—	—
{ *Mergus merganser*, goosander	—	+	+	+	?	—

*casual in Atlantic sector.

	TROP-ICAL WEST ATLAN-TIC	TEMP-ERATE WEST ATLAN-TIC	ARCTIC	TEMP-ERATE EAST ATLAN-TIC	MEDI-TERR-ANEAN	TROPI-CAL EAST ATLAN-TIC
Mergus serrator, red-breasted merganser	—	+	+	+	—	—
Phalaropus fulicarius, grey phalarope	—	*just*	+	*just*	—	—
Phalaropus lobatus, red-necked phalarope	—	+	+	+	—	—

(iii) NORTH ATLANTIC NON-BREEDING VISITORS AND CASUALS

PRIMARY

Aptenodytes patagonica, king-penguin (introduced)
Diomedea exulans, wandering albatross
Diomedea melanophris, black-browed albatross
Diomedea chlororhynchos, yellow-nosed albatross
Diomedea chrysostoma, grey-headed albatross
Phoebetria palpebrata, light-mantled sooty albatross
Daption capensis, Cape pigeon
Puffinus gravis, Tristan great shearwater
Puffinus griseus, sooty shearwater
Pterodroma inexpectata, Peale's or scaled petrel
Pterodroma neglecta, Kermadec petrel
Pterodroma arminjoniana, Trinidad petrel
Pterodroma leucoptera, collared petrel
Oceanites oceanicus, Wilson's petrel
Fregetta tropica, black-bellied storm-petrel
Sula capensis, Cape gannet
Larus californicus, California gull (perhaps a race of *L. argentatus*)
Larus ichthyaëtus, great black-headed gull
Sterna trudeaui, Trudeau's tern
Sterna balaenarum, Damara tern
Thalasseus bergii, swift tern
Thalasseus elegans, elegant tern
[*Gygis alba*, fairy tern (probably)]
Aethia psittacula, paroquet auklet
Aethia cristatella, crested auklet
Lunda cirrhata, tufted puffin

SECONDARY

Somateria fischeri, spectacled eider

NOTE: *Macronectes giganteus*, the giant fulmar of the antarctic and subantarctic, has been recorded (1846 or 1847) from the Rhine near Mainz in Germany. Most authorities now place this record in the *limbo* of 'hypothetical' cases.

BIBLIOGRAPHY

ORNITHOLOGISTS HAVE BECOME slaves to the established system of bibliographical citation, under which it is the custom to cite the original authority for every fact quoted, with the date of publication of his work, full title of the paper, the correct abbreviation of the title of the journal according to the *World List of Scientific Periodicals*, etc., etc. As a result various scholarly and admirable books have become adorned with super-bibliographies the publication of which must have increased the setting cost of the books by at least ten per cent., sometimes by several hundreds of pounds. These bibliographies certainly show that the author has taken the trouble to go to original sources for his information, and make it very easy for other scholars to tread the same paths: they also, of course, give credit where it is due. Thus the bibliography of E. A. Armstrong (1947) contains about a thousand citations, occupying 38 pages in smallish type; that of J. Huxley (1942) nearly a thousand, occupying 35 pages; that of R. C. Murphy (1936) about a thousand occupying 32 double-column pages; that of F. Salomonsen (1950-51), admittedly selective, over five hundred occupying 18 double-column pages. If Fisher (1952) had published his full formal bibliography of the fulmar he would have quoted 2,378 works; if cited in full in smaller type than the main text of the book these would have occupied about 125 pages; in the smallest possible type between sixty and seventy pages.

In the course of writing this book we have consulted about five thousand original notes, papers and books; our resulting collection of slips is nevertheless only a practical, working bibliography of the sea-birds of the North Atlantic. If we were to expand it to a complete bibliography we should doubtless end up with at least ten thousand entries, even if we rigidly confined them to purely scientific publications. If we were to publish it as it is it might be of use to a few scholars who probably know more about the literature than we do; but it would certainly increase the price of this book beyond the reach of those for whom we intend it!

We have therefore confined our bibliography generally to classic publications which (in our opinion) represent important stages in the development of human knowledge of North Atlantic sea-birds, and to publications particularly relevant to facts in the text which (in our judgment) are not common knowledge or which are based on research or observation of particular interest or originality. The whole bibliography is thus selected by subjective judgment; and disappointed scholars are cordially invited to correspond with us if thus frustrated.

We would like to take the opportunity to add that, in our opinion, the time has come for all bibliographies to works of zoological synthesis to be selective. No historian today, writer of a history book of the rarest degree of specification, would attempt to quote the original source for every fact. But many zoological writers rudely interrupt their own text with cross-references to bulky triumphs of slip-index work, which deserve publication on their own—as original contributions to the science of Bibliography—or not at all. We ourselves have no feeling other than satisfaction in discarding nine-tenths of the slip-index we have laboriously and carefully compiled.

AINSLIE, J. A. and ATKINSON, R. (1937). On the breeding habits of Leach's fork-tailed petrel. *Brit. Birds, 30:* 234-48, 276-77.

ALEXANDER, W. B. (1928). Birds of the ocean. New York and London, G. P. Putnam's Sons.

ALLEN, G. M. (1931). The birds of Liberia. *Report of the Harvard-African Expedition upon the African Republic of Liberia and the Belgian Congo,* vol. *1:* 636-748.

ANDERSEN, K. (1894). *Diomedea melanophrys,* boende paa Faerøerne. *Vidensk. Medd. Naturh. Foren. København, 1894:* 241-64.

ANDERSON, J. (1746). Nachrichten von Island, Grönland und der Strasse Davis, zum wahren Nutzen der Wissenschaften und der Handlung. Hamburg.

ANDRÉE, S. A. (1931). Andrée's first diary, pp. 347-412 of S. A. Andrée, N. Strindberg and K. Fraenkel (1931). The Andrée Diaries. London, John Lane, transl. Edward Adams-Ray.

ANON (1838). Grönlands historiske Mindesmærker, udgivne af de Kong Nordiske Oldskriftselskab. Kjöbenhavn, vol. *1.*

——— (1952). Gannet-hunting on Sulisgeir . . . *Scotsman,* 27 Sep.

ARMSTRONG, E. A. (1940). Birds of the grey wind. London, New York and Toronto, Oxford University Press.

——— (1947). Bird display and behaviour. London, Lindsay Drummond.

ATKINSON, R. and AINSLIE J. A. (1940). The British breeding status of Leach's fork-tailed petrel. *Brit. Birds, 34:* 50-55.

AUDUBON, J. J. (1831-39). Ornithological biography, . . . Edinburgh, 5 vols.

——— (1840-44). Birds of America; from drawings made in the United States and their territories. New York and Philadelphia, first 8vo ed.

AUSTIN, O. L. Jr. (1928). Migration-routes of the arctic tern (*Sterna paradisaea* Brünnich). *Bull. N.E. Bird-Banding Assoc. 4:* 121-25.

——— (1932). The birds of Newfoundland Labrador. *Mem. Nuttall Orn. Cl.* no. 7; 229 pp.

——— (1932 onwards). Valuable papers on terns (chiefly *Sterna hirundo*) too numerous to cite, in *Bird-Banding, 3* and volumes to date.

BAILEY, A. M. (1948). Birds of arctic Alaska. *Colorado Mus. Nat. Hist. Popular Ser.* no. 8; 317 pp.

BAILEY, H. H. (1913). The Birds of Virginia. Lynchburg, Va.

——— (1925), The birds of Florida; . . . Baltimore, Maryland.

BANNERMAN, D. A. (1930-31). The birds of tropical West Africa. London, Crown Agents for the Colonies (Oliver & Boyd), vols. *1 & 2.*

BARTHOLOMEW, G. A. A. (1942). The fishing activities of double-crested cormorants on San Francisco Bay. *Condor 44:* 13-21.

——— (1943). The daily movements of cormorants in San Francisco Bay. *Condor, 45:* 3-18.

——— (1943b). Contests of double-crested cormorants for perching sites. *Condor, 45:* 186-95.

BARTHOLOMEW, J. (1950). The advanced atlas of modern geography. London and New York, Meiklejohn and McGraw-Hill.

BARTSCH, P. (1919). The bird rookeries of the Tortugas. *Smithson. Rep. 1917:* 469-500.

BAXTER, E. V. and RINTOUL, L. J. (1953). The birds of Scotland . . . Edinburgh and London, Oliver and Boyd, 2 vols.

BEEBE, W. (1935). Rediscovery of the Bermuda cahow... *Bull. N.Y. Zool. Soc. 38:* 187-90.

BELCHER, Sir C. and SMOOKER, G. D. (1935). in Birds of the colony of Trinidad and Tobago. *Ibis* (13) *5:* 294-97.

BENT, A. C. (1919). Life histories of North American diving birds. Order Pygopodes. *Bull. U.S. Nat. Mus.* no. 107; 237 pp.

—— (1921). Life histories of North American gulls and terns. Order Longipennes. *Bull. U.S. Nat. Mus.* no. 113; 345 pp.

—— (1922). Life histories of North American petrels and pelicans and their allies. . . . *Bull. U.S. Nat. Mus.* no. 121; 181. pp.

BERTELSEN, A. (1921). Fuglene i Umánaq distrikt. *Medd. Grønland, 62:* 139-214.

BERTRAM, G. C. L. and LACK, D. (1933). Notes on the birds of Bear Island. *Ibis* (13) *3:* 283-301.

BICKERTON, W. (1912). The home-life of the terns or sea swallows. London, Witherby.

BIERMAN, W. H. and VOOUS, K. H. (1950). Birds observed and collected during the whaling expeditions of the *Willem Barendsz* in the Antarctic, 1946-1947 and 1947-1948. *Ardea, 37:* 123 pp.

BLEZARD, E. (ed.), GARNETT, M., GRAHAM, R. and JOHNSTON, T. L. (1943). The birds of Lakeland. *Trans. Carlisle Nat. Hist. Soc. 6:* 170 pp., publ. Arbroath, Buncle.

BOND, J. (1950-51). Check-list of birds of the West Indies. Philadelphia, Acad. Nat. Sci. (200 pp. 1950; first suppl. 22 pp. 1951).

BOWDISH, B. S. (1900). A day on De Cicheo Island. *Oologist, 17:* 117.

BREUIL, H. and others (1911). Les cavernes de la région Cantabriques. Monaco.

BROOKS, A. (1939). Migrations of the skua family. *Ibis* (14) *3:* 324-28.

—— (1943). The status of the California gull. *Auk, 60:* 15-20.

BUCKLEY, T. E. and HARVIE-BROWN, J. A. (1891). A vertebrate fauna of the Orkney Islands. Edinburgh, David Douglas.

BULLER, W. L. (1873). A history of the birds of New Zealand. London.

—— (1888). A history of the birds of New Zealand. London, 2nd ed., 2 vols.

—— (1905). Supplement to the *Birds of New Zealand*. London, 2 vols.

BUTURLIN, S. A. (1906). The breeding grounds of the rosy gull. *Ibis* (8) *6:* 131-39, 333-37, 661-66.

BUXTON, J. and LOCKLEY, R. M. (1950). Island of Skomer. London and New York, Staples Press.

CARTWRIGHT, G. (1792). A journal of transactions and events, during a residence of nearly sixteen years on the coast of Labrador. . . . Newark, 3 vols.

CASTERET, N. (1947). My caves. London, Dent.

CHISLETT, R. (1952). Yorkshire Birds. London and Hull, A. Brown & Sons.

CLARK, G. (1948). Fowling in prehistoric Europe. *Antiquity, 22:* 116-30.

CLARKE, W. E. (1895). On the recent visitation of the little auk (*Mergulus alle*) to Scotland. *Ann. Scot. Nat. Hist. 1895:* 97-108.

CLARKE, W. E. (1898). On the avifauna of Franz Josef Land. . . . *Ibis* (7) *4:* 249-77.
—— (1912). The little auk visitation of 1911-12. *Scot. Nat. 1912:* 77-81.
—— (1912b). Studies in bird migration. London, Gurney and Jackson, 2 vols.
COLLINGE, W. E. (1924-27). The food of some British wild birds. A study in economic ornithology. York, publ. by author.
CONDER, P. J. (1949). Individual distance. *Ibis, 91:* 649-55.
CONNELL, R. (1887). St. Kilda and the St. Kildians. London and Glasgow.
COOKE, R. (1946). Black terns breeding in Sussex. *Brit. Birds, 39:* 71-72.
COTT, H. B. (1948). Edibility of the eggs of birds. *Nature, 161:* 8-11.
—— (1949). The palatability of the eggs of birds. *Ool. Rec. 23:* 1-9.
—— (1951-52). The palatability of the eggs of birds: . . . *Proc. Zool. Soc. Lond. 121:* 1-41. *122:* 1-54;
—— (1953). The exploitation of wild birds for their eggs. *Ibis, 95:* 409-49, 643-75.
COTTAM, C. and UHLER, F. M. (1937). Birds in relation to fishes. *U.S. Bur. Biol. Survey, B:* 5-83.
CURRY-LINDAHL, K. (1947). Några Svenska Fåglar. Stockholm, Natur och Kultur.
DARLING, F. F. (1938). Bird flocks and the breeding cycle a contribution to the study of avian sociality. Cambridge, University Press.
—— (1947). Natural history in the Highlands and Islands. London, Collins' *New Naturalist.*
DARWIN, C. (1871). The descent of man, and selection in relation to sex. London.
—— (1920). The origin of species by means of natural selection or the preservation of favoured races in the struggle for life. London, John Murray, reprint of 6th ed. (First ed. 1859).
DAVIS, M. and FRIEDMANN, H. (1936). The courtship display of the flightless cormorant. *Sci. Monthly, 42:* 560-63.
DEACON, G. E. R. (1945). Water circulation and surface boundaries in the oceans. *Quart. J. Roy. Metereol. Soc. 71:* 11-25.
DEBES, L. (1673). Faeroae et Faeroa Reserata. Copenhagen.
DELACOUR, J. (1947). Birds of Malaysia. New York, the MacMillan Co.
DELONG, E. (ed.) (1883). The voyage of the *Jeannette.* The ship and ice journals of George W. DeLong, Lieutenant-Commander U.S.N., and Commander of the Polar Expedition of 1879-1881. London, Kegan Paul, 2 vols.
DEMENT'EV, G. P., GLADKOV, N. A., PTUSHENKO, E. S., SPANGENBERG, E. P. and SUDILOVSKAYA, A. M. (1951). Ptitsy Sovetskogo Soyuza. Moskva, Gosudarstvennoye Izdatel'stvo "Sovetskaya Nauka," vol. *1.*
DEMENT'EV, G. P., GLADKOV, N. A. and SPANGENBERG, E. P. (1951). Ptitsy Sovetskogo Soyuza. Moskva, Gosudarstvennoye Izdatel'stvo "Sovetskaya Nauka," vol. *3.*
DEWAR, J. M. (1939). Timing the under-water activities of diving birds. *Brit. Birds,* 38: 58-61.
DILL, H. R. and BRYAN, W. A. (1912). Report on conditions on the Hawaiian bird reservation with list of the birds found on Laysan. *U.S. Dep. Agric. Biol. Surv. Bull.* no. 42; 7-24.
DIXON, C. (1885). The ornithology of St. Kilda. *Ibis* (5) *3:* 69-97.
—— (1896). British sea birds. London, Bliss, Sands & Foster.

DROST, R. (1939). Erfolgreiche Brut der Dreizehenmöve, *Rissa tridactyla* (L.) auf Helgoland. *Orn. Monatsb. 47:* 179-80.

DUFFEY, E. and SERGEANT, D. E. (1950). Field notes on the birds of Bear Island. *Ibis, 92:* 554-63.

DUTCHER, W. (1904). Report of the A.O.U. Committee on the protection of North American birds, for the year 1903. *Auk, 21:* 97.

DWIGHT, J. (1925). The gulls (Laridae) of the world; their plumages, moults, variations, relationships and distribution. *Bull. Amer. Mus. Nat. Hist. 52:* 63-401.

EDMUNDS, M. H. (1952). Albatross in Derbyshire. *Field, 200: 424.*

ELLIOTT, J. S. (1895). Observations on the fauna of St. Kilda. *Zoologist* (3) *19:* 281-86.

EMERSON, W. O. (1904). The Farallone Islands revisited, 1887-1903. *Condor, 6:* 61-68.

FABER, F. (1822). Prodromus der isländischen Ornithologie. Kobenhavn.

—— (1824-27). Beiträge zur arktischen Zoologie. Oken's Isis, *1824:* 447-64, 779-92, 967-82; *1826:* 702-14, 791-807, 909-27, 1048-64; *1827:* 43-73, 633-88.

—— (1825-26). Über das Leben der hochnordischen Vögel. Leipzig.

FALLA, R. A. (1934). The distribution and breeding habits of petrels in northern New Zealand. *Rec. Auckland Inst. Mus. 1:* 245-60.

—— (1937). Birds. *Rep. B.A.N.Z. Antarct. Res. Exped.* (B) *2:* 288 pp.

FEILDEN, H. W. (1872). The birds of the Faeroe Islands. *Zoologist* (2) *7:* 3210-25, 3245-57, 3277-94.

—— (1890). The deserted domicile of the diablotin in Dominica. *Trans. Norf. Nat. Soc. 5:* 24-39.

FERDINAND, L. (1947). Studier af Fuglelivet paa Færørne. *Dansk. Orn. Foren. Tidsskr. 41:* 1-37.

FISCHER, F. and VON PELZELN, A. (1886). Vögel von Jan Mayen. *Mitt. Orn. Ver. "Schwalbe", 10:* 193-97, 205-12, 217-19; transl. W. E. Clarke (1890). The birds of Jan Mayen Island. *Zoologist* (3) *14:* 1-16, 41-51.

FISHER, J. (1940). Watching birds. Harmondsworth, Penguin Books.

—— (1947). Bird Recognition I: Sea-birds and waders. Penguin Books.

—— (1951). Voyage to Rockall. *Bird Notes, 24:* 302-09.

—— (1952). The Fulmar. London, Collins, *New Naturalist.*

FISHER, J. and VEVERS, H. G. (1943-44). The breeding distribution, history and population of the North Atlantic gannet (*Sula bassana*). *J. Anim. Ecol. 12:* 173-213; *13:* 49-62.

—— (1951). The present population of the North Atlantic gannet. *Proc. X. Int. Orn. Congr. Uppsala, 1950:* 463-67.

FISHER, J. and WATERSTON, G. (1941). The breeding distribution, history and population of the fulmar (*Fulmarus glacialis*) in the British Isles. *J. Anim. Ecol. 10:* 204-72.

FLEMING, C. A, and others (1953). Checklist of New Zealand birds. Wellington, Orn. Soc. N.Z.

FORBUSH, E. H. (1925). Birds of Massachusetts and other New England States. Boston, Mass. Dep. Agric., 3 vols.

FOSTER, R. J., BAXTER, R. L. and BALL, P. A. J. (1951). A visit to Grímsey (Iceland) July-August 1949. *Ibis, 93:* 53-59.

FRAZAR, M. A. (1887). An ornithologists's summer in Labrador. *Orn. Ool. 12:* 1-3, 17-20, 33-35.

GÄTKE, H. (1895). Heligoland as an ornithological observatory, the result of fifty years' experience. Edinburgh, transl. R. Rosenstock.

GAUSE, G. F. (1934). The struggle for existence. Baltimore, Williams & Wilkins Co.

GÉROUDET, P. (1946). La vie des oiseaux. Les Palmipèdes. Neuchâtel and Paris, Delachaux and Niestlé, *les Beautés de la Nature*.

GIBSON, J. A. (1951). The breeding distribution, population and history of the birds of Ailsa Craig. *Scot. Nat. 63:* 73-100, 159-77.

GIBSON-HILL, C. A. (1947). British sea birds. London, Witherby.

GLAUERT, L. (1946). The little shearwater's year. *Emu, 46:* 187-92.

GLEGG, W. E. (1945, 1947). Fishes and other aquatic animals preying on birds. *Ibis, 87:* 422-33. *89:* 433-35.

——— (1949). Great auks reported from Lofoten Islands. Explanation introduction of king penguins. *Bull. Brit. Orn. Cl. 69:* 120-21.

GODMAN, F. DU CANE (1907-10). A monograph of the petrels. London, Witherby.

GOETHE, F. (1937). Beobachtungen und Untersuchungen zur Biologie der Silbermöwe *(L.a. argentatus)* auf der Vogelinsel Memerstand. *J. Orn. 85:* 1-119

GRABA, C. J. (1830). Tagebuch, geführt auf einer Reise nach Färö im Jahre 1828. Hamburg.

GRAY, R. and SOUTHWELL, T. (1886). Voyage of the *Eclipse* to the Greenland seas, Capt. David Gray, Commander. *Zoologist* (3) *10:* 50-54.

GREEN, J. F. (1887). Ocean birds. London, R. H. Porter.

GRIEVE, S. (1885). The great auk, or garefowl *(Alca impennis*, Linn.) its history, archaeology and remains. London and Edinburgh, Jack.

GRIFFIN, D. R. (1940). Homing experiments with Leach's petrels. *Auk, 57:* 61-74.

——— (1943). Homing experiments with herring gulls and common terns. *Bird-banding, 14:* 7-33.

——— (1944). The sensory basis of bird navigation. *Quart. Rev. Biol. 19:* 15-31.

GRIFFIN, D. R. and HOCK, R. J. (1948). Experiments on bird navigation. *Science, 107:* 347-49.

——— (1949). Aeroplane observations on homing birds. *Ecology, 30:* 176-98.

GRINNELL, J. and MILLER, A. H. (1944). The distribution of the birds of California. *Pacif. Cst. Avif.* no. 27; 608 pp.

GRISCOM, L. (1939). Migration of the red phalarope off Massachusetts. *Auk, 56:* 185.

——— (1949). The birds of Concord. Cambridge, Mass., Harvard U.P., *New England Bird Studies, 2:* 340 pp.

GRISCOM, L. and FOLGER, E. V. (1948). The birds of Nantucket. Cambridge, Mass., Harvard U.P., *New England Bird Studies, 1:* 156 pp.

GROSS, A. O. (1912). Observations on the yellow-billed tropic-bird *(Phaethon americanus* Grant) at the Bermuda Islands. *Auk, 29:* 49-71.

——— (1935). The life history cycle of Leach's petrel *(Oceanodroma leucorhoa leucorhoa)* on the outer sea islands of the Bay of Fundy. *Auk, 52:* 382-99.

——— (1944). The present status of the double-crested cormorant on the coast of Maine. *Auk, 61:* 513-37.

——— (1945). The present status of the great black-backed gull on the coat of Maine. *Auk, 62:* 241-56.

GROSS, A. O. (1945b). The laughing gull on the coast of Maine. *Bird-banding, 16:* 53-58.

—— (1947). Recoveries of banded Leach's petrels. *Bird-banding, 18:* 117-26.

—— (1951). The herring gull - cormorant control project. *Proc. X. Int. Orn. Congr. Uppsala, 1950:* 532-36.

GURNEY, J. H. (1913). The gannet. A bird with a history. London, Witherby.

HANTZSCH, B. (1905). Beitrag zur Kenntnis der Vogelwelt Islands. Berlin, Friedländer.

—— (1928-29). Contribution to the knowledge of the avifauna of northeastern Labrador. *Canad. Field-Nat. 42:* 2-9, 33-40, 87-94, 123-25, 146-48, 172-77, 201-07, 221-27; *43:* 11-18, 31-34, 52-59.

HARRISSON, T. H. and HURRELL, H. G. (1933). Numerical fluctuations of the great black-backed gull (*Larus marinus* Linn.) in England and Wales. *Proc. Zool. Soc. London* (A) *103:* 191-209.

HARTLEY, C. H. and FISHER, J. (1936). The marine foods of birds in an inland fjord region in West Spitsbergen. *J. Anim. Ecol. 5:* 370-89.

HARVIE-BROWN, J. A. (1895). Albatross in the Orcadian seas. *Ann. Scot Nat. Hist. 1895:* 57.

—— (1900). Albatross near Faroe. *Zoologist* (4) *4:* 324.

HAVERSCHMIDT, F. (1933). Beobachtungen in der Kormoran-kolonie bei Lekkerkerk. *Beitr. Fortpfl.-biol. Vög. 9:* 1-14.

HAWKSLEY, O. (1949). Transatlantic arctic tern recoveries. *Bird-banding, 20:* 185-86.

HEATHCOTE, N. (1900). St. Kilda. London, etc., Longmans Green.

HEINROTH, O. and HEINROTH, M. (1924-33). Die Vögel Mitteleuropas . . . Berlin.

HEWITT, O. H. (1950). Fifth census of non-passerine birds in the bird sanctuaries of the north shore of the Gulf of St. Lawrence. *Canad. Field-Nat. 64:* 73-76.

HOLLOM, P. A. D. (1940). Report on the 1938 survey of black-headed gull colonies. *Brit. Birds, 33:* 202-21, 230-44.

—— (1940b). Additions to the report on black-headed gull colonies. *ibid. 34:* 93.

HOLM, G. (1918). Gunbjørns-Skær og Korsøer. *Medd. Grønland, 56:* 289-308.

HOLMES, P. F. (1939). Some oceanic records and notes on the winter distribution of phalaropes. *Ibis* (14) *3:* 329-42.

HORREBOW, N. (1752). Tilforladeliga Efterretninger om Island . . . Kjöbenhavn.

HØRRING, R. (1937). Birds *in* Report of the Fifth Thule Expedition 1921-24. Zoology. Copenhagen, vol. *2:* 1-134.

HØRRING, R. and SALOMONSEN, F. (1941). Further records of rare or new Greenland birds. *Medd. Grønland, 131:* no. 5., 86 pp.

HOWARD, H. (1950). Fossil evidence of avian evolution. *Ibis, 92:* 1-21.

HUTCHINSON, G. E. (1950). Survey of contemporary knowledge of biogeochemistry 3. The biogeochemistry of vertebrate excretion. *Bull. Amer. Mus. Nat. Hist. 96:* 554 pp.

HUXLEY, J. S. (1914). The courtship habits of the great-crested grebe (*Podiceps cristatus*). *Proc. Zool. Soc. Lond. 1914:* 491-562.

—— (1942). Evolution the modern synthesis. London, Geo. Allen & Unwin Ltd.

VAN IJZENDOORN, A. L. J. (1950). The breeding-birds of the Netherlands. Leiden, E. J. Brill.

JACKSON, F. G. (1899). A thousand days in the Arctic. London and New York, Harper Bros., 2 vols.

JESPERSEN, P. (1924). The frequency of birds over the high Atlantic Ocean. *Nature*, *114*: 281-83.

——— (1929). On the frequency of birds over the high Atlantic Ocean. *Verh. VI. Int. Orn. Kongr. København, 1926:* 163-72.

——— (1930). Ornithological observations in the North Atlantic Ocean. 'Dana' *Oceanogr. Reps.* no. 7; 36 pp.

——— (1933). Observations on the oceanic birds of the Pacific and adjacent waters. *Vidensk. Medd. Dansk. naturh. Foren. 94:* 187-221.

——— (1946). The breeding birds of Denmark. Copenhagen, Munksgaard.

JOHNSON, R. A. (1940). Present range, migration and abundance of the Atlantic murre in North America. *Bird-banding, 11:* 1-17.

——— (1941). Nesting behavior of the Atlantic murre. *Auk, 58:* 153-63.

JONES, J. M. (1859). The naturalist in Bermuda; a sketch of the geology, zoology, and botany of that remarkable group of islands; together with meteorological observations. London.

KAY, G. T. (1947). The young guillemot's flight to the sea. *Brit. Birds, 40:* 156-57.

——— (1948). The gannet in Shetland in winter. *Brit. Birds, 41:* 268-70.

——— (1949). The young gannet. *Brit. Birds, 42:* 260-63.

KEIGHLEY, J. and LOCKLEY, R. M. (1947). Fledging-periods of the razorbill, guillemot and kittiwake. *Brit. Birds, 40:* 165-71.

——— (1948). The incubation and fledging-periods of the razorbill. *Brit. Birds, 41:* 113-14.

KIRKMAN, F. B. (1937). Bird behaviour. A contribution based chiefly on a study of the black-headed gull. London and Edinburgh, Nelson & Jack.

KOLTHOFF, G. (1901). Till Spetsbergen och nordöstra Grönland År 1900. Stockholm.

KRAMER, G. (1952). Experiments on bird orientation. *Ibis, 94:* 265-85.

KRASOVSKII, S. K. (1937). The biological basis for the economic exploitation of bird-cliffs and on the biology of the guillemot (*Uria lomvia* L.). *Trans. Arctic Inst. Leningrad, 77:* 33-91.

KRITZLER, H. (1948). Observations on behavior in captive fulmars. *Condor, 50:* 5-15.

KUMLIEN, L. (1879). Contributions to the natural history of Arctic America. *Bull. U.S. Nat. Mus.* no. 15; Birds, pp. 69-105.

LABAT, J. B. (1722). Nouveau voyage aux isles de l'Amérique contenant l'histoire naturelle de ces pays, l'origine, les moeurs, la religion, et le gouvernement des habitans anciens et moderns, etc. Paris, vol. 2.

LACK, D. (1944). Ecological aspects of species-formation in passerine birds. *Ibis, 86:* 260-86.

——— (1945). The ecology of closely related species with special reference to cormorant (*Phalacrocorax carbo*) and shag (*P. aristotelis*). *J. Anim. Ecol. 14:* 12-16.

LANDT, J. (1800). Forsøg til en Beskrivelse over Faerøerne. København.

——— (1810). A description of the Feroe Islands, . . . London, transl. of above.

LAWRENCE, G. N. (1878). Catalogue of the birds of Dominica from collections made for the Smithsonian Institution by Frederick A. Ober, together with his notes and observations. *Proc. U.S. Nat. Mus. 1:* 48-69.

LAWRENCE, G. N. (1891). Description of new subspecies of Cypselidae of the genus *Chaetura*, with a note on the diablotin. *Auk, 8:* 59-62.

LEWIS, H. F. (1925 onwards). Papers, too numerous to cite, principally on the sea-bird sanctuaries of the Gulf of St. Lawrence, in *Canad. Field-Nat. 39* onwards.

—— (1929). The natural history of the double-crested cormorant (*Phalacrocorax auritus auritus* (Lesson)). Ottawa, Ru-Mi-Lou Books.

—— (1931). Additional information concerning the double-crested cormorant, *Phalacrocorax auritus auritus* (Lesson). *Auk, 48:* 207-14.

—— (1941). Breeding European cormorants of North America. *Auk, 58:* 360-63.

—— (1941b). Ring-billed gulls of the Atlantic coast. *Wilson Bull. 53:* 22-30.

—— (1941c). Remarks on the birds of Anticosti Island. *Wilson Bull. 53:* 73-84.

LOCKLEY, R M. (1932). On the breeding habits of the storm-petrel, with special reference to its incubation and fledging- periods. *Brit. Birds, 25:* 206-11.

—— (1934). On the breeding-habits of the puffin: with special reference to its incubation and fledging- periods. *Brit. Birds, 27:* 214-23.

—— (1934b). The private life of the guillemot. *Countryman, 10:* 103-15.

—— (1936). On the breeding birds of the Westmann Islands. *Ibis* (13) 6: 712-18.

—— (1938). I know an island. London, etc., Harrap.

—— (1942). Shearwaters. London, Dent.

—— (1946). Birds of the sea. Harmondsworth, Penguin Books.

—— (1947). Letters from Skokholm. London, Dent.

—— (1952). Notes on the birds of the islands of the Berlengas (Portugal), the Desertas and Baixo (Madeira) and the Salvages. *Ibis, 94:* 144-57.

—— (1953). Puffins. London, Dent.

LOCKLEY, R. M. and SALMON, H. M. (1934). The gannet colonies of Iceland. *Brit. Birds, 28:* 183-84.

LONGSTAFF, T. G. (1924). Notes from Spitsbergen, 1923. *Ibis* (11) 6: 480-95.

LØPPENTHIN, B. (1946). Fortegnelse over Danmarks Fugle. København, Dansk. Orn. Foren.

—— (1948). Recent changes in the list of Danish breeding birds. *Ibis, 90:* 86-90.

LORENZ, K. (1935). Der Kumpan in der Umwelt des Vogels. *J. Orn. 83:* 137-213, 289-413; transl. (1937).

—— (1937). transl. of above as "The companion in the bird's world." *Auk, 54:* 245-73.

LØVENSKIOLD, H. L. (1947-50). Håndbok over Norges Fugler. Oslo, Gyldendal Norsk Forlag.

LOWE, P. R. (1911). A naturalist on desert islands. London.

—— (1914). Our common sea-birds. London.

LUMSDEN, W. H. R. and HADDOW, A. J. (1946). The food of the shag (*Phalacrocorax aristotelis*) in the Clyde sea area. *J. Anim. Ecol. 15:* 35-42.

MANNING, T. H. (1949). On the birds of north-western Ungava. Appendix to Mrs. T. Manning "A summer on Hudson Bay." London, Hodder & Stoughton.

MANNING, T. H. (1952). Birds of the west James Bay and southern Hudson Bay coasts. *Bull. Nat. Mus. Canada* no. 125; 114 pp.

MARCHANT, S. (1952). The status of the black-headed gull colony at Ravenglass. *Brit. Birds, 45:* 22-27.

MARPLES, G. and MARPLES, A. (1934). Sea terns or sea swallows. Their habits, language, arrival and departure. London, Country Life.

MARSHALL, A. J. (1949). Weather factors and spermatogenesis in birds. *Proc. Zool. Soc. Lond. 119:* 711-16.

MARSHALL, F. H. A. (1936). Sexual periodicity and the causes which determine it. The Croonian lecture. *Philos. Trans. Roy. Soc.* (B) *226:* 423-56.

MARTIN, M. (1698). A late voyage to St. Kilda, . . . London (other eds. 1753, 1774, 1809, 1818, 1934).

MATHIESON, J. (1927). Life on St. Kilda. *Scotsman,* 21 Oct.

MATTHEWS, G. V. T. (1952). Preliminary report on homing experiments with Manx shearwaters from Skokholm, 1951. *Skokholm Bird Obs. Rep. 1951:* 31-33.

MATTHEWS, L. H. (1929). The birds of South Georgia. *Discovery Rep. 1:* 561-92.

—— (1949). The origin of stomach oil in the petrels, with comparative observations on the avian proventriculus. *Ibis, 91:* 373-92.

—— (1950). Stomach oil in fulmars. *Ibis, 92:* 153.

MAYAUD, N. (1947). Phalaropes and gannets off the west coast of Africa. *Bull. Brit. Orn. Cl. 67:* 54-55.

—— (1953). Liste des oiseaux de France. *Alauda, 21:* 1-63.

MAYR, E. (1938). Birds on an Atlantic crossing. *Proc. Linn. Soc. N.Y.* no. 49; 54-58.

—— (1940). Speciation phenomena in birds. *Amer. Nat. 74:* 249-78.

—— (1942). Systematics and the origin of species from the viewpoint of a zoologist. New York, Columbia University Press.

MAYR, E. and AMADON, D. (1951). A classification of recent birds. *Amer. Mus. Novit.* no. 1496; 42 pp.

MEINERTZHAGEN, R. (1925). The distribution of the phalaropes. *Ibis* (12) *1:* 325-44.

—— (1935). The races of *Larus argentatus* and *Larus fuscus;* with special reference to Herr. B. Stegmann's recent paper on the subject. *Ibis* (13) *5:* 762-73.

MENDALL, H. L. (1936). The home-life and economic status of the double-crested cormorant, *Phalacrocorax auritus auritus* (Lesson). *Maine Bull. 39:* no. 3; 143 pp.

MILES, J. A. R. and SHRIVASTAV, J. B. (1951). Ornithosis in certain sea-birds. *J. Anim. Ecol. 20:* 195-200.

MILES, J. A. R. and STOKER, M. G. P. (1948). Puffinosis, a virus epizootic of the Manx shearwater (*Puffinus p. puffinus*). *Nature, 161:* 1016-17.

MILLER, A. H. (1943). Census of a colony of Caspian terns. *Condor, 45:* 220-25.

MILLER, L. and VAN ROSSEM, A. J. (1929). Nesting of the laughing gull in southern California. *Condor, 31:* 141-42.

MOHR, N. (1786). Forsøg til en islandsk Naturhistorie. København.

MONRO, D. (1774). Description of the Western Isles of Scotland, called Hybrides. Edinburgh.

MOREAU, R. E. (1923). Herring-gull eating its own chick. *Brit. Birds, 16:* 221-22.

—— (1949). The neglected sea-bird stations of Africa. *Ibis, 91:* 352-53.

—— (1950). The breeding seasons of African birds—2. Sea birds. *Ibis, 92:* 419-33.

MOSELEY, H. N. (1879). Notes by a naturalist on the *Challenger*. London.

MOWBRAY, L. (1908). The cahow: discovery in Bermuda of fossil bones and feathers ...*Amer. J. Sci.* (4) *25*: 361-62.

MÜLLER, H. C. (1862). Færöernes Fuglefauna med Bemærkninger om Fuglefangsten. *Vidensk. Medd. naturh. Foren. Kbh. 1862*: 1-78.

MURDOCH, J. (1885). Birds, *in* Report of the international polar expedition to Point Barrow, Alaska, ...Washington.

MURPHY, R. C. (1918). A study of the Atlantic *Oceanites*. *Bull. Amer. Mus. Nat. Hist. 38*: 117-46.

―― (1936). Oceanic birds of South America. New York, MacMillan Co. & Amer. Mus. Nat. Hist., 2 vols.

―― (1952). The Manx shearwater, *Puffinus puffinus*, as a species of world-wide distribution. *Amer. Mus. Novit.* no. 1586; 21 pp.

MURPHY, R. C. and MOWBRAY, L. S. (1951). New light on the cahow, *Pterodroma cahow*. *Auk*, *68*: 266-80.

MURPHY, R. C. and SNYDER, J. P. (1953). The "*Pealea*" phenomenon and other notes on storm petrels. *Amer. Mus. Novit.* no. 1596; 16 pp.

MURPHY, R. C. and VOGT, W. (1933). The dovekie [*Alle alle*] influx of 1932. *Auk*, *1933*: 325-49.

MURRAY, J. and HJORT, J. (1912). The depths of the ocean. London, MacMillan.

MACAULAY, K. (1764). The history of St. Kilda . . . London.

MACGILLIVRAY, J. (1842). Account of the island of St. Kilda, . . . *Edinb. New Philos. J. 32*: 47-70.

MACGILLIVRAY, W. (1824). Descriptions, characters and synonyms of the different species of the genus *Larus*. *Mem. Wernerian Nat. Hist. Soc. 5*: 247-76.

―― (1837-52). A history of British birds, indigenous and migratory. London, 5 vols.

M'KENZIE, Sir G. (1818). An account of Hirta and Rona given to Sir Robert Sibbald, by the Lord Register. *Misc. Scot. 2*: no. 2; 79-81.

MACKENZIE, N. (1905). Notes on the birds of St. Kilda. *Ann. Scot. Nat. Hist. 14*: 75-80, 141-53.

MACPHERSON, H. A. (1897). A history of fowling . . . Edinburgh.

NANSEN, F. (1897). Farthest north. London, Constable, 2 vols.

NEWCOMB, R. L. (1888). Our lost explorers: the narrative of the *Jeannette* arctic expedition.... Hartford, Conn.

NEWTON, A. (1861). Abstract of Mr. J. Wolley's researches in Iceland respecting the garefowl or great auk. *Ibis, 3*: 374-99.

―― (1868). The zoological aspect of game laws. *Rep. Brit. Assoc. Norwich.*

―― (1898). On the Orcadian home of the garefowl (*Alca impennis*). *Ibis* (7) *4*: 587-92.

NICHOLS, J. T. and MOWBRAY, L. L. (1916). Two new forms of petrels from the Bermudas. *Auk, 33*: 194-95.

NICHOLSON, E. M. (1950). Regions of the North Atlantic. *Bull. Brit. Trust Orn.* no. 36; 5, 8-9.

―― (1951). Birds of the North Atlantic. *Proc. X. Int. Orn. Congr. Uppsala, 1950*: 600-02.

NOBLE, G. K. and WURM, M. (1943). The social behavior of the laughing gull. *Ann. N.Y. Acad. Sci. 45*: 179-220.

NORTON, A. H. and ALLEN, R. P. (1931). Breeding of the great black-backed gull and double-crested cormorant in Maine. *Auk, 48:* 589-92.

OBER, F. A. (1880). Camps in the Caribbees. Boston.

ÓLAFSSON, E. and PÁLSSON, B. (1772). Reise igiennem Island. Sorøe.

—— (1774-75). Reise durch Island. Copenhagen and Leipzig.

—— (1802). Voyage en Islande,. . . Paris, 5 vols., transl. of above by Gauthier-de-Lapeyronie.

—— (1805). Travels in Iceland: performed by order of his Danish Majesty . . . , by *Messrs.* Olafsen and Povelsen. Translated from the Danish. London, Richard Phillips's Collection of Modern and Contemporary Voyages and Travels, vol. *2:* no. 1; 162 pp.

OLAVIUS, O. (1780). Oeconomisk Reise igiennem de nordvestlige, og nordlige og nordöstlige Kanter af Izland. Kobenhavn, 2 vols.

PALMER, R. S. (1941). A behavior study of the common tern (*Sterna hirundo hirundo* L.). *Proc. Boston Soc. Nat. Hist. 42:* 1-119.

—— (1941b). White-faced terns. *Auk, 58:* 164-78.

—— (1949). Maine birds. Based largely on data gathered by Arthur Herbert Norton. *Bull. Mus. Comp. Zool. 102:* 656 pp.

—— (1950). Corrigenda to Maine birds. *Bull. Maine Audubon Soc. 6:* 20.

PALUDAN, K. (1947). Alken. København, Munksgaard.

—— (1951). Contributions to the breeding biology of *Larus argentatus* and *Larus fuscus. Vidensk. Medd. Dansk naturh. Foren. 114:* 1-128.

PARRY, W. E. (1824). Journal of a second voyage for the discovery of a north-west passage from the Atlantic to the Pacific; . . . London.

—— (1828). Narrative of an attempt to reach the North Pole, . . . London.

PATTEN, C. J. (1902). The aquatic birds of Great Britain and Ireland. London.

PEARSON, T. G., BRIMLEY, C. S. and BRIMLEY, H. H. (1919). Birds of North Carolina. Raleigh, N. C., N.C. Geol. & Econ. Surv., vol. *4.*

PEDERSEN, A. (1930). Fortgesetzte Beiträge zur Kenntnis der säugetier- und Vogelfauna der Ostküste Grönlands . . . . *Medd. Grønland, 77:* 341-508.

PERRY, R. (1940). Lundy isle of puffins. London, Lindsay Drummond.

—— (1948). Display of the arctic skua. *Country Life, 103:* 375.

—— (1948b). Pirate gull of the Shetlands. *ibid. 104:* 84-85.

—— (1948c). Shetland sanctuary. London, Faber & Faber.

—— (1950). The young gannet. *Brit. Birds, 43:* 343-44.

PETERS, H. S. and BURLEIGH, T. D. (1951). The birds of Newfoundland. St. John's, Dept. Natural Resources.

PETERS, J. L. (1931). Check list of birds of the world. Cambridge, Mass., Harvard University Press, vol. *1.*

—— (1934). —— vol. *2.*

PETERSON, R. T. (1950). Birds over America. New York, Dodd, Mead & Co.

PITT, F. (1929). Notes on the effect of temperature upon the breeding behaviour of birds, with special reference to the northern golden plover (*Charadrius apricarius altifrons*), and the fieldfare (*Turdus pilaris*). *Ibs* (12) *5:* 53-71.

PLATH, K. (1914). With the tropic-birds in Bermuda. *Ibis* (10) *2:* 552-59, pls. 21-24.

PLESKE, T. (1928). Birds of the Eurasian tundra. *Mem. Boston Soc. Nat. Hist. 6:* 107-485.

PORTIELJE, A. F. J. (1927). Zur Ethologie bezw. Psychologie von *Phalacrocorax carbo subcormoranus* (Brehm). *Ardea, 16:* 107-23.
—— (1928). Zur Ethologie bezw. Psychologie der Silbermöwe (*Larus argentatus argentatus* Pont.). *Ardea, 17:* 112-49.
PREYER, W. (1862). Über *Plautus impennis* Brünn. Heidelberg; and *J. Orn. 10:* 110-24, 337-56.
RANKIN, M. N. and DUFFEY, E. A. G. (1948). A study of the bird life of the North Atlantic. *Brit. Birds, 41:* suppl., 42 pp.
REID, S. G. (1884). The birds of Bermuda. Part 4 *of* Contributions to the natural history of the Bermudas. *Bull. U.S. Nat. Mus.* no. 25 165-279.
RICHDALE, L. E. (1943). The white-faced storm petrel or takahi-karemoana. *Trans. Proc. Roy. Soc. N.Z. 73:* 9-115, 217-32, 335-50.
—— (1950). The pre-egg stage in the albatross family. Dunedin, Biol. Monogrs. no. 3; 92 pp.
—— (1952). Post-egg period in albatrosses. Dunedin, Biol. Monogrs. no. 4; 166 pp.
RICHTER, R. (1937). Einiges über die Lebensweise des Eissturmvogels (*Fulmarus glacialis* L.). *J. Orn. 85:* 187-200.
RIVIÈRE, B. B. (1930). A history of the birds of Norfolk. London, Witherby.
ROBERTS, B. B. (1940). The life cycle of Wilson's petrel *Oceanites oceanicus* (Kuhl). *British Graham Land Expedition 1934-37 Sci Reps. 1:* 141-94. London, British Museum.
—— (1941). A bibliography of Antarctic ornithology. *Ibid. 1:* 336-67.
RÖMER, F. and SCHAUDINN, F. (1900). Die Vögel, *in* Fauna Arctica . . . Jena, Fischer, vol. *1:* part 1; 66-84.
ROWAN, M. K. (1952). The greater shearwater *Puffinus gravis* at its breeding grounds. *Ibis, 94:* 97-121.
ROWAN, W. (1915). The Blakeney Point ternery. *Brit. Birds, 8:* 250-66.
—— (1918). Power of control over deposition of eggs. *Brit. Birds, 12:* 42-43.
RUBOW, C. (1911). Hættemaagen (*Larus ridibundus*). Kjøbenhavn.
—— (1911). The life of the common gull told in photographs. London, Witherby (transl. from Danish ed., publ. 1910).
SALOMONSEN, F. (1935). Aves *in* The Zoology of the Faroes. Copenhagen, Carlsberg.
—— (1941b). The black-winged guillemot (*Uria grylle* mut. *motzfeldi* Benicken, *Medd. Grønland, 131:* no. 6; 21 pp.
—— (1941c). Tretaaet Maage (*Rissa tridactyla* (L.) som Ynglefugl i Danmark. *Dansk. Orn. Foren. Tidsskr. 35:* 159-79.
—— (1943). Betydningen af social stimulans for Yngleforholdene i Fuglekolonier. *Dansk. Orn. Foren. Tidsskr. 37:* 1-11.
—— (1943b). Fugletællinger 1936-1942 paa Hirsholmene og Christiansø. *Dansk. Orn. Foren. Tidsskr. 37:* 151-81.
—— (1944). The Atlantic Alcidae. *Göteborgs Vetensk. Samh. Handl. 3B:* 1-138.
—— (1945). Gejrfuglen, et Hundredaars Minde. *Dyr i Natur og Museum, 1944-45:* 99-110
—— (1947). Maagekolonierne paa Hirsholmene. *Dansk. Orn. Foren. Tidsskr. 41:* 174-86.
—— (1950-51). Grønlands Fugle. København, Ejnar Munksgaard.

SALOMONSEN, F. (1952). Femte foreløbige liste over genfundne grønlandske ring-fugle. *Dansk. Orn. Foren. Tidsskr. 46:* 110-17.

SANDS, J. (1878). Out of the world; or, life in St. Kilda. Edinburgh, 2nd ed.

SCHALOW, H. (1904). Die Vögel der Arktis, vol. *4:* part 1 of F. Römer and F. Schaudinn. Fauna Arctica. Jena, Gustav Fischer.

SCHULZ, H. (1947). Die Welt der Seevögel ein Führer durch die Vogelbrutstätten der deutschen Küsten. Hamburg, Lettenbauer.

SCOTT, W. E. D. (1891-92). Observations on the birds of Jamaica, West Indies. *Auk, 8:* 249-56, 353-65; *9:* 9-15, 120-29, 273-77, 369-75.

SEEBOHM, H. (1883-85). A history of British birds, . . . London, 4 vols. vol *3:* 286).

SELOUS, E. (1905). The bird-watcher in the Shetlands. London, Dent.

—— (1906-10). Observations on sexual selection in birds, including a day-to-day diary on the breeding habits of the ruff. *Zoologist* (12 parts), 1906-10.

—— (1927). Realities of bird life. London, Constable

SERGEANT, D. E. (1951). Ecological relationships of the guillemots *Uria aalge* and *Uria lomvia. Proc. X. Int. Orn. Congr. Uppsala, 1950:* 578-87.

—— (1952). Little auks in Britain, 1948 to 1951. *Brit. Birds, 45:* 122-33.

SERVENTY, D. L. (1939). Notes on cormorants. *Emu, 38:* 357-71.

SERVENTY, D. L., CLANCEY, P. A. and ELLIOTT, H. F. I. (1953). The Derbyshire albatross. *Brit. Birds, 46:* 307-10.

SHUFELDT, R. W. (1916). The bird caves of the Bermudas and their former inhabit-ants. *Ibis* (10) *4:* 623-35.

SLADEN, W. J. L. (1952). Arctic skua in the Antarctic. *Ibis, 94:* 543.

SOLLAS, W. J. (1924). Ancient hunters and their modern representatives. London, MacMillan, third ed., (first ed. 1911).

SOPER, J. D. (1928). A faunal investigation of southern Baffin Island. *Bull. Nat. Mus. Canada, 53:* 1-143.

—— (1934). Interesting bird records from southern Baffin Island. *Canad. Field-Nat. 48:* 41-44, 65-68, 79-82.

—— (1946). Ornithological results of the Baffin Island expeditions of 1928-1929 and 1930-1931, together with more recent records. *Auk, 63:* 1-24.

SOUTHERN, H. N. (1937). Habits of the common tern. *Field, 169:* 290.

—— (1939). The status and problem of the bridled guillemot. *Proc. Zool. Soc. Lond. (A) 109:* 31-41.

—— (1943). The two phases of *Stercorarius parasiticus* (Linnaeus). *Ibis, 85:* 443-85.

—— (1944). Dimorphism in *Stercorarius pomarinus* (Temminck). *Ibis, 86:* 1-16.

—— (1951). Change in status of the bridled guillemot after ten years. *Proc. Zool. Soc. Lond. 121:* 657-71.

SOUTHERN, H. N. and REEVE, E. C. R. (1941). Quantitative studies in the geo-graphical variation of birds.—The common guillemot (*Uria aalge* Pont.). *Proc. Zool. Soc. Lond. (A) 111:* 255-76.

SOUTHWELL, T. (1904). On the whale fishery from Scotland, . . . *Ann. Scot. Nat. Hist. 13:* 77-90.

—— (1948). The tern colonies of the Dry Tortugas Keys. *Auk, 65:* 1-19.

STANFORD, W. P. (1953). Winter distribution of the grey phalarope. *Phalaropus fulicarius. Ibis, 95:* 483-91.

SPRUNT, A. (1938). The southern dovekie flight of 1936. *Auk. 54:* 85-94.

STEGMANN, B. (1934). Ueber die Formen der grossen Möwen (subgenus *Larus*) und ihre gegenseitigen Beziehungen. *J. Orn. 82:* 340-80.

STEVEN, G. A. (1933). The food consumed by shags and cormorants around the shores of Cornwall (England). *J. Marine Biol. Assoc. 19:* 277-92.

STONE, W. and others (1931). Check-list of North American birds prepared by a committee of the American Ornithologists' Union. Lancaster, Pa., A.O.U., 4th ed.

STORER, R. W. (1952). A comparison of variation, behavior and evolution in the sea bird genera *Uria* and *Cepphus*. *Univ. Calif. Publ. Zool. 52:* 121-222.

STUART, D. (1948). Vital statistics of the Mochrum cormorant colony. *Brit. Birds, 41:* 194-99.

STUBBS, F. J. (1913). Asiatic birds in Leadenhall Market. *Zoologist* (4) *17:* 156-57.

SURREY-DANE, D. (1948). A disease of Manx shearwaters (*Puffinus puffinus*). *J. Anim. Ecol. 17:* 158-64.

SURREY-DANE, D., MILES, J. A. R. and STOKER, M. G. P. (1953). A disease of Manx sheerwaters: further observations in the field. *J. Anim. Ecol. 22:* 123-33.

SVABO, J. K. (1783). Indberetninger, indhentede paa en, Allernaadigst befalet, Reise i Faerøe, i Aarene 1781 og 1782. Kjøbenhavn.

SWAINSON, W. and RICHARDSON, J. (1832). The birds, vol. *2* of J. Richardson (1832). Fauna Boreali-Americana; . . . London, 4 vols.

TAIT, W. C. (1924). The birds of Portugal. London, Witherby.

TÅNING, Å. V. (1933). The winter quarters of the phalaropes. *Ibis* (13) *3:* 132-33.

TAVERNER, P. A. (1933). A study of Kumlien's gull (*Larus kumlieni* Brewster). *Canad. Field-Nat. 47:* 88-90.

—— (1934). Birds of Canada. *Canad. Dep. Mines Bull.* no. 72; 445 pp.

TEMPLEMAN, W. (1945). Observations on some Newfoundland sea-birds. *Canad. Field-Nat. 59:* 136-47.

DU TERTRE, J. B. (1654). Histoire générale des isles des Christophie, de la Guadeloupe, de la Martinique, et autres dans l'Amérique. Paris.

THOMPSON, B. H. (1932). History and present status of the breeding colonies of the white pelican (*pelecanus erythrorhynchas*) in the United States. *Contr. U.S. Wildlife Div. Occ. Pap.* no. 1; 82 pp.

THOMSON, A. L. (1939). The migration of the gannet: results of marking in the British Isles. *Brit. Birds, 32:* 282-89.

THORPE, W. H. (1945). The evolutionary significance of habitat selection. *J. Anim. Ecol. 14:* 67-70.

TIMMERMANN, G. (1938-49). Die Vögel Islands. *Vísindafélag Íslendinga,* no. 21; 1-109, no. 24; 111-238, no. 28; 239-524.

TINBERGEN, N. (1931). Zur Paarungsbiologie der Fluszseeschwalbe (*Sterna hirundo hirundo* L.). *Ardea, 20:* 1-18.

—— (1951). The study of instinct. Oxford University Press.

—— (1952). On the significance of territory in the herring gull. *Ibis, 94:* 158-59.

—— (1952b). A note on the origin and evolution of threat display. *Ibis, 94:* 160-62.

—— (1953). The herring-gull's world. London, Collins' *New Naturalist.*

TURNER, E. L. (1914). Cormorants in Norfolk. *Brit. Birds, 8:* 130-42.

TURNER, L. McS. (1886). Birds, pp. 115-96 *of* Contributions to the natural history of Alaska. Washington.

VALEUR, P. (1947). Havhesten og havsula på Rundøy. *Naturen Bergen, 71:* 370-79.

VERHEYEN, R. (1951). Les oiseaux d'Eau de Belgique (á l'exception des anatidés et des échassiers.) Bruxelles, Inst. roy. Sci. Nat. Belg.

VESEY-FITZGERALD, D. (1941). Further contributions to the ornithology of the Seychelles Islands. *Ibis* (14) *5:* 518-31.

WATSON, J. B. (1908). The behavior of noddy and sooty terns. *Pap. Tortugas Lab. Carnegie Inst. Wash. 2:* 187-225.

WATSON, J. B. and LASHLEY, K. S. (1915). An historical and experimental study of homing. *Pap. Dep. Marine Biol. Carnegie Inst. Wash. 7:* 9-104.

WEGENER, A. (1924). Origin of continents and oceans. London, Methuen, transl. Skert.

WETMORE, A. (1918). The birds of Desecheo Island, Porto Rico. *Auk, 35:* 333-40.
—— (1926). Observations on the birds of Argentina, Paraguay, Uruguay, and Chile. *Bull. U.S. Nat. Mus.* no. 133; 434 pp.

WETMORE, A. and SWALES, B. H. (1931). The birds of Haiti and the Dominican Republic. *Bull. U.S. Nat. Mus.* no. 155; 483 pp.

WIGLESWORTH, J. (1903). St. Kilda and its birds. Liverpool.

WILKINS, G. H. (1923). Report on the birds collected during the voyage of the *Quest* (Shackleton-Rowett expedition) to the southern Atlantic. *Ibis* (11) *5:* 4745 511.

WILLIAMS, L. (1942). Display and sexual behavior of the Brandt cormorant. *Condor, 43:* 85-104.

WILLIAMSON, K. (1939). The great auk (*Alca impennis* L.) in Man. *J. Manx Mus. 4:* 168-72.
—— (1945). The economic importance of sea-fowl in the Faeroe Islands. *Ibis, 87:* 249-69.
—— (1945b). Some new and scarce breeding species in the Faeroe Islands. *Ibis, 87:* 550-58.
—— (1946). Birds in Faeroe folk-lore. *Northw. Nat. 21:* 7-19, 155-66.
—— (1948). The Atlantic islands: a study of the Faeroe life and scene. London, Collins.
—— (1949). The distraction behaviour of the arctic skua. *Ibis, 91:* 307-13.
—— (1950). Fair Isle Bird Observatory first annual report 1949. Edinburgh, Fair Isle Bird Observatory Trust.
—— (1950b). Fair Isle Bird Observatory notes on selected species spring 1949. *Scot. Nat. 62:* 17-25.
—— (1951, mimeod.). The arctic skua study, 1951. *Fair Isle Bird Obs. Bull. 1951:* no. 4; 3-10.

WILLIAMSON K. and PETERSEN Á BOTNI, N.F. (1947). Notes on the occurrences and habits of some passage-migrants and rare vagrants in the Faeroe Islands. *Ibis, 89:* 105-17.

WINN, H. E. (1950). The black guillemots of Kent Island, Bay of Fundy. *Auk, 67:* 477-85.

WINNALL, R. N. (1948). Cory's shearwater off Aberdeenshire. *Brit. Birds, 41:* 88-89.

WITHERBY, H. F., JOURDAIN, F. C. R., TICEHURST, N. F. and TUCKER, B. W. (1938-41). The handbook of British birds. London, Witherby, 5 vols.

WOLLEY, J. (1850). Some observations on the birds of the Faroe Islands. *Jardine's Contributions to Ornithology, 1850:* 106-17.

WORM, O. [Olaus Wormius] (1655). Museum Wormianum; seu, Historia rerum rariorum, tam naturalium, quam artificialum, tam domesticarum, quam exoticarum, quae Hafniae Danorum in aedibus authoris servantur. Lugduni Batavorum [Amsterdam].

WRIGHT, H. W. (1913). The birds of San Martin Island, Lower California. *Condor, 15:* 207-10.

WYNNE-EDWARDS, V. C. (1930). Birds of the north Atlantic. *Discovery, 11:* 359-62.

—— (1935). On the habits and distribution of birds on the North Atlantic. *Proc. Boston Soc. Nat. Hist. 40:* 233-346.

—— (1952). Zoology of the Baird expedition (1950). I. The birds observed in central and south-east Baffin Island. *Auk, 69:* 353-91.

WYNNE-EDWARDS, V.C., LOCKLEY, R. M. and SALMON, H. M. (1936). The distribution and numbers of breeding gannets *(Sula bassana* L.). *Brit. Birds, 29:* 262-76.

INDEX TO VERTEBRATE SPECIES IN A SYSTEMATIC ORDER

Plate references in italics

MAMMALS

BIRDS

INDEX TO AUTHORITIES

Those mentioned only in the Bibliography are not listed